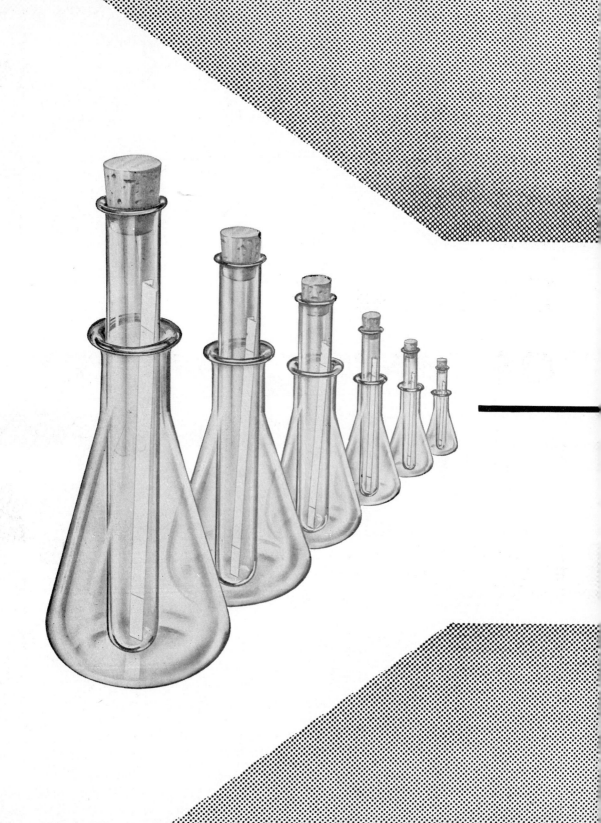

Experiments in
ORGANIC CHEMISTRY

THIRD EDITION, REVISED

Louis F. Fieser

SHELDON EMERY PROFESSOR OF
ORGANIC CHEMISTRY, HARVARD UNIVERSITY

D. C. HEATH AND COMPANY   BOSTON

LIBRARY OF CONGRESS CATALOG NUMBER: 55-7396

Preface

Although this book is based on the editions published in 1935 and 1941, most of the previous experiments that have been retained are considerably revised. For example, improved procedures are given for the preparation of an alkene (cyclohexene), of mandelic acid, nitrobenzene, aniline, anthraquinone, *p*-chlorotoluene, and acetylsalicylic acid. New experiments are presented on elution and paper-strip chromatography, enzymatic and spontaneous resolution, synthesis of ninhydrin, isolation of plant and animal products, synthesis of *cis*- and *trans*-stilbene, tolan, and related products (the infrared and ultraviolet spectra of which are reproduced). Another new chapter is an exercise in cost calculation.

One modification aimed at increased stimulation of thought and interest is inclusion of more experimental problems and unknowns. Fractional distillation, done with an inexpensive but efficient column packing, is applied to identification of the components of a binary mixture and determination of their ratio. Triphenylcarbinol synthesized from benzoic acid is used for the problem formulated in the cover design ($HX = HCl$, HBr, HI, $HCl–SnCl_2$). Problems in identification of unknowns are included in the experiments on carbonyl compounds, amines, amino acids, and sugars, as well as in a chapter devoted to qualitative analysis. A technique for measuring milligram quantities of solids and liquids with equipment no more elaborate than a triple-beam balance and a ruler makes possible Rast molecular weight determination, determination of the ratio of decolorizing carbon to an adsorbate, and preparation of derivatives on a millimole scale. Synthetic reaction sequences with alternative routes and procedures are also aimed at increased initiative on the part of the student.

The scale of experimentation is at the conventional macro level in representative experiments, but more generally semimacro or semimicro experimentation is specified in the interest of better technique, increased number of experiments in the time available, and saving in cost of both chemicals and apparatus. A few new pieces of apparatus suggested as aids to better and more convenient experimentation are available from a supplier [1] at modest cost.

An *Instructor's Manual*, available on request to the publisher, lists chemicals and apparatus required with details of suppliers and costs; notes on the experiments, including explanations, experimental results, answers to questions, and references; and

[1] The Wilkens-Anderson Company (Waco), 4525 West Division Street, Chicago 51, Illinois.

acknowledgments. The cost estimates indicate substantial reduction in cost of both chemicals and apparatus.

Part II of the book has been revised in accordance with the results of a poll of opinion on the usefulness of the different sections. Those that seemed of limited interest have been omitted. Others are rearranged and condensed. The previously brief section of notes on reagents has been expanded through the work of Mary Fieser to a chapter that lists 320 reagents of general and special use, with 870 literature references. The notes on the properties, sources, and uses of the reagents are presented in condensed form appropriate for research chemists, but they may be stimulating to students in a beginning course. A table of derivatives at the end of the book that includes references to the chapter on reagents may be useful in the investigation of unknowns. The table of formula calculations has been expanded to C_{50} and H_{75}.

Concerning the revision: This printing incorporates a certain number of small modifications suggested by experiences here and elsewhere. The apparatus and assemblies now preferred (Figs. 2.4, 3.1, 4.2, 6.7a, 6.9a) are those demonstrated in the film "Techniques of Organic Chemistry" (distributor: Young America Films, N.Y.).

Experience to date suggests the desirability of assigning to all class members only one or two sections of each of the Chapters 2–8 and of reserving for the better experimentalists the preparation of ninhydrin (even though the fourth and sixth steps have now been better standardized).

Louis F. Fieser

Cambridge, Massachusetts

Contents

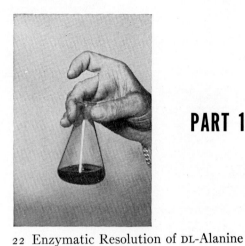

PART 1

PART 2

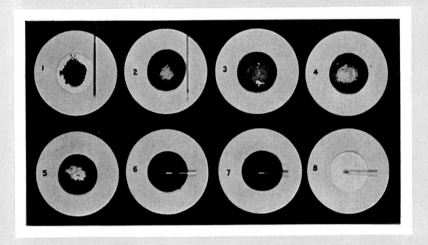

Fig. 0.1. Weights

1. Decolorizing carbon (Norit); 100-mg. and 10-mg. samples.
2. Iodoform; 100-mg. and 10-mg. samples.
3. 100 mg. Anthracene, crystalline.
4. 100 mg. Anthracene, amorphous (precipitated from ethanol solution with water).
5. 25 mg. Hydrocortisone, an average daily dose.
6. 1.4 mg. Thiamine hydrochloride, daily requirement.
7. 1.5 mg. Riboflavin, daily requirement.
8. 1 mg. Vitamin B_{12}, nearly a three-year supply (daily requirement 1γ).

Fig. 0.4. Winding the coil of resistance wire

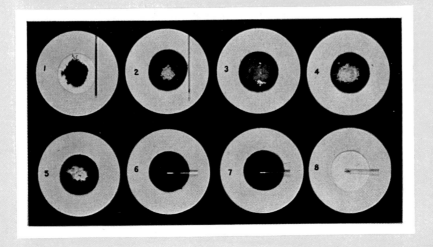

Fig. 0.1. Weights

1. Decolorizing carbon (Norit); 100-mg. and 10-mg. samples.
2. Iodoform; 100-mg. and 10-mg. samples.
3. 100 mg. Anthracene, crystalline.
4. 100 mg. Anthracene, amorphous (precipitated from ethanol solution with water).
5. 25 mg. Hydrocortisone, an average daily dose.
6. 1.4 mg. Thiamine hydrochloride, daily requirement.
7. 1.5 mg. Riboflavin, daily requirement.
8. 1 mg. Vitamin B_{12}, nearly a three-year supply (daily requirement 1γ).

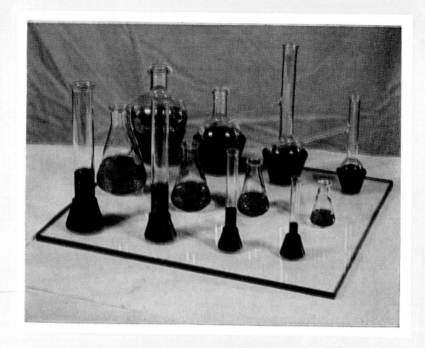

Fig. 0.2. Vessels filled to their practical working capacity

(Except when used as receivers)

	TEST TUBES, MM.				ERLENMEYER FLASKS, ML.				ROUND FLASKS, ML.			
Size, in mm. or ml.	25 × 150	20 × 150	13 × 100	10 × 75	125	50	25	10	200	100	50	10
Actual capacity, ml.	54	35	10	4	140	60	30	13	215	105	50	13
Practical capacity, ml.	15	10	3	1	75	30	15	5	115	60	27	5

Fig. 0.3. Construction of a hot plate

Fig. 0.4. Winding the coil of resistance wire

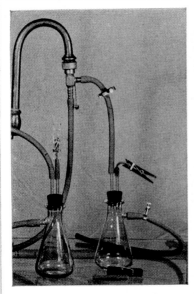

Filter flask with gauge

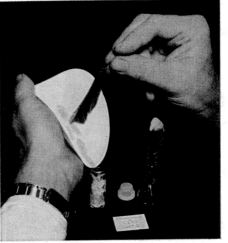

Screen for microburner

Storage cabinet (Capillary dropping tubes deliver micro drops of known weight; calibrated tubes of three sizes measure solids by millimeters of column length.)

Feather

Fig. 0.5. Useful accessories

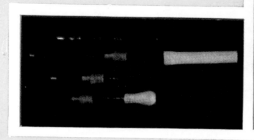

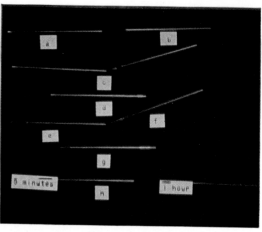

Rast determination of molecular weight
(Sealing an evacuated capillary)

Color test in a capillary tube

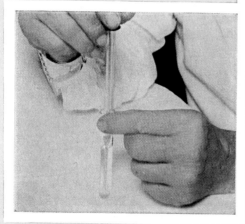

Test for a reducing sugar with blue tetrazolium at the following dilutions: Tube 1, 1:1,000,000; Tube 2, 1:10,000,000; Tube 3, 1:100,000,000; Tube 4, same as 3 but extracted with butanol.

Extraction of an acid from ether
with alkali

Fig. 0.6. Microtechniques

Fig. 0.7. Extraction of the acidic plant pigment lapachol from ether with aqueous buffers

In each separatory funnel a solution of 100 mg. of lapachol in 100 ml. of ether has been equilibrated with 100 ml. of a buffer solution (made from tablets) of pH marked on the flask and visualized on Hydrion test papers. The amounts extracted in the aqueous buffers as red anion (A^-), easily determined by colorimetry, are: pH 8.00, 4.7 mg.; pH 8.60, 16.6 mg.; pH 9.20, 43.7 mg.

It may be assumed that the ratio of the concentrations of unionized acid (HA) in the ether and water phases is a constant, K, or $K = [HA]^{ether}/[HA]^{water}$. Since $K_a = [H^+][A^-]/[HA]^{water}$, and since the pigment in the aqueous phase is present almost exclusively as anion, the measurable distribution ratio C is given by the expression

$$C = \frac{[Total\ pigment]^{ether}}{[Total\ pigment]^{water}} = \frac{[HA]^{ether}}{[A^-]} = \frac{[H^+]K}{K_a}$$

An *extraction constant E* is defined as the hydrogen ion concentration corresponding to the ratio C = 100 (whence $K/K_a = 100/E$) and is employed as the negative logarithm, pE, values for which can be calculated from the colorimetric measurements cited and the pH of the buffer from the equation

$$pE = \log C + pH - 2$$

Thus at pH 8.00

$$pE = \log 95.3/4.7 + 8.00 - 2 = 7.31$$

The other determinations give agreeing values: 7.30 and 7.31. The pE value of a given compound characterizes its hydrophilic-lipophilic balance.

Fig. 0.8. Paper chromatography

Ascending-flow chromatograms running on creased paper strips dipping into phenol solution; the long strip in the rear is in a test tube inserted into a graduate. The circles of filter paper were spotted with solutions of six amino acids and sprayed with ninhydrin (left) and permanganate (right); cystine, methione, and tyrosine give yellow spots.

Paper strip dispenser with millimeter scale and measuring lines on the top edge. Amino acid test solutions, each in a vial with a plastic cap through which extends a toothpick for application of the solution to a strip. (Extra toothpicks to the right.) Matching colors on the cap, the vial, and the baseboard minimize chance of return to wrong location.

Developed chromatograms on 25-cm. and 10-cm. paper strips. A spot shows the distance an amino acid has traveled from the starting line (bottom) to the finish line (top) when the solvent has traveled the whole way. The three test tubes contain pigments formed from proline and ninhydrin and distributed between water and benzene.

PART I

Introduction   CHAPTER I

Chapters 2–8 of this manual deal with techniques for purification of organic compounds by distillation, crystallization, and extraction and for determination of purity from boiling point and melting point data, color, and distribution characteristics. These techniques are fundamental to almost all experimentation in the organic laboratory and will be used extensively in later preparations and syntheses, and in identification of unknowns; hence it is important that the principles are understood thoroughly and that proficiency is gained in the manipulations involved. To this end both experimental problems and unknowns are included in these opening chapters.

Many of the experiments of this book are on a semimacro scale, that is, with 1–2 g. of solid or 10–20 ml. of liquid, and a number are on a semimicro scale involving 100–200 mg. of both solids and liquids. As compared with experimentation with 10–20 g. of solid or 100–200 ml. of liquid, semimacro-semimicro manipulation is neater and effects considerable saving of time and expense. Furthermore, this is the way research and development chemists usually operate except for preparation of large quantities of starting material or when the rarity of the substance under investigation necessitates use of the more exacting technique of micro manipulation (10–20 mg.). Some of the analytical experiments of the manual involve detection or determination of a few micrograms of material.

For semimacro-semimicro work to be done expertly, as it is hoped users of this book will learn to do, some accessory equipment is desirable, if not indispensable. Several accessories, some of them new, are described in Chapters 1–8. Simply constructed items such as stirring rods, wash bottles, capillary dropping tubes,

Semimacro and semimicro experimentation

FIG. 1.1 Dowel stand

1. Baseboard, 1″ × 6″ × 6″; deep-bored holes made with a $\frac{7}{16}$″ drill and an outsize $\frac{3}{4}$″ drill.

2. Two $\frac{3}{4}$″ dowels 18″ long, holes cut with $\frac{1}{2}$″ drill.

3. One plain $\frac{7}{16}$″ dowel, 12″ long.

4. Two slip collars $\frac{3}{4}$″ × $1\frac{1}{2}$″ × $3\frac{1}{2}$″; holes cut with $\frac{15}{32}$″ and outsize $\frac{3}{4}$″ drills.

5. Four $3\frac{3}{4}$″ clothespins with spring clips screwed to heads.

FIG. 1.2 Brick base

and measuring tubes are obligatory and should be made when you reach the point where their use and construction are discussed. Other useful accessories, if not stocked by your laboratory from indicated wholesale sources, can be purchased at a five and ten cent store. General utility items recommended are the dowel stand (Fig. 1.1) and filter block (Fig. 1.3), which are adapted to many uses, either alone, in combination, or in combination with ring stands. The dowel stand is made from familiar, inexpensive parts. A clothespin is so constructed that it fits into the holes snugly at different depths. When a slip collar is mounted on one of the long uprights (right rear) it is adjustable to any height and is held in place by leverage action; it can be locked in place by a push pin inserted in a pin hole in the wood. The small hole of the collar slips loosely over a $\frac{7}{16}$″ dowel (front) or a ring stand, and the height is adjustable by moving the spring clothes clip. The double grip steel spring clip has rounded sections $\frac{7}{16}$″ and $\frac{3}{4}$″ i.d., one or the other of which will receive easily and hold firmly glass apparatus of all sizes from $\frac{7}{16}$″ to $1\frac{3}{16}$″ (8–25 mm.) in diameter. The apparatus can be mounted quickly and is adjustable up or down with ease. As an alternative to the wooden baseboard, a generally useful base can be made from a cord brick (Fig. 1.2, left). This brick is provided with holes both to save freightage weight and to improve bonding. The holes on both sides are smoothed with a round file to receive the $\frac{3}{4}$″ dowel upright and a firm fit is made by inserting a collar made from a strip of 0.01″ copper foil. Rubber feet for the bottom (center) can be made by cementing on sections of rubber suction tubing with liquid solder (aluminum powder in a nitrocellulose adhesive), and the base finished with aluminum paint delivered from a spray can. The $\frac{7}{16}$″ dowel is supported firmly with one drilled cork at the top as shown and another at the bottom. Holes used for test tubes should be plugged at the bottom with a section of cork stopper. A separatory funnel can be supported in a test tube as shown.

The filter block (Fig. 1.3) has a grooved section for holding thick-walled suction tubing and so supporting small filter flasks (in the two ways shown in Fig. 6.6). The block also has pegs for drying and storing apparatus, holes for stirring rods, and holes for supporting Pyrex test tubes of the following sizes:

25 × 150 mm.	13 × 100 mm.
20 × 150 mm.	10 × 75 mm.

The grooved section of the filter block and the slip collar of the dowel stand are both of such width ($1\frac{1}{2}$″) that they serve as supports for a Cenco microburner (height $2\frac{1}{2}''$), the H-base of which has feet that can be snapped over the edges of the wood.

If the dowel stand and filter block are not included in the kit supplied, you may care to construct your own. The designs shown can be modified or simplified. Thus a simple grooved block corresponding to the end section of the block shown serves adequately as a support for filter flasks and for a microburner;

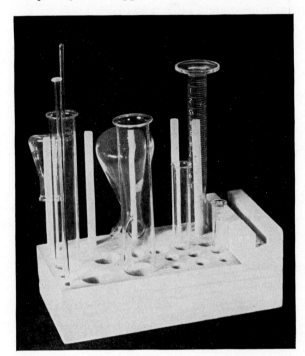

FIG. 1.3 Filter block

one of the collars of the dowel stand having just the smaller of the two holes can be slipped over a ring stand and used as an adjustable-height support for a microburner. If you make your own dowel stand, use a $\frac{3}{4}''$ drill for cutting the larger holes in the baseboard, and sandpaper the two ends of the dowels to fit. You may be able to improve upon the designs or to invent new ways of accomplishing the same objectives.

The new procedures, techniques, and apparatus that appear for the first time in this edition of the manual are the outcome of considerable experimentation by the author. The yields and working times cited are those obtained with the experience gained in repeating the experiments, sometimes dozens of times, in order to work out details, and if you do not match the results on your first trial you should not feel discouraged (or be given a low grade!). In the early experiments, follow the detailed directions carefully and without hurry, acquire such accessory equipment as you need, try to develop a good technique, and try to approach the yields cited. Once you have gained mastery of fundamental operations, try to quicken your pace by organizing your work to avoid idle laboratory time. If operation A requires unattended heating or cooling for a certain period of time, start operation B. Considerable time can be saved by cleaning each piece of equipment immediately after it has been used, for you will know then what type of contaminant is present and you will be able to remove it more easily than after it has dried and hardened.

Note. The hardwood slip collar as supplied makes a tight fit with the Cenco microburner (page 3), but it may dry out and shrink. If the fit is too loose, soak the wood in water for half-hour periods until the fit is satisfactory. In case it becomes swollen to oversize, heat it in a beaker on the steam bath until it fits.

The distillation apparatus shown in Fig. 2.1 consists of a 50-ml. distilling flask equipped with a thermometer with its bulb in the vapor space, a condenser, a receiving flask (Erlenmeyer),

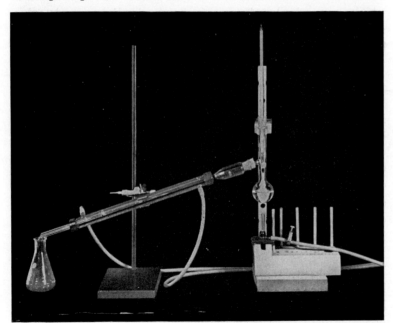

FIG. 2.1   Distillation apparatus

and a microburner mounted on a filter block. The flow of gas is adjusted with a pinchcock. [If pure water is heated in the distilling flask with a small flame the vapor pressure of the liquid, that is the tendency of molecules to escape from the surface, increases until it becomes equal to the atmospheric pressure.] Continued heating supplies heat of vaporization necessary for conversion of liquid to gas, and vapors rise into the neck of the flask

Boiling point of a
pure liquid

and at first condense and run back. When the neck has been warmed sufficiently, the vapors begin flowing out through the side arm into the condenser. Distillation is conducted slowly but steadily so that the thermometer bulb always carries a drop of condensate and is always bathed in a flow of vapor; liquid and vapor are then in equilibrium and the temperature recorded is the true boiling point. If excessive heat is applied and the vapor becomes superheated, the drop will disappear, the liquid-vapor equilibrium will be upset, and the temperature will rise above the boiling point.

Whereas superheating of the vapor can be avoided by exercising suitable care, some superheating of the liquid is almost inevitable, because the heat supplied is not all immediately dissipated by vaporization. Hence if the thermometer bulb were immersed in the boiling liquid it might record a temperature a little above the boiling point. A thermometer in the vapor space, however, will record the true boiling point even of a liquid in which a nonvolatile substance is dissolved. For example, when a solution of sugar in water is distilled the boiling point recorded on a thermometer in the vapor phase is 100° (at 760 mm.) throughout the distillation, whereas the temperature of the boiling liquid is initially somewhat above 100° and continues to rise as the sugar solution becomes more concentrated. The vapor pressure of the solution is dependent upon the number of water molecules present in a given volume, and hence with increasing concentration of nonvolatile sugar molecules and decreasing concentration of water the vapor pressure at a given temperature decreases and a higher temperature is required for boiling. However, sugar molecules do not leave the solution, and the drop clinging to the thermometer bulb, like the distillate of which it is a sample, is pure water in equilibrium with pure water vapor.

When a distillation is done in a system open to the air and the boiling point is the temperature at which the pressure of the boiling liquid is equal to that of the atmosphere, the prevailing barometric pressure should be noted and allowance made for appreciable deviations from the normal pressure of 760 mm. by reference to Table 2.1. Distillation can also be done at the vacuum of an oil or water pump with substantial reduction of boiling point.

Mixtures of the miscible liquids carbon tetrachloride (b.p. 76.7°) and toluene (b.p. 110.6°) distil at temperatures intermediate between the two boiling points and the composition of the distillate changes progressively during the process. Since the two substances are mutually soluble, each is diluted by the other, with consequent reduction in the vapor pressure that it can exert at a given temperature. However, the liquids exert a common pressure against the atmosphere and boiling occurs when the sum of the two partial pressures equals atmospheric pressure.

An azeotropic mixture is a mixture of liquids of a certain definite composition that distils at a constant temperature without change in composition. The boiling point is usually lower than that of the lowest boiling component, but it is sometimes higher

TABLE 2.1

VARIATION IN BOILING POINT WITH PRESSURE

Pressure	Water	Benzene
780 mm.	100.7°	81.2°
770 mm.	100.4°	80.8°
760 mm.	100.0°	80.1°
750 mm.	99.6°	79.9°
740 mm.	99.3°	79.5°
584 mm.*	92.8°	71.2°

* Instituto de Quimica, Mexico City, altitude 7700 ft. (2310 meters).

than that of the highest boiling component; it is never in an intermediate range. Ordinary ethyl alcohol is an azeotrope of b.p. 78.1° composed of 95.5% (by weight) ethanol, b.p. 78.4°, and 4.5% of water. An azeotropic mixture of 32.4% ethanol and 67.6% benzene (b.p. 80.1°) boils at 68.2°. A ternary azeotrope, b.p. 64.9°, contains 74.1% benzene, 18.5% ethanol, and 7.4% water. Absolute ethanol is made by adding benzene to 95% alcohol and removing the water in the volatile azeotrope.

EXPERIMENTS

1. Calibration of Thermometer

Test the 0° point with a well-stirred mixture of crushed ice and distilled water. Put 10 ml. of water in a 25 × 150-mm. test tube, clamp the tube in a vertical position, add one carborundum boiling stone to prevent bumping,[1] boil gently, and hold a thermometer in the boiling vapor, and check the 100° point. Then immerse the bulb in the boiling liquid and see if you can observe any superheating.

[1] For efficiency of operation, freedom from dust, uniformity, cheapness, and ready visibility in a reaction product, carborundum stones are recommended above all others. One pound of No. 12 carborundum (The Carborundum Co., Niagara Falls, N.Y.) provides each of 90 students with over 300 stones (5 g. in a small cork-stoppered shell vial).

2. Apparatus (see Fig. 2.1)

Use a 50-ml. distilling flask and a short condenser (50 cm. overall). Cork stoppers are used since rubber swells in organic solvents, particularly in benzene, which is one of the liquids to be

distilled. Since benzene is highly flammable, the cork fittings must be perfectly tight. Select a cork that initially fits only 4–5 mm. into the opening and soften it by rolling it under a wooden block; this treatment reduces the size and diminishes the chance of the cork splitting when bored. Select a borer that will give a hole slightly smaller than required, hold it in the right hand and work it into the cork held in the left hand. After each twist grasp the cork at a new place and check the alignment. When

the cork has been cut halfway through, withdraw the borer, push out a plug if present, and cut the remainder of the hole from the other side. Test the fit of the tube to be inserted and, with frequent further testing, ream the hole with a round file applied from both sides until the tube can be inserted without undue force but still fits tightly. Grasp the tube or thermometer close to the end to be inserted and work it carefully into the cork by twisting. If it is held very far from the cork it is liable to break and cause a severe cut. The bulb of the thermometer should be slightly below the opening of the side arm and in the center of the neck.

3. Distillation of Benzene and of Benzene–Water

Introduce 20 ml. of benzene and a boiling stone into the flask (dry), make sure that all connections are tight, and heat the flask directly with a small flame until boiling starts. Then adjust the flame until the distillate drops at a regular rate of about one drop per second. Slight cloudiness of the first condensate indicates the presence of a trace of water in the benzene or of a film of moisture in the flask. When the condensate is clear and the requirements for vapor-liquid equilibrium are satisfied, the boiling point should become constant. Apply appropriate corrections for barometric pressure and thermometer errors.

When half of the benzene has distilled remove the flame, let the flask cool a little, and add about 1 ml. of water. Note that benzene is insoluble in water. Distil the mixture and note the boiling point and the character of the condensate. When you think that all the water has been removed from the boiling flask and that it contains pure benzene, discontinue the distillation, let the flask cool and empty it, and clean and dry the apparatus. The condenser can be cleaned by clamping it in a vertical position, placing under it the receiving flask emptied of its contents (discard), and rinsing the tube with a few ml. of acetone, which dissolves both water and benzene and evaporates rapidly (b.p. 56°). For both convenience and economy of solvent, wash acetone can be dispensed from a 50-ml. Calcutta wash bottle (Fig. 2.2), operated by pointing the tip downward and allowing the base of the flask to be warmed in the palm of the hand.[2] If the condenser is simply let stand upright it will dry in a few minutes.

FIG. 2.2 **Calcutta wash bottle**

Drying can be hastened by drawing air through the apparatus at the suction of the water pump (some compressed air sources are suitable for drying but others contain substantial amounts of moisture).

4. Carbon Tetrachloride–Toluene

Measure 10 ml. each of carbon tetrachloride (b.p. 76.7°) and toluene (b.p. 110.6°) into the 50-ml. distilling flask (dry), introduce a boiling stone, and put a 10-ml. graduate in place as the receiver (Fig. 2.3). The tip of the condenser should touch the graduate so that liquid will flow in steadily and not by drops. Distil the mixture at a regular rate and record the results as follows:

Fraction	B.p.	Volume, ml.	Fraction	B.p.	Volume, ml.
I	To 82°		IV	104–111°	
II	82–93°		Residue		
III	93–104°		Loss		

FIG. 2.3 **(Scale extended with gummed label)**

[2] An empty Ronsonol lighter-fuel can with a switch-spout is a convenient wash bottle for acetone. The plastic cap can be removed for filling by prying it carefully with a coin. To replace it, press down on pieces of wood or coins resting on each shoulder of the cap.

5. Azeotropic Distillation

Rinse the cooled flask and the condenser with a little acetone and let them drain and dry. Then introduce 10 ml. of 95% ethanol and 5 ml. of benzene (and a boiling stone). Distil the mixture, collect the distillate in a dry 10-ml. graduate, and plot boiling point against milliliters of distillate. Note the approximate boiling point and volume of each fraction. At the end, test the small residual liquid in the flask for the presence of benzene by smelling it and pouring it into water. In the light of your observations and the introductory discussion, identify the different fractions of distillate.

QUESTIONS

1. Can you account for the observed boiling point of benzene-water mixtures relative to that of benzene? Note that the two liquids are immiscible and hence that molecules of A do not dilute molecules of B; the presence of A does not reduce the partial vapor pressure exerted by B against the external pressure, and vice versa. The total pressure is equal to the sum of the two partial pressures.

2. If a liquid is found to boil at a constant temperature over the whole range of the distillation, could you infer that it is a pure substance?

3. If two miscible liquids are found to boil at exactly the same temperature, could the conclusion be drawn that they are identical?

FIG. 2.4 Graduate with flared mouth (Kimball 20025)

Your experience in the preceding distillation of a mixture of carbon tetrachloride and toluene should have shown that a single distillation effects little separation of these components, which differ in boiling point by only 34°. The distribution of distillate observed in an experiment conducted on a larger scale is shown in the third column of Table 3.1; the boiling point ranges show

TABLE 3.1

FRACTIONATION WITHOUT A COLUMN

MIXTURE: 60 ml. Carbon Tetrachloride (b.p. 76.7°),
60 ml. Toluene (b.p. 110.6°)

Fraction	Temp. interval	VOLUME OF FRACTION IN ML.			
		1st Dist'n	2nd Dist'n	3rd Dist'n	4th Dist'n
I	To 82°	0	8.5	19.3	28.5
II	82–93°	45.0	44.3	30.5	21.0
III	93–104°	44.5	31.2	23.8	15.3
IV	104–111°	26.7	29.0	34.5	39.3
Residue	....	1.8	1.5	2.2	2.0
Losses	....	2.0	3.5	4.2	4.2

that fraction II is a little richer than the others in the more volatile carbon tetrachloride and that IV is richer in toluene. Further concentration of the components in the two end fractions can be achieved by distilling each appreciable fraction and combining more and less volatile parts with appropriate parts of other fractions. Thus in the second distillation the 45.0 ml. of II afforded 8.5 ml. of distillate appropriate for flask I and a residue that when combined with original fraction III yielded 44.3

ml. of distillate of b.p. 82–93° and a less volatile part that was combined with IV. The process is tedious and the net result of four distillations is discouraging.

A fractionating column such as that shown in Fig. 3.1 effects in a single operation what amounts to several separate simple

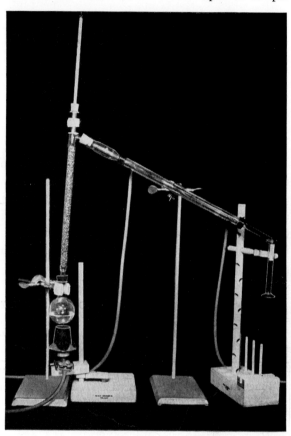

FIG. 3.1 Distillation with a fractionating column

distillations. The column has a packing that provides a cooling space where part of the vapor of the boiling mixture condenses and trickles down through the crevices in the packing; the less volatile component tends to condense first. Fresh vapor from the flask forces its way up through the descending condensate with attendant heat interchange, since the vapor is hotter than the liquid. A more volatile part of the liquid vaporizes and a less volatile part of the vapor condenses. Equilibrations occur in all parts of the column and the vapor that eventually passes into the receiver is highly enriched in the more volatile component, while the condensate that continually drops back into the flask is scrubbed of the volatile liquid and enriched in the less volatile one.

With the column illustrated in Fig. 3.1 and specified for the experiments below, it is possible to effect sharp separations such as that indicated in the distillation curve of Fig. 3.2 for a mixture of liquids boiling only 35.3° apart. To obtain so successful a result, however, one must use a very small flame protected from drafts and boil the liquid slowly and steadily enough to allow full heat equilibration between liquid and vapor in the column. Column efficiency is improved by insulating the column and by introducing a small condenser at the very top of the column to effect partial condensation of the already highly rectified vapor.

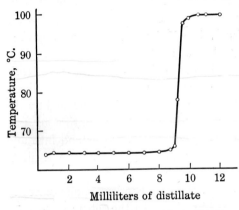

FIG. 3.2 **Fractionation of a mixture of methanol (b.p. 64.7°) and water**

The simple apparatus specified permits observation of the functioning of a column and will demonstrate the enormous efficiency over simple distillation.

Since the separation effected in a fractionating column is dependent upon heat equilibration in multiple processes of vaporization and condensation, the efficiency of separation increases with increasing heat of vaporization of the liquids concerned. Table 3.2 shows that water by far surpasses any of the organic solvents

TABLE 3.2

PROPERTIES OF SOLVENTS

Solvent	B.p.	Latent heat of vaporization [a]	Surface tension [b] (20°)
Acetone	56.5°	125.3	23.7
Methanol	64.7°	261.7	22.6
Hexane	68.7°	79.2	18.4
Carbon tetrachloride	76.7°	46.4	26.8
Benzene	80.1°	93.5	29.0
Water	100.0°	536.6	72.7
Toluene	110.6°	86.8	28.4

[a] Calories per gram at the b.p.
[b] Dynes per centimeter.

listed; it is a particularly favorable component for separation from a mixture. Water also surpasses organic liquids in surface tension, a property that determines the behavior of a condensate on a glass surface, as will be apparent from one of the experiments. The high heat of vaporization, the high surface tension, and a boiling point that is high for a substance of so low molecular weight (compare ammonia) are all consequences of a high degree of association of molecules in liquid water.

EXPERIMENTS

1. Apparatus (Fig. 3.1)

The fractionating column is a tube with side arm packed loosely with a stainless steel sponge.[1] The 100-ml. boiling flask with flared neck is connected to the column by means of a No. 2 Neoprene adapter, and a short condenser (50 cm. overall) delivers into a 10-ml. graduate, the inside wall of which is touched by the condenser so that the flow of condensate is continuous (see Fig. 2.3). The side arm of the column should extend into and touch the narrow part of the condenser in order that the distillate will flow in evenly at this point as well.

Success in a fractional distillation is dependent upon very careful adjustment of the rate of heating. In the set-up of Fig. 3.1 the heating is done by a microburner mounted on a slip collar that fits loosely on a $\frac{7}{16}''$ dowel and rests on a clothes clip. Fine temperature control is made by adjustment of the distance of the flame from the flask. The flame is protected by a chimney supported, as shown in Fig. 3.3, by piercing a $2\frac{1}{2}'' \times 2\frac{1}{2}''$ square of copper gauze with an awl, enlarging the hole with a cork-borer sharpener, and slipping over the burner a $\frac{1}{2}''$ section of cork and then the gauze, and folding the corners up over the chimney.

The experiments below should demonstrate the mode of operation and efficiency of a fractionating column. Follow the direc-

In case slip collar does not fit, see note on p. 4.

Note for the instructor

[1] A stainless steel scouring sponge obtainable at an F. W. Woolworth or S. S. Kresge store is pulled out to a strand about 20'' long and half of this is packed loosely into the column with a $\frac{3}{16}''$ dowel. A piece of Fiberglas is taped on at the top for insulation. The efficiency is at least as good as that of the same tube packed with glass helices or glass beads and immeasurably better than with a packing of short sections of glass tubing, and no indentures at the base of the column are required and no porcelain plate is needed. The packing can be used to convert an ordinary distilling flask into a reasonably good fractionation flask (Chapter 26.2). If the liquid is not known to be inert to the packing a test should be made before distillation is tried.

Suppliers. Fractionation tube, overall length 42 cm., o.d. 18 mm., Wilkens-Anderson No. 5817. Round bottomed flasks, 100-ml. with flared neck: Schott-Jena DIN 12351, Fish-Schurman Corp., New Rochelle, N.Y.; Wilkens-Anderson No. 5578.

tions carefully and do not hurry. If your distillation curve for either of the known mixtures is irregular and does not indicate clearly the composition of the mixture, repeat the fractionation before investigation of the unknown.

2. Methanol–Water

Fractionally distil a mixture of 10 ml. of methanol and 10 ml. of water. Adjust the boiling flask to a height about 7 cm. above the tip of the microburner and apply the smallest flame (just nonluminous) that will stay lit. Increase the heat until active boiling begins and note how the boiling stone operates. Con-

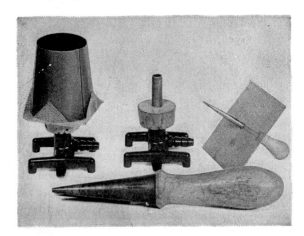

FIG. 3.3 Chimney holder for burner

tinue to heat rather rapidly (to save time) until a ring of condensate has risen from one half to three quarters the way to the top of the column. If you cannot at first see this ring, locate it by touching the column with the fingers. The temperature rise from this point on should be very gradual, in order that the column may acquire a steady temperature gradient. Do not apply more heat until you are sure that the ring of condensate has stopped rising. Then increase the heat by raising the burner a little closer to the boiling flask. In a properly conducted operation the vapor-condensate mixture reaches the top of the column only after 7–10 min. Once distillation has commenced it should continue steadily without any drop in temperature at a rate not greater than 1 ml. in $1\frac{1}{2}$–2 min. Observe the flow at the tip of the side arm and keep it steady by slight increases in heat (raise the burner) as required. Record the temperature as each ml. of distillate collects, and make more frequent readings (0.5 ml.) when the temperature starts to rise abruptly. Stop the distillation when a second steady temperature is reached (about 12 ml.).

15

{ Plot a distillation curve and record what you observed inside the column in the course of the fractionation. }

Let the column cool and then wash it with acetone and let this drain. Then stopper the column at the top and bottom, connect the side arm through a calcium chloride tube to the suction pump, and evacuate until there is no further cooling effect and the column has warmed to room temperature.

3. Carbon Tetrachloride–Toluene

Fractionate a mixture of 10 ml. each of the two liquids and plot a distillation curve. If a little moisture appears at the top of the column wrap the part of the tube above the side arm with cotton, glass wool, or a collar of Fiberglas insulation (see Fig. 3.1, Wilkens-Anderson No. 5817). Compare your results with those reported in Table 3.1 for distillation without a column.

4. Unknown

An unknown, prepared by the instructor, is a mixture of any two of the solvents listed in Table 3.2 that are mutually soluble and differ in boiling point by more than 20°. The unknown mixture should contain not more than 10 ml. of the more volatile component to 10 ml. of the other component.[2] Fractionate the unknown, identify the components from the boiling points, and estimate the composition of the mixture from the distillation curve.

QUESTIONS

1. Explain the change observed in the column as methanol is being displaced by water.

2. Outline a specific procedure for the preparation of completely pure methanol starting with a mixture of 100 ml. each of methanol and water.

3. If carbon tetrachloride were to be isolated in pure form from a mixture of 100 ml. each of this solvent with toluene, in what respects should the procedure differ from that outlined in (2)?

4. The components of the methanol–water and carbon tetrachloride–toluene mixtures differ from each other in boiling point by nearly the same increment. Explain why the separation was more efficient with one solvent pair than with the other.

5. Which pair of miscible solvents listed in Table 3.2 offer the best possibility for separation by fractional distillation and which should be the most difficultly separable?

[2] Methanol forms azeotropes of boiling points and percentages of methanol as follows: n-hexane, 50.6°, 28%; carbon tetrachloride, 76.8°, 20.6%; benzene, 58.3°, 39.6%; toluene, 63.8°, 69%.

Melting Points

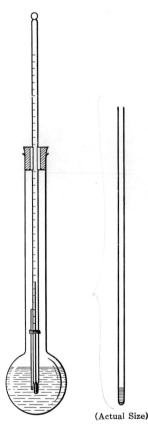

(Actual Size)

The melting point of an organic solid can be determined by introducing a tiny amount of the substance into a small capillary tube (Fig. 4.1), attaching this to the stem of a thermometer centered in a heating bath, heating the bath slowly, and observing the temperatures at which melting begins and is complete. Pure samples usually have sharp melting points, for example 149.5–150° or 189–190°; impure samples of the same compounds melt at lower temperatures and over a wider range, for example 145–148° or 187–189°. The contaminant that depresses the melting point and extends the melting range may be an indefinitely characterized resinous material or it may be a trace of a second chemical entity of melting point either higher or lower than that of the major component. Under equilibrium conditions (no supercooling) the temperature at which a pure solid melts is identical with that at which the molten substance solidifies or freezes. Just as salt lowers the freezing point of water, so one compound (A) depresses the melting point of another (B) with which it is mixed. If pure A melts at 150–151° and pure B at 120–121°, mixtures of A with small amounts of B will melt unsharply at temperatures below 150° and mixtures of B containing A will melt below 120°. Both the temperature and sharpness of melting are useful criteria of purity.

A third substance C may have exactly the same melting point as A, namely 150–151°, but if a mixed melting point determination is made, that is if A and C are mixed and the melting point of the mixture is observed, the one substance will be found to depress the melting point of the other. Depression of melting point or nondepression is invaluable in the identification of unknowns. An unknown D found to melt at 150–151° can be sus-

FIG. 4.1 Melting point flask and capillary tube

The Pyrex flask is 22 cm. long, the neck is 18 mm. o.d., the bulb 50 mm. o.d. Available from Macalaster Bicknell Co., Cambridge, Mass.

pected of being identical with one or the other known substances A and C; observation that the mixture AD shows a melting point depression would exclude identity with A, and failure of C to depress the melting point of D would prove C and D identical.

If a substance melts at 150° or higher, the thread of mercury in the upper part of the thermometer is cooler than that in the bulb and hence the temperature recorded is a little lower than the actual bath temperature. The extent of the error due to stem exposure depends upon the design of the thermometer and the type of heating bath used; it may amount to 2–5° at 200°, 3–10° at 250°. An approximate correction for stem exposure can be calculated from the formula:

$$\text{Stem correction (°C)} = 0.000154\ (t - t')N$$

where the fraction represents the difference in the coefficients of expansion of glass and of mercury, t is the temperature read, t' is the average temperature of the exposed column of mercury (determined, approximately, by reading the temperature of a second thermometer whose bulb is placed midway between the bath and the point on the first thermometer corresponding to t), and N represents the length, measured in degrees, of the thread exposed between the top of the heating liquid and the point t. The convention for reporting a corrected melting point is: m.p. 283.5–284.5° (corr.). The error can be eliminated by use of a heating bath designed to accommodate a series of short thermometers that can be totally immersed.

EXPERIMENT

1. Apparatus (Fig. 4.1)

The thermometer is fitted through a cork, a section of which is cut away for pressure release and so that the scale is visible. A single-edge razor blade is convenient for cutting, and the cut can be smoothed or deepened with a triangular file. The round bulb of the flask causes convection currents to rise evenly along the outer walls and then descend and converge at the center, hence care must be taken to center the thermometer. The long neck prevents spilling and fuming and minimizes the error due to stem exposure. The bulb of the flask (dry!) is three-quarters filled with dibutyl phthalate containing 0.4% of hydroquinone (inhibits discoloration and oxidation to phthalic anhydride).

The molecular weight determination described in Section 6 requires such fine temperature adjustment and so close observation of the sample that the experiments that precede it should be used to gain necessary experience in the adjustment and operation of an adequate assembly, such as that illustrated in Fig. 4.2. The melting-point flask is mounted with a clamp on a ring stand, and a slip collar carrying a microburner with chimney fits loosely on a $\frac{7}{16}''$ dowel at a height determined by the position of the spring clothes clip. If a lens is desired for viewing the sample or reading the thermometer (or both), it can be mounted on a piece of tubing (preferably Tygon) held in the ring of a test tube holder.[1]

The capillary melting point tubes are made by drawing out 12-mm. tubing. The large tube is rotated in the hottest part of the Bunsen burner flame until it is very soft and begins to sag. It should not be drawn at all during the heating. Remove it from the flame, hesitate for a second or two, and then draw it out steadily but not too rapidly to arm's length. With some practice it is possible to produce 10–15 good tubes in a single drawing. The long tube can be cut into sections nicely with the sharp edge of a broken clay plate. Alternately, bring a sharp file resting on your forefinger underneath the tube, put your thumb over the place to be cut, and gently draw in the file so as to produce a slight scratch. On applying gentle pressure with the thumb the tube will now break cleanly. The tube is sealed by rotating the end in the edge of a small flame. The proper size of the tube is indicated in the sketch, Fig. 4.1.

Spatulas that are useful for filling the capillary tubes and that meet other requirements of the experiments of this manual are shown in Fig. 4.3. They can be kept clean by polishing with steel wool. They should not be used as stirring rods and will be ruined if they are heated in a flame.

FIG. 4.2 Melting point assembly

Fisher glass-tubing scorer recommended for cutting glass

2. Operation

Put a small pile of the sample about 3–4 mm. in diameter on a filter paper and crush it to a powder with a small spatula. Scrape the powder into a mound and use the spatula as a stop while pushing the open end of a capillary tube into the sample to scoop it up. The sample may be shaken down to the bottom by gentle stroking with a file, or it may be tamped down by dropping the tube through a long vertical tube onto a hard surface. The column of solid should be no more than 2–3 mm. in length and it should be tightly packed. If the sample is in the form of a compact cake it is often convenient to fill the capillary by cutting

---

[1] A lens 4 cm. in diameter with a 5-cm. handle currently costs 19 cents at an F. W. Woolworth or S. S. Kresge store.

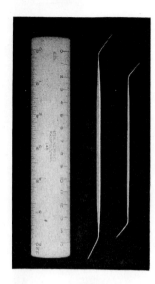

FIG. 4.3 Spatulas of sterling silver

The spatulas are 5″ and 7″ in length and the blade of the larger one is ¼″ wide. Available from R. F. Simmons Co., Attleboro, Mass.

out a tiny cylinder with the open end of the tube and then shaking it down. If a fluffy or sticky sample plugs the tube and fails to be shaken down try using just a tiny fragment of material at a time.

The melting point capillary is held to the thermometer by a small rubber band made by cutting a thin slice off the end of a piece of tubing; the band may require replacement from time to time. Insertion of a fresh tube under the rubber band is facilitated by leaving a used tube in place. The sample should be close to and on a level with the center of the thermometer bulb, which must be fully submerged and centered in the flask. If the approximate melting temperature is known, the bath can be heated rapidly until the temperature is about 20° below this point, but the heating during the last 15–20° must be slow and regular (2° rise per minute). Observe both the sample and the thermometer and record the temperatures of initial and terminal melting. The Pyrex flask can be detached and cooled for a second determination as follows: with an air blast if the temperature is above 150°; if the bath is no hotter than 150° it may be submerged for 30-sec. periods in a 600-ml. beaker of water.

If determinations are to be done on two or three samples that differ in melting point by as much as 10°, two or three capillaries can be secured to the thermometer together and the melting points observed in succession without removal of the thermometer from the bath. As a precaution against interchange of tubes while they are being attached, use some system of identification, such as one, two, and three dots made with a marking pencil.

3. Known

Determine the melting point of either urea (m.p. 133°) or cinnamic acid (m.p. 133°). Repeat the determination and if you do not check your first result within 1° do a third one.

4. Mixture

Make mixtures of urea and cinnamic acid in the approximate proportions 1:4, 1:1, and 4:1 by putting side by side small piles of the two substances of sizes estimated to be in the right ratio and then mixing them. Note the ranges of melting but use the temperatures of complete liquefaction (and the m.p. 133° for each pure component) for construction of a rough diagram.

5. Unknown

Determine the melting point of an unknown, which may be any one of the following:

Acetanilide   *m*-Dinitrobenzene
Benzoic acid   Salicylic acid
Cinnamic acid   Succinic acid

Look up the melting points of these substances in a handbook, the Merck Index, or a catalogue, and identify your unknown by carrying out a mixed melting point determination with an authentic sample.

6. Rast Molecular Weight Determination [2]

A dissolved substance depresses the freezing (or melting) point of the solvent to an extent that is dependent upon the ratio of solute to solvent molecules and upon the susceptibility of the particular solvent used, as measured by the value of its cryoscopic constant. The freezing point of a fixed weight of benzene is depressed a constant number of degrees by a certain molecular proportion of any soluble, unionized solute, and observation of the extent of the depression (Δt) and knowledge of the cryoscopic constant C for benzene permits calculation of the molecular weight.

$$\text{Mol. wt.} = \frac{\text{Solute, g.}}{\text{Solvent, g.}} \left| \frac{C}{\Delta t} \right.$$

The constant C can be expressed in terms appropriate to the practice of using very dilute solutions for avoiding errors that otherwise decrease accuracy. One gram of a substance of molecular weight 100 produces the depressions noted when dissolved in 100 g. of each of the following solvents: benzene, $0.510°$; acetic acid, $0.390°$; water, $0.185°$. If the molecular weight of the solute is 200 or 300 the depressions are one-half or one-third those cited. With these and other common solvents the depressions are so small that molecular weight determinations can be made only with use of a precision instrument such as the Beckmann thermometer. Camphor is a special solvent because its cryoscopic constant is eight times that of benzene and twenty times that of water. It is a solid, m.p. about $173°$, but in the molten state it has high solvent power for organic compounds and affords solid solutions whose melting points can be determined in capillary tubes with an ordinary thermometer, which suffices for observation of the depression of $4.0°$ produced by 1 g. of a compound of

[2] It is suggested that a student who has developed reasonable competency in making his own melting point capillaries be given the option of using the more uniform manufactured capillaries, at least for this and other quantitative experiments (Chapters 5, 6, 11). Kimble glass capillaries 1.5–2 × 90 mm. sealed at one end are recommended.

molecular weight 100 dissolved in 100 g. of camphor. Rast's method is to prepare such a solid solution, determine the depression, and calculate the molecular weight:

$$\text{Mol. wt.} = \frac{\text{Substance, g.}}{\text{Camphor, g.}} \left| \frac{40,000}{\Delta t} \right.$$

Camphor is a natural product and is also manufactured synthetically on a large scale for use as plasticizer for nitrocellulose to produce celluloid. The melting behavior is peculiar, since even the purest material melts over a considerable temperature range: the solid softens, then it turns to a glassy semisolid, then a clear liquid appears in the upper part of the tube and a skeleton of crystals remains in the lower part and slowly decreases in size and eventually disappears. The point of disappearance of the last crystal, the melting point, can be determined with accuracy. If the bath is allowed to cool very slowly an equally accurate determination can be made of the freezing point, the temperature at which the first tiny crystals of camphor separate. That the freezing point is usually found to be about 2° below the melting point is probably due to supercooling of the unstirred solution. Dilute solid solutions (1–6%) of solid organic compounds in camphor behave similarly; the transition temperatures are lower, the melting ranges wider, and the difference between melting and freezing point somewhat greater. High accuracy in determining the extent of depression is attainable with the apparatus of Fig. 4.2 by attaching to the thermometer one tube containing pure camphor and another containing a mixture of camphor and the substance under investigation. Errors due to inaccuracy of the thermometer or to stem exposure are thus cancelled. Very slow heating and cooling and very careful observation are required. It is necessary also to seal off the capillary at a point that will be below the level of the heating fluid, for if there is any vapor space above this level camphor will sublime into the cooler area and leave a residual melt enriched in the solute. The capillary is evacuated prior to sealing to facilitate formation of a firm seal without increasing the fragility of the tube. The technique is of general use, since some compounds undergo air oxidation when heated in open capillary tubes and true melting points are obtainable only when the determinations are made in evacuated tubes.

Problem

One unknown contains X grams of acetanilide (C_8H_9ON) per 100 g. of camphor and the other contains X grams of benzophenone ($C_{13}H_{10}O$) per 100 g. of camphor.[3] The problem is to determine the melting and freezing points of the two unknowns and of camphor simultaneously, establish which unknown is acetanilide and which is benzophenone, and calculate the value of X, common to both samples. Care should be taken to fill, seal, and mount the tubes properly, for once this is done the determinations can be repeated until you have gained sufficient experience to obtain checking results in which you can have confidence.

Procedure

Push the open end of a melting point capillary into powdered unknown A or B or camphor contained in a short specimen tube and tamp down the solid until you have a column about 5 mm. long. Mark each tube and record what it contains. The tube is connected to the suction pump with an adapter (Fig. 4.4) consisting of a glass tube capped with a rubber vaccine stopper[4] with a hole pierced through it with an awl or ice pick. Lubricate the end of the hole extending toward the wide part of the stopper, grasp the capillary very close to the sealed end, and thrust it through nearly to the full length. Connect to the suction pump, restore the markings if necessary, and make a guiding mark 1.5 cm. from the closed end where a seal is to be formed. Grasp the end of the tube with one hand and the adapter with the other, hold the point of sealing near the small flame of a microburner, steady your hands on the bench so that neither will move much when the tube is melted, and then hold the tube in the flame until the walls collapse to form a flat seal and remove it at once. Take the tube out of the adapter and if the two straight parts are not in a line soften the seal and correct the alignment.

Mount tubes of A, B, and camphor side by side on the thermometer under a rubber band, insert the thermometer, and make sure that all the seals are completely submerged. The bath may be heated rapidly to about 130°, but from this point on the temperature rise should be as slow as it possibly can be made. At the outset a very small flame about 7 cm. below the flask should produce a slow, gradual rise of 1° in 30–40 sec. Determine the point of disappearance of the last crystal for each sample

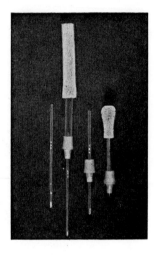

FIG. 4.4 Evacuation and sealing of capillary

---

[3] Weigh $X/10$ g. of substance and 10 g. of camphor in a test tube, stopper loosely, melt without undue overheating, pour the melt into a mortar, swirl until solid, then at once dislodge the solid and while it is still hot grind it lightly and not too long. Concentrations of 1–6% are satisfactory.

[4] West Co. (Philadelphia) No. 1A red or amber rubber vaccine stoppers are listed by Arthur H. Thomas Co. as rubber stoppers 2319-B.

Notes for the instructor

in succession and then continue heating until the bath is about 2° above the melting point of camphor, and do not stop at this point to interpret the results. Instead, lower the flame by small increments until the temperature starts to fall and then adjust the heating so that the temperature falls 1° in 30–40 sec. Determine each freezing point in turn and then keep the bath at about 140° while calculating the depressions in melting and freezing point. If the two depressions are very divergent, or if the difference between m.p. and f.p. for either A or B is much greater than that for camphor, repeat all the determinations.

In order to assess the data calculate the value of X for each separate determination from the equation:

$$X = \frac{\Delta t}{\ } \left| \frac{\text{Mol. wt.}}{400} \right.$$

Tabulate the results, put the more divergent values in parentheses, and average the others. Does any pair of determinations on A and B leave doubt as to the identity of the unknowns? When the true value of X is disclosed, calculate the molecular weights based on your best Δt values and estimate the limit of accuracy of the method. On the estimate that a 3-mm. column of camphor in a capillary tube weighs 1 mg., calculate the weights of acetanilide and benzophenone used in your determinations.

On completion of the experiment

Since the melting point apparatus will be required for the next experiment it may be put away in assembled form. When parts are required for other purposes the heating flask should be let cool, stoppered tightly with a cork, and put away.

Weights and Measures | CHAPTER 5

Frontispiece Fig. 0.1 presents a comparison of the volumes occupied by equal weights of common solid materials and shows weighed samples of substances of interest for their color or because of the physiological activity that they exhibit, in some instances in extremely minute doses. Because solids vary widely in density, and since a crystalline solid occupies a greater volume than an amorphous sample of the same substance, an estimation of weight based on visual inspection is a mere guess that may be in error by a factor of 2–10. Since later experiments require accurate estimation of quantities too small to be measured on a 100-g. triple beam balance, indeed of the magnitude of the smaller samples of Fig. 0.1, a procedure is given below for measuring the weight of a sample from the volume it occupies in a calibrated capillary melting point tube.

Fig. 0.2 shows a series of vessels containing about the maximum amount of liquid that each should contain if the liquid is to be distilled or heated to dissolve a solute. The measurements given in the caption show that the actual volume of a standard flask is usually a little greater than the nominal volume. Although volumes of 1 ml. and more can be measured accurately with an appropriate graduate, occasions arise where a rough estimate is adequate and measurement in a graduate inconvenient, for example when a solution that half fills a 125-ml. Erlenmeyer flask is to be evaporated to a volume of 15 ml. and the concentrated solution let stand for crystallization. A simple solution is to measure 15 ml. of methanol or acetone into a second 125-ml. Erlenmeyer flask and to use this as a gauge. A low-boiling organic solvent of low surface tension is preferable to water because the emptied flask drains and dries faster.

The smallest of the test tubes shown in Fig. 0.2, the 10 × 75 mm. size, is recommended for use in making solubility tests both for economy of materials and because the tube serves as an adequate graduate for measuring the small volumes of solvent required: 0.5 ml. of liquid forms a 1-cm. column, the 1.0 ml. of yellow solution in the illustration forms a 2-cm. column. A method of measurement of greater precision that is applicable to still smaller volumes is described below.

EXPERIMENTS

1. Weights

Make marks with a wax pencil 9, 13, and 22 cm. from a cleanly cut end of a piece of 7-mm. (o.d.) soft glass tubing. Cut the tube at the 22-cm. mark by making a scratch with a file, moistening it, placing your thumbs together just opposite the file scratch, and exerting a slight outward pressure. Then heat the tube in a microburner at the midpoint, between the 9 and 13 cm. marks, and draw it down to the first stage shown in Fig. 5.1. Then, in turn, seal off each half as shown, heat each seal until soft, and press the tube down onto a flat, heat-resistant surface (a coin) to form two flat-ended cylindrical tubes a little over 10 cm. long. Do not fire polish the open end, but rather blunt the outer edge with a file. Prepare a second pair of measuring tubes of 5-mm. soft glass. Select the better tube of each size for calibration and put the others aside as substitutes that can be assumed to be of the same inside diameter as those calibrated. Fill the 7-mm. measuring tube with sodium bicarbonate by the technique used for filling a melting point capillary: thrust the open end into a pile of solid backed by a spatula, and shake it down by the agitation provided by light stroking with a file. Do not pack the solid in as tightly as possible, but rather develop your own technique for packing it, by stroking with file (see 4.2), in a way that you can reproduce. When the tube is filled, measure the length of the column of solid and then, by stroking with a file, shake out the bicarbonate onto a tared paper and weigh it. Calculate the weight of bicarbonate per unit of length of column, i.e., mg. per mm. Now fill the 5-mm. tube to the same standard degree of density, measure the length of the column, and to determine the weight, invert this tube over the 7-mm. tube and empty its contents into the larger tube by stroking with a file. Pack the column by your standard technique, measure the length, calculate the weight that filled the 5-mm. tube, and so establish the calibration of this tube in mg. of bicarbonate per mm. of length. A

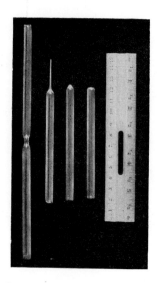

FIG. 5.1 Preparation of a 7-mm. measuring tube

melting point capillary serves as the smallest measuring tube. Fill and calibrate it by reference to the calibrated 5-mm. tube.

Shake the solid out of the tubes, blow out any adhering particles with an air blast, and store the tubes for use whenever you wish to measure small amounts of bicarbonate. For measurement of another solid, you can either repeat the whole calibration, or merely determine the density of the solid relative to that of sodium bicarbonate by filling the 7-mm. tube and weighing the contents.

2. Volumes

Small volumes can be measured with capillary dropping tubes (Fig. 5.2), which are required also for other techniques. Two tubes can be made at a time by marking a length of 8-mm. soft glass tubing at distances of 11, 15, and 26 cm., cutting the tube at the 26-cm. mark, and heating it at the middle and drawing it down. The capillary tip can be cut off cleanly to a length of 5–6 cm. after scratching it with the sharp edge of a piece of clay plate; the other end should be fire polished. The rubber bulb is like that of an ordinary medicine dropper.

Adjust the bulb to the extreme end of the capillary dropping tube, insert the tip into water, squeeze out all the air possible, and draw as much water as you can into the tube. Eliminate air bubbles so that the tube is filled solidly with liquid from tip to meniscus. Weigh a 10-ml. Erlenmeyer flask on a triple beam balance to 0.01 g., introduce the water into it by micro drops, and count the drops. From the gain in weight of the flask and the specific gravity of water, calculate the ml. delivered by your tube per micro drop. Then, by addition or removal of an appropriate number of micro drops, adjust the volume in the 10-ml. flask to exactly 1.0 ml., draw this amount of water completely into the tube and mark the level of the meniscus with a rubber band. To check your first measurement, draw in concentrated hydrochloric acid to the 1-ml. mark, count the drops delivered, and see if the weight is close to the expected value (see back cover of book). If so, you have a calibrated tube with which you can measure 1 ml. of any liquid by volume, or measure fractional volumes of water or of concd. hydrochloric acid by micro drops. Whereas the weight per drop of an aqueous solution as concentrated as the 36% acid is slightly different from that for water, the calibration by drops established for water can be used for measurement of dilute (5–10%) aqueous solutions of acids and bases. To determine if the water calibration applies also to

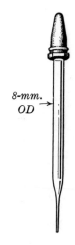

8-$mm.$
OD →

FIG. 5.2 Capillary dropping tube

Approximation: 50-mm.
column in standard capillary
(Note 2, p. 21)

organic liquids, count the number of drops delivered by 1.0 ml. of methanol. [Explain the result (see Table 3.2)].

3. Titration

To check one calibration against the other, measure 1 millimole (1/1000 mole) of sodium bicarbonate into a 10-ml. Erlenmeyer flask, dissolve it in 1 ml. of water, and determine the pH by dipping a strip of Hydrion paper into the solution and at once comparing the color with the color charts on the two sides of the plastic container. Measure 1.0 ml. of concd. hydrochloric acid into a 10-ml. graduate, dilute with water to a volume of 10 ml., and calculate the number of drops of the dilute solution required to give 1 millimole of acid (see back cover). Run about 80% of the theoretical amount of acid into the bicarbonate solution, check the pH, and then complete the titration by dropwise addition until you reach the end point of pH 4. Compare calculated and found values. Before discarding the solution let a piece of used Hydrion paper soak in it for a time to determine if the pigment is water soluble, for if so a paper should never be left long in a solution being tested.

4. Applications

The above techniques are useful in the investigation of unknowns. The specific gravity of a liquid unknown can be determined in the course of calibrating a dropping tube already calibrated for water. A capillary tube for measurement of a solid unknown can be calibrated by the simple method described in the last paragraph of Section 1. A test of an aqueous solution of a liquid or solid unknown with Hydrion paper will reveal the presence of acidic or basic groups and indicate the strength, and a titration will establish the number of ionic groups if the molecular weight is known. Even if the substance is nonionic, knowledge of the approximate molecular weight should facilitate identification. A Rast determination can be made by preparing a mixture of 100 mg. of substance and 3 g. of camphor by the procedure described in Note 3 of Chapter 4 and determining the melting point depression.

5. Storage of Tubes

A protective cabinet for storage of measuring tubes (Fig. 5.3) can be made by securing sponge rubber strips to a cigar box. To make a pair of strips with matching grooves, cut off two pieces of $\frac{9}{16}'' \times \frac{1}{2}''$ Dor-Tite [1] about $\frac{1}{2}''$ longer than required, leave the

---

[1] Durkee-Atwood Co., Minneapolis 13.

protective cloth in place, and tape the strips side by side onto a ruler (or the side of a filter block). To trim the ends neatly to the measurement desired, put a drop of glycerol at the place to be cut and slowly work a sharp razor blade through the rubber and cloth. A tool for making a groove to fit a 5-mm. tube is made by clamping a pair of razor blades to a quarter. Two quarters

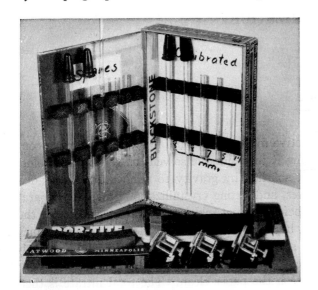

FIG. 5.3 Storage cabinet

gives the right spacing for 7- and 8-mm. tubes; a cut to accommodate a capillary tube is made with the blades clamped to each other. The cores are cut out, and a straight line is drawn on the box to mark the place where the strip is to be mounted, since it usually cannot be moved without damage from the position of initial attachment. Then insert a blade under the protective cloth and remove it, without touching the tacky surface, and carefully put the strip in place. Note that in the open position the lid of the box serves as a convenient rack for pipettes. One side can be reserved for calibrated tubes and the other for spares and for dropping tubes used for other purposes. If a section of the tip of a dropping tube breaks off, the tube may still be usable but requires recalibration.

CHAPTER **6** | Crystallization

A highly effective method of purifying a solid substance consists in dissolving it in a suitable solvent at the boiling point, filtering the hot solution by gravity to remove any suspended insoluble particles, and letting crystallization proceed. Separation of crystals before the hot solution has all passed through the filter paper can be largely prevented by determining the minimum volume of solvent required to effect solution and then adding a deliberate excess (20–100%). A little more fresh hot solvent is required to wash the paper clean. The total filtrate is then evaporated to the original optimal volume and let stand undisturbed at room temperature until the solution has acquired the temperature of the surroundings and crystals have ceased to increase in number or size; the flask is then chilled in an ice bath to promote further crystallization. The crystals that have separated in this first crop are collected by suction filtration and washed free of mother liquor with a little fresh, chilled solvent. The combined mother liquor and washings can be concentrated to a small volume and let stand for separation of a second crop. The quality of each crop is ascertained by melting point determination.

Samples to be purified frequently contain soluble extraneous coloring matter that gives rise to solutions and crystals that are yellowish when they should be colorless or of an off color rather than a pure color. Some soluble pigments can be adsorbed on finely divided carbon and removed, whereas others are not appreciably adsorbed. Colored impurities of the latter type, like colorless impurities, tend to remain in the crystallization mother liquor and are eliminated when the crystals are collected and washed. Hence if the initial solution is yellowish, brownish, or has a dull or off color it is treated with decolorizing carbon, but if the process is only partially effective it is not repeated. Norit, one commercially available decolorizing carbon (also called animal charcoal, bone black), is specified throughout this manual both because it is generally satisfactory and for brevity. The fine carbon particles present a large, active surface for adsorption of dissolved substances, particularly the polymeric, resinous, and reactive by-products that appear in traces in most organic reaction mixtures. Norit is added to the hot solution prior to filtration and the solution is kept hot for a brief period, shaken to wet the carbon, and filtered. Adsorption occurs very rapidly and no advantage is gained by boiling the suspension for several minutes. Norit actually is less effective at a high than a low temperature, and the only point of operating at the boiling temperature is to keep the substance being crystallized in solution. It is a mistake to use more Norit than that actually needed, for an excess may adsorb some of the sample and cause losses.

The specification that the hot solution saturated with solute at the boiling point be let stand undisturbed means that crystallization is allowed to proceed without subsequently moving the flask, jarring the bench on which it is resting, or inserting a thermometer or stirring rod. For estimation of the temperature, the flask should be touched very lightly between the thumb and a finger without any movement of the flask. Crystallization does not start at once but after an induction period ranging from several minutes to an hour or two, even though the temperature has dropped well below that at which the solution is saturated with solute. The phenomenon of supersaturation makes crystallization a remarkably effective means of purification and separation. Suppose that substances A and B have exactly the same solubility in a given solvent and that a 9A:1B mixture is let crystallize undisturbed from a solution saturated at the boiling point. Molecules of the more abundant A eventually form the first crystal and this acts as seed which induces separation of further crystals of A molecules, while B remains in supersaturated solution, perhaps even after crystallization of A has ceased. The crystals, collected without any agitation of the mixture beyond that necessary, will be found enriched in A beyond the 9:1 ratio, and the mother liquor will contain most or all of the B. Supersaturation of the hot solution may be upset by rapid cooling, stirring, or even a slight motion of the flask, and then A and B may both start to crystallize and the process is spoiled. By proper, undisturbed crystallizations either one of a pair of substances of the same solubility can be isolated if it is present in sufficiently preponderant amount. Experiment 31.4 includes isolation in pure form from a reaction mixture of two compounds that differ considerably in solubility. The more abundant and less soluble C crystallizes first, and successive crops of it are obtained by concentrating the mother liquor and adding a tiny seed crystal of C. The more soluble D initially remains in the mother liquor, but when this is so enriched that D is the dominant component, the unseeded solution slowly deposits pure D.

The properties and current relative costs of solvents commonly used for crystallization are listed in Table 6.1. A general rule

TABLE 6.1

COMMON SOLVENTS

Solvent	B.p.	F.p.	Sp. gr.	Miscibility with water	Flammability	Cost, dollars per gallon [a]
Water	100°	0°	1.0	+	o	.0002
Methanol	64.7°	< 0°	0.79	+	+	.27
95% Ethanol	78.1°	< 0°	0.81	+	++	.41
Acetic acid	118°	16.7°	1.05	+	+	.87
Acetone	56.5°	< 0°	0.79	+	+++	.53
Ether	34.6°	< 0°	0.71	−	++++	.60
Petroleum ether	30–60°	< 0°	0.64	−	++++	.24
Ligroin	65–75°	< 0°	0.67	−	+++	.21
Benzene	80.1°	5°	0.88	−	++++	.42
Chloroform	61.2°	< 0°	1.48	−	o	2.10
Carbon tetrachloride	76.7°	< 0°	1.59	−	o	1.13

[a] Prices shown are for large quantities (in 1955).

of solubility is that like dissolves like. Methanol (CH_3OH), ethanol (C_2H_5OH), and acetic acid (CH_3COOH) are all hydroxylic and they are all miscible with one another and with water; they resemble one another in that they are able to dissolve substances of specific types, particularly hydroxylic compounds, and are less effective solvents for structurally dissimilar compounds such as hydrocarbons. The solvent power increases with increasing boiling point; for example, ethanol dissolves about twice as much of a given solute as does methanol. On the other hand, ethanol is more costly than methanol. Since losses entailed in dilution prior to filtration, in evaporation, and in washing are about equal, methanol is the more economical solvent. The chlorinated hydrocarbons chloroform and carbon tetrachloride are particularly expensive. Ligroin is a mixture of aliphatic hydrocarbons comparable to petroleum ether but with a higher boiling point range; it has comparable but greater solvent power. A substance that dissolves easily in petroleum ether or ligroin is almost invariably insoluble in water. Acetone is similar in solvent action to ethanol, and ether is similar to benzene.

Two miscible solvents of different solvent power constitute a useful solvent pair. The hydrocarbon naphthalene is insoluble in water but so soluble in methanol that it crystallizes from this solvent only if the solution is highly concentrated and the temperature low. It can be crystallized efficiently from a suitably proportioned methanol-water mixture; the hydrocarbon is dissolved in excess methanol and water is added little by little at the boiling point until the solution is saturated.

Solvent pairs

Other useful solvent pairs are listed in Table 6.2. If solubility tests conducted with 20-mg. samples of the material to be crys-

TABLE 6.2

SOLVENT PAIRS

Methanol–Water	Ether–Methanol
Ethanol–Water	Ether–Acetone
Acetic acid–Water	Ether–Petroleum ether
Acetone–Water	Benzene–Ligroin

tallized show that it is readily soluble in one member of a solvent pair and sparingly soluble in the other, a solution of the sample in the first solvent can be adjusted to conditions suitable for crystallization by dilution with the second solvent.

EXPERIMENTS

1. Apparatus

The Erlenmeyer flask (Pyrex) is particularly well adapted to all operations of crystallization. For dissolving the solid the flask can be grasped at the neck with the thumb and finger and the flask heated on a steam bath or hot plate or, if the liquid is water, over a free flame, and the contents agitated by swirling the flask, that is, imparting a circulatory motion of wider circumference at the bottom of the flask than at the top (Fig. 6.1); the conical shape prevents spilling of liquid. If lumps or large crystals of solid are slow in dissolving, the process can be hastened by crushing the material against the bottom of the flask with a flattened stirring rod, made by heating the end of a piece of 4-mm. glass rod to redness and pressing it onto a flat surface, such

FIG. 6.1 Erlenmeyer flask being swirled

33

FIG. 6.2 Pouring a hot liquid

Collection of crystals

---

as a coin. To pour out hot liquid cover the hand with a folded towel and grasp the flask (Fig. 6.2). Use of a test tube holder is not advised because the control is too remote; a fair expedient is to use finger protectors made by slitting lengthwise 1″-sections of rubber tubing. When a solution is let stand for crystallization the flask is stoppered to prevent evaporation and formation of a crystal crust; for final chilling the flask is rested in a beaker of appropriate size containing ice and water.

The filters should be stemless (to avoid crystallization in the stem) and are supported merely by resting in the mouth of the receiving flask. Proper matching sizes of flasks, filters, and papers are indicated in Fig. 6.3.[1]

The classical apparatus (Fig. 6.4) for collection of crystals by suction filtration is a Büchner funnel fitted to a filter flask with a rubber stopper. To cut the large hole required put a drop of glycerol as lubricant at the place to be cut and twist in a sharp cork borer with a vigorous circulatory motion but with exertion of only slight pressure; excessive pushing leads to an irregular hole of very small diameter.[2] Neoprene filter adapters (Fig. 6.5) are much nicer to use and do not swell in solvents or age, as rubber does; short of being boiled with nitric acid or put in a flame they should last indefinitely. Suitable assemblies and the

FIG. 6.3 Assemblies for gravity filtration

Note for the instructor

---

*Insertion and removal
of tubes from
stoppers*

[1] Recommended per student: one Schott-Jena G-20 funnel without stem of sizes 2.5, 4.0, 5.5, and 6.0 cm. Alternative: one Kimble funnel No. 29,000 of each of the sizes shown; local glassblower to cut the stem of the 25-mm. funnel to a length of 10 mm. and remove the stems of the other funnels completely. Whatman No. 1 filter paper is satisfactory.

[2] On insertion of a glass tube into a rubber stopper the stopper should be moistened with glycerol. A stopper frozen to a glass tube is easily loosened by painting glycerol around the tube on both sides, inserting the small end of a 7″ spatula (Fig. 4.3) between the rubber and glass, and working it around the circumference of the tube on one side and then the other.

proper sizes of filter paper are shown in Fig. 6.5.[3] The small funnel on the right is a Hirsch funnel and the two other porcelain funnels are Büchner funnels. The glass funnel has the advantage that the inside, where residues often lodge, is visible.

A filter flask is connected to a suction pump with special suction tubing made with thick walls so that it will not collapse under vacuum. This tubing is so heavy that the 50-ml. and 125-ml. filter flasks will tip over easily unless provided with a support, such as a filter block (Fig. 6.6). Suction tubing ($\frac{3}{16}''$) fits snugly into the groove at a level with the side arm of a 50-ml. flask; for support of a 125-ml. flask the suction tubing is pushed into the groove only at the far side. Larger filter flasks have adequate stability and require no support. An alternative device for supporting small filter flasks illustrated in Fig. 6.6 is a simple adapter consisting of a glass tube with two right-angle bends such that one terminus points north and the other east.

A filter flask, or other vessel that is to be evacuated, is not connected to the water pump directly but through a second vessel that serves as a reservoir for equalization of pressure and as a trap for mother liquor that may be carried over in a foam from a filter flask. A 250-ml. filter flask is a convenient reservoir-trap,

Crystallization

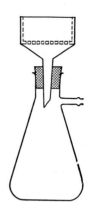

FIG. 6.4 Büchner funnel and filter flask

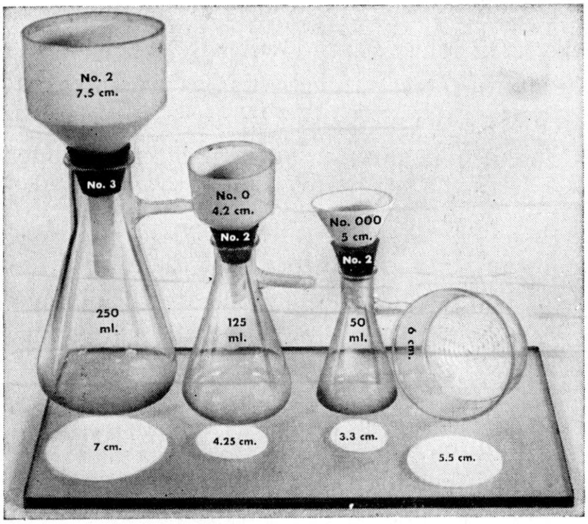

FIG. 6.5 Matching filter assemblies

[3] Neoprene filter adapters are available from Arthur H. Thomas Co.; a set of Nos. 2(2), 3, and 4 is recommended. They are also useful for holding test tubes and flasks (Fig. 0.2) and as stopper shields (Fig. 23.2). The 250-ml. filter flask recommended is of Kimble glass; the smaller ones, Pyrex Erlenmeyer flasks with side arms, are available on order from Corning Glass Works. The porcelain funnels are standard Coors items: Hirsch No. 000, Büchner No. 0 and No. 2. The glass funnel, recommended as an alternate to the No. 2 porcelain funnel, is a Schott-Jena slit-sieve Büchner funnel No. 4236, supplied by Fish-Schurman Corp.

Note for the instructor

and Fig. 6.7 shows how it can be provided with a valve for ready release of vacuum in case a filtrate starts to foam. A 7-cm. length

FIG. 6.6 Filter blocks and a filter flask adapter (Adapter designed by William J. Leanza)

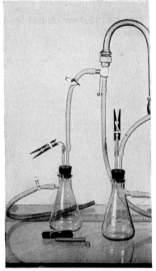

FIG. 6.7 Suction pump trap with valve-pressure gauge

FIG. 6.7a Simplified trap (Waco 5556)

of 6-mm. thin-walled rubber tubing is slid between the jaws of a clothes clip and kept in place by a band cut from the same tubing. When the valve is put in place in the manner shown in the un-attached assembly on the right, the 6-mm. tube is slipped over the glass tube just far enough to space the end of the clothes clip $2\frac{1}{2}$ cm. from the end of the glass tube. The assembly on the left is shown connected to a water suction pump with $\frac{3}{16}''$ suction tubing. For demonstration of the operation of the valve as a pressure gauge, the screw pinch clamp lower left was closed, the pump was operated until the clip, functioning as a pointer, had reached the position of maximum descent shown, and the second pinch clamp was closed. The position of the pointer will differ-entiate between an efficient and faulty suction pump and will reveal leaks, for example in an assembly for vacuum distillation. The pressure gauge can be used also to adjust the rate of flow of water through the pump to produce a moderate vacuum ade-quate for filtration of a crystallizate from a volatile solvent such as ether.

Equipment for crystallization is not complete without one or two wash bottles, in addition to an acetone wash bottle. A wash bottle of distilled water is indispensable, and the classical design shown in Fig. 6.8 is recommended over a variety of others. It is easily constructed from a 500-ml. Pyrex Florence flask, 7-mm. tubing, and a No. 5 fusiform rubber stopper, as shown in the illustration (stopper and tube assembly available from Wilkens-Anderson Co., No. 2110 F). One can direct the stream of water forced out by pressure from the lips by guiding the flexible tip with the forefinger. After an initial delivery, the few drops of water remaining in the tip can be forced out separately by a quick breath of air. A large volume of water, for example 25, 50, or 100 ml., can be measured rapidly into a graduate by inverting the wash bottle and delivering the liquid into the container through the mouthpiece. Cut off the flow a little short of the mark and complete the addition by using the wash bottle in the normal fashion. It is convenient to have available also a similar wash bottle for methanol.

For safe delivery of the gentle heat required to dissolve a solid to be crystallized, an electrical hot plate has advantages over a steam bath and is usually preferred by experienced workers to whom the high cost of commercial hot plates is not a deterrent. Fig. 6.9 illustrates steps in the construction of a hot plate that can be made in a short time at very low cost [4] (Fig. 6.9a shows a Waco adaptation of the same basic principle). It is made from an emptied codfish can or similar tin can large enough to accommodate the standard 3″ heating element of a coffee maker, shown on the right resting on an unemptied can of suitable size (diameter $3\frac{5}{16}$″, height $2\frac{7}{16}$″). The coil of the standard heater supplies ten times the heat desirable in a laboratory unit and is to be replaced by one prepared as described below. The can is cut preferably with a tool-steel opener that folds the cut edge smoothly against the rim. Three equidistant openings are made in the side wall, one to receive the protruding part of the heating element and the others for ventilation and cooling. Each opening should be 2.6 cm. wide and extend from a point 1 cm. from the sealed end of the can to the rim of the open end. Make a pattern from a strip of cardboard that just encircles the can; mark the design in pencil and then cut with a razor blade. Tape the pattern onto the can in a position to avoid the seam and scratch lines with an awl to mark the boundaries of the openings. Then, with a coping saw (Fig. 6.9, rear), make horizontal cuts through the 2.6-cm. lines at the top and bottom; the ends of the cuts can be finished trimly with a spare saw blade from which one of the pins has been withdrawn. Next mark a vertical line sectioning each area to be opened in half and, preferably with a cold chisel operating on an anvil, cut along these dividing lines; when the metal is nearly all cut through, flexing of the tin in and out with the fingers effects full separation. Each half-section can then be folded with the fingers sharply on the marking line and then bent nearly flush with the inner wall. Intermediate stages of cutting and bending are shown in Fig. 6.9 (central can) and Fig.

[4] A simpler hot plate is described in the instructor's manual.

Crystallization

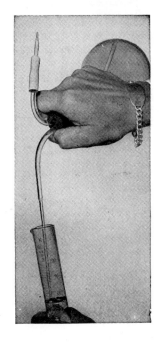

FIG. 6.8 Water wash bottle

6.12 (can on the right). An insulating circle of asbestos is inserted against the inner surface of the sealed end of the can and the modified heating element is entered next to it and secured in place by spreading three of the bent sections of tin. Wooden cover knobs can be bolted in place through holes made with an awl.

The heating coil is made by winding No. 32 nichrome resistance wire from a spool onto an arbor, as shown in Figs. 6.10 and 6.11.

FIG. 6.9   Construction of hot plate

FIG. 6.9a   Waco hot plate (6612)

The arbor, made of $\frac{5}{32}''$ brass rod, has a handle 4 cm. distant from a 40 cm.-long shaft. It turns in pieces of suction tubing held in place by a 6″ applicator stick that also serves as a spacer. The magnifying glass is grasped in the jaws of a clothes clip supported by slipping one of its handles into the slot of a clothespin. At the start the arbor is withdrawn in the direction of the handle until the other end is just protruding from the bearing on the left (Fig. 6.10). The wire is led around the peg of the filter block (Fig. 6.11) and taped onto the arbor, which is then wound with the crank so that it travels slowly in the direction of the second bearing. The point where the wire feeds onto the arbor should be kept close to the first bearing. With care one can produce a tight coil with each ring touching the next. In case of a gap, reverse the crank slightly to loosen the coil and tighten with an awl or with the fingers. Proper winding is important because the measure of the amount of wire to use is a 10-cm. coil packed tightly on the arbor (23 ft.). When this point is reached, tape the feed end of the coil, cut the wire 1–2 inches from the coil, take out the arbor and then carefully remove both tapes. Stretch the coil section by section until, in the resting position, it spreads evenly over the whole length of the arbor. With slight further stretching insert the coil into the grooves of the ceramic base of the heating element, insert the two ends of the wire through holes in the base, and connect them to the stripped ends of rubber-coated No. 18 parallel cord fitted at the other end with an Academy automatic plug. The lead holes in the ceramic base and the connections can be covered with Tileko waterproof cement or Sauereisen cement and the plate sprayed inside and out with aluminum paint.

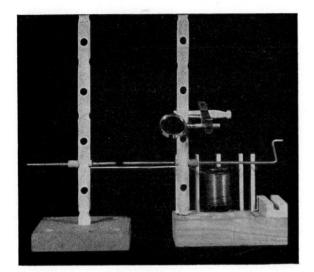

FIG. 6.10

The hot plate is then ready for operation (Fig. 6.12, left). If properly constructed the plate should heat 75 ml. of mineral oil or concd. sulfuric acid to 140–150°; since the maximal temperature is reasonably constant, occasions may arise for using such a bath for conducting a reaction at the temperature concerned, as in the illustration (test tube). The plate draws only about 70 watts and hence many of them can be connected to the same line without risk of blowing a fuse. Trial of the bare heating element (Fig. 6.12, right) will show that at full heat the wire does not glow, and ether dropped on it does not ignite.

FIG. 6.11

EXPERIMENTS

1. Solubility Tests

To test the solubility of a solid, transfer an amount roughly estimated to be about 20 mg. with a small spatula into a 10 × 75-mm. test tube and add about 0.5 ml. of solvent, either delivered from a calibrated capillary dropping tube or estimated as a 1-cm. column in the small test tube. Stir with a fire-polished stirring rod (4-mm.), break up any lumps, and see if the solid is readily soluble in the solvent in question at room temperature. If the substance is found to be readily soluble in cold methanol, ethanol, acetone, or acetic acid, add a few drops of water from a wash bottle to see if solid precipitates and, if it does, heat the mixture, adjust the composition of the solvent pair to produce a hot solution saturated at the boiling point, let the solution stand undisturbed, and note the character of the crystals. If a substance

FIG. 6.12

fails to dissolve in a given solvent in the cold, heat the suspension and see if solution occurs; if the solvent is flammable, heat the test tube on the steam bath or in a small beaker of water kept warm on the steam bath or a hot plate. If the solid all dissolves it can be declared readily soluble in the hot solvent; if some but not all dissolves, it is moderately soluble, and small amounts of further solvent should then be added until solution is complete. When a solution of substance in hot solvent has been obtained, cool the solution under the tap, and if necessary rub the walls with a stirring rod, to make sure that the concentration is such that crystallization is possible. Then reheat to dissolve the solid, let the solution stand undisturbed, and inspect the character of the ultimate crystals.

Make solubility tests on the following compounds in each of the solvents listed, note the degree of solubility in the solvents, cold and hot, and determine suitable solvents, solvent-pairs, or other expedients for crystallization of each substance. Record the crystal form, at least to the extent of distinguishing between needles (pointed crystals), plates (flat and thin), and prisms. How do your observations conform to the generalization that like dissolves like?

Substances:

Resorcinol, $C_6H_4(OH)_2$, a dihydroxy compound.

Anthracene, $C_{14}H_{10}$, an aromatic hydrocarbon.

Benzoic acid, C_6H_5COOH, a hydroxylic compound.

Sodium naphthionate, $(C_{10}H_8N)SO_3Na$, an organic compound with an inorganic group. Compare it with sodium sulfate.

Solvents:

Water, hydroxylic, ionic.

Benzene, an aromatic hydrocarbon.

Ligroin, a mixture of aliphatic hydrocarbons.

2. Clarification

Phthalic acid containing 0.25% of the dye Martius Yellow [5] (Chapter 42) is to be treated with Norit in two different ways to remove the more strongly adsorbed dye and produce pure, colorless phthalic acid.

(a) You are first to make an accurate determination of the amount of Norit just required to effect complete clarification of an aliquot part of a solution prepared by swirling a mixture of 1.0 g. of crude phthalic acid and 25 ml. of water in a 125-ml. Erlenmeyer flask over a free flame. Put the flask on either a steam bath or a hot plate to keep warm, and introduce a calibrated capillary dropping tube with the 1-ml. point marked with a rubber band rather than wax, which would melt. Calibrate a melting point capillary for measuring Norit. For an initial trial, measure out any arbitrarily chosen quantity of Norit up to 25 mg. into a 13 × 100-mm. test tube. Rest a 4.2-cm. funnel in the mouth of a second test tube, fold a paper of appropriate size (Fig. 6.3), fit it into the funnel, and moisten it with a little water from a wash bottle so that it stays in place. Make sure that the upper part of the dropping tube is warm enough to prevent crystallization by drawing in hot liquid and expelling it a few times, and then measure 3.0 ml. of solution into the test tube containing Norit. Boil the suspension for a moment or two to wet the carbon particles and effect thorough mixing, let the particles settle, and inspect the supernatant liquor for color. Since even precipitated carbon often has a deceiving effect on the appearance, filter the hot solution into a second test tube and see if the filtrate

Determination of ratio of adsorbent to adsorbate

[5] A mixture of 100 g. of phthalic anhydride, 310 mg. of the ammonium salt of 2,4-dinitro-1-naphthol, 41 g. of sodium hydroxide, and 500 ml. of water is warmed to effect solution, acidified, cooled, and the pale yellow solid collected.

is colorless, or a lighter yellow than before treatment. A very faint color is sometimes detectable only when the solution is viewed on a line close to the axis of the tube. Discard the solution and repeat the test several times, with increasing or decreasing amounts of Norit as suggested by previous tests, and determine the maximal amount of Martius Yellow that can be completely adsorbed on 10 mg. of Norit.

Calculation of ratio

As an approximation it may be assumed that the Norit used had a surface area of 800 sq. meters per gram, or 80% that of the best carbons, especially prepared and carefully stored. The area is thus $8 \times 10^2 \times 10^4 = 8 \times 10^6$ cm.^{2}/g., or $8 \times 10^6 / 1 \times 10^{-16}$ $= 8 \times 10^{22}$ sq. Å/g., or $8 \times 10^{22} / 100 = 8 \times 10^{20}$ sq. Å/10 mg. of Norit. If the Martius Yellow molecules are assumed to be 10 Å wide and 20 Å long and if dye molecules cover all available surface of a 10-mg. sample of adsorbent, the number of molecules adsorbed is $8 \times 10^{20} / 10 \times 20 = 4 \times 10^{18}$ molecules, or $4 \times 10^{18} /$ 6.0228×10^{23} (Avogadro's number) $= 6.7 \times 10^{-6}$ moles of Martius Yellow. The molecular weight of the dye ($C_{10}H_6O_5N_2$) is 234.16, and hence the weight of dye estimated to be adsorbed under ideal conditions by 10 mg. of Norit is $6.7 \times 10^{-6} \times 234.16$ $\times 1000 = 1.6$ mg. Compare this calculated value with the value that you found experimentally and suggest factors that may have contributed to a discrepancy. Were the conditions of your experiment ideal for adsorption of Martius Yellow?

(b) Next crystallize 1.0 g. of the crude phthalic acid from water with use of 1.5 times the amount of Norit that you found required for decoloration (200 mg.). First heat the solid in a 50-ml. Erlenmeyer flask with 5 ml. of water and add more water at the boiling point, 1 ml. at a time, and determine the amount of water required to dissolve the sample. Let the yellow solution cool a little and note that phthalic acid crystallizes rapidly and abundantly. Since the solubility of the acid in cold water is low (0.54 g. per 100 g. at 14°), difficulty in the filtration can be avoided by use of a large excess of solvent. Add enough more water to make up the volume to 25 ml., add the Norit, heat to the boiling point, and filter the hot solution by gravity into a second Erlenmeyer flask. In filtration of a carbon-containing suspension, always pour the liquid first onto the upper part of the section of paper that is reinforced by the extra folds, for this minimizes passage of carbon particles through the paper. In case the first few drops of filtrate do contain carbon, watch for the point where the filtrate is clear, change to a clean receiving flask, and reheat and refilter the first filtrate. Sometimes filtra-

Clarification by gravity filtration

tion is slow because a funnel fits so snugly into the mouth of a
flask that pressure develops. If you note that raising the funnel
by the fingers increases the flow of filtrate, make a tiny, flat
spacer by folding a small strip of filter paper two or three times
and insert it between the funnel and the flask. To rinse the
emptied flask, add 1-2 ml. of water, heat to boiling, and pour
the hot wash liquor in a succession of drops around the upper
rim of the filter paper. The emptied flask, the filter, and the
filter paper containing Norit are to be put aside for processing
as described below. Reheat the filtrate to dissolve any solid that
has separated, and let the solution stand undisturbed for crystallization. As crystals separate, record the crystalline form and
any other distinguishing characteristics. After crystallization at
room temperature has ceased, put the flask in a beaker of ice and
water. In collecting the product by suction filtration use a spatula to dislodge crystals and ease them out of the flask. If crystals
remain after the flask has been emptied, filtrate can be poured
back into the crystallization flask for washing as often as desired,
since it is saturated with solute. Fresh solvent (water from a
wash bottle) should be used only in a final wash to free the crystals of mother liquor. The product should be colorless and the
yield 0.83–0.85 g.

Note that the Norit collected on the filter should contain 2.5
mg. of Martius Yellow. This dye is an acid, and although it is
not dislodged from the adsorbent by either alkali or methanol
alone it can be eluted with methanolic alkali. Unfold the paper
containing Norit and adsorbed Martius Yellow, hold it over the
funnel resting on the emptied flask and, with a stream of methanol delivered from a Calcutta wash bottle, wash the carbon
particles into the flask; use about 10 ml. of methanol. Add 1
ml. of 10% sodium hydroxide solution,[6] digest the mixture on
the steam bath for a few minutes while fitting the used filter paper
into the same funnel and resting this in the neck of a clean flask.
Filter the hot, yellow solution, rinse the carbon with methanol,
and then wash the Norit back into the emptied flask as before
and extract again; filter into a clean flask in order to observe
the intensity of color. Repeat the extraction two or three times

---

[6] To 40 g. of sodium hydroxide pellets in a 500-ml. Erlenmeyer flask add 360 ml.
of distilled water and swirl occasionally until solution is complete (if tap water is
used the solution has to be filtered). Store the solution in a labelled 16-oz. tincture
bottle, the neck and mouth of which should be greased to prevent creeping of the
solution and formation of a deposit of sodium carbonate. See back cover of book
for specific gravity, etc. Use of Fisher Scientific Company's Gram-Pac containing
25 g. of sodium hydroxide eliminates the operation of weighing.

more until the methanolic sodium hydroxide extract is only feebly colored. Then combine the alkaline extracts, add enough hydrochloric acid to discharge the yellow color due to Martius Yellow anion, and stopper and label the container and put it away for a later attempt to isolate the dye that it contains. In the meantime see if you can devise a procedure for attaining this objective.

(c) A second method of clarification applicable to acids and bases that form water-soluble salts demonstrates the speed of adsorption and the efficiency of Norit at room temperature. Place 1.0 g. (0.006 mole) of crude phthalic acid in a 50-ml. Erlenmeyer flask, add 0.51 g. (0.006 mole) of sodium bicarbonate, and then add 20 ml. of water in small portions with swirling to break the foam. A clear yellow solution should result. Fit a 50-ml. filter flask with a Hirsch funnel and paper, moisten the paper with water, and apply gentle suction. Measure 150 mg. of Norit into a 13 × 100-mm. test tube, fill the tube with water, close the end with the thumb and shake to moisten the carbon, and then pour the suspension onto the funnel and rinse the tube with water. A thin but even pad of decolorizing carbon should result. Detach the flask and pour out the water; then reconnect and filter the yellow solution through the pad. If the color is not completely removed make a new pad and repeat the process.

Since phthalic acid is dibasic, treatment of 0.006 mole of it with 0.006 mole of bicarbonate gives a solution of sodium hydrogen phthalate. This solution is useful as a buffer, that is a solution of a pH that changes only slightly on addition of small amounts of either a strong acid or a strong base. The carefully measured pH of this buffer is 3.92; test your solution with Hydrion paper and see how the pH corresponds to the figure given. Then add concd. hydrochloric acid by micro drops until the solution is titrated to pH 1–2, let crystallization proceed, and collect the product.

3. Separation of a Mixture

Since naphthalene ($C_{10}H_8$, m.p. 80°) and diphenyl ($C_{12}H_{10}$, m.p. 69°) are aromatic hydrocarbons of nearly the same solubility as well as melting point, a 1:1 mixture is very difficult to separate by crystallization. The mixture, m.p. 42–48°, is much more soluble than either component and tends to remain in supersaturated solution. Seeding of a saturated solution with either component causes slow separation of a small crop of crystals melting in the range 40–48°. However naphthalene forms a molecular complex with picric acid, a picrate, and diphenyl does not, and since the complex is much less soluble than either component, naphthalene can be isolated in the form of this derivative. The picrate, m.p. 149–150°, is split by treatment with ammonia solution to form the water-soluble ammonium salt of picric acid.

Naphthalene-picric acid complex

In a 20 × 150-mm. test tube dissolve 2.0 g. of the 1 : 1 naphthalene–diphenyl mixture in 4 ml. of methanol and transfer the hot solution with a capillary dropping tube to a hot solution prepared by warming 3.0 g. of picric acid ($C_6H_3O_7N_3$) with 20 ml. of methanol in a 50-ml. Erlenmeyer flask. To rinse the test tube add 1 ml. of methanol, warm, draw hot liquid into the dropper to warm and rinse it; the wash liquor can be transferred almost quantitatively. If crystals separate during the addition, reheat to dissolve them, let the solution stand, and watch it to observe the initial separation and rapid growth of yellow needles of naphthalene picrate. Then cool in a beaker of ice and water, and cool a little methanol for washing. Collect the crystals on a Hirsch funnel and use only very gentle suction, for otherwise the low-boiling solvent evaporates unduly from the filtrate. Rinse the flask with the minimum amount of chilled solvent to avoid loss of product. Let the crystals dry and determine the weight and m.p.

Caution: picric acid dyes the skin

To recover the diphenyl, transfer the yellow filtrate to a 125-ml. Erlenmeyer flask and add 2 ml. of concd. ammonia solution and 75 ml. of distilled water. Collect the precipitated hydrocarbon on a small Büchner funnel and wash it free of yellow ammonium picrate with water. Naphthalene is recovered from its picrate by dissolving this in hot methanol and adding 2 ml. of concd. ammonia solution and 75 ml. of distilled water. Since the samples of the two hydrocarbons are to be crystallized from methanol, drying of the samples prior to crystallization is unnecessary.

To crystallize each hydrocarbon, dissolve it in a small volume of hot methanol and, if the solution is not perfectly clear, dilute with excess solvent, filter by gravity, and evaporate to an appropriate volume. On pouring a hot solution in methanol or other organic solvent into a filter, a crust of solid often appears in or around the neck of the delivery flask. To recover this, add a little fresh solvent to the flask, warm it, draw up hot solvent into a capillary dropper to warm it as well, and then draw up all the hot liquid, hold the neck of the delivery flask over the funnel, and drop liquid onto the neck to rinse it. Solid often separates around the opening of a stemless funnel as hot solution filters

Crystallization from an organic solvent

through it. If so, lift the funnel temporarily to introduce a boiling stone and then boil the solution gently on a steam bath or hot plate so that hot liquid condensing on the funnel and returning to the flask gradually dissolves the solid. Evaporation of the filtered solution to a point suitable for crystallization should be done on the steam bath with an aspirator tube, inserted into the

FIG. 6.13   Aspirator tube

neck of the flask and connected to the suction pump, for entrainment of inflammable vapor. A convenient arrangement is shown in Fig. 6.13.

After first crops of naphthalene and diphenyl have been obtained, second crops can be secured by evaporation or, more easily, by heating the combined mother liquor and washings to the boiling point, adding water cautiously to the point of cloudiness, and then a little methanol to clear the solution.

Record the crystal form, m.p., odor, and per cent recovery of each hydrocarbon; in the case of naphthalene calculate also the per cent yield as picrate.

4. Purification of an Unknown[7]

With a total supply of 2.0 g. of a crude unknown, you are to ascertain the properties of the major component from appro-

[7] Many accumulated student preparations can be rendered suitable for use as unknowns; example: 500 g. *p*-nitroaniline, 50 g. *p*-bromoacetanilide, 20 g. sand, 10 g. ashes.

priate tests, devise a method for purification, and submit as much pure product as you can, together with evidence of its purity. The characterizing tests should include melting point determination, tests for solubility and crystallizability in organic solvents, solvent pairs, and water. If the substance is water-soluble, determine if it is acidic or basic. Conserve your material by using very small samples for the tests. After a test in a volatile solvent has been completed, the solvent can be evaporated by heating the tube on the steam bath and the residue used for another test. In case you use Norit for clarification of a solution of substance in an organic solvent take the precaution to let the boiling solution cool slightly and swirl it well to relieve superheating before addition of the decolorizing carbon; otherwise the fine particles are liable to initiate vigorous boiling with loss of liquid out of the mouth of the flask.

CHAPTER 7 | Extraction

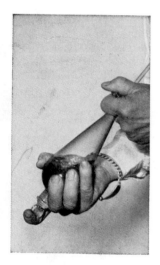

FIG. 7.1 **Separatory funnel**

A frequently used method of working up a reaction mixture is to dilute the mixture with water and extract with ether in a separatory funnel (Fig. 7.1). When the stoppered funnel is shaken to distribute the components between the immiscible solvents ether and water, pressure always develops through volatilization of ether from the heat of the hands, and liberation of a gas (CO_2) will increase the pressure. Consequently, the funnel is so grasped that the stopper is held in place by one hand and the stopcock by the other, as illustrated. After a brief shake or two the funnel is held in the inverted position shown and the stopcock opened cautiously to test the extent of pressure and to release it. After the orienting test the mixture can be shaken more vigorously and tested further. When equilibration is judged to be complete, the slight, constant terminal pressure due to ether is released, the stopper is rinsed with a few drops of ether delivered by a Calcutta wash bottle or a capillary dropping tube, and the layers are let settle. The organic reaction product is distributed wholly or largely into the upper ether layer, whereas inorganic salts, acids, and bases pass into the water layer, which can be drawn off and discarded. If the reaction was run in alcohol or acetone solution the bulk of the solvent is removed in the water layer and the rest can be eliminated in two or three washings with 1–2 volumes of water conducted with the techniques used in the first equilibration. Ways of supporting a separatory funnel are shown in Figs. 0.7 and 1.2.

Acetic acid is also distributed largely into the aqueous phase, but if the reaction product is a neutral substance the residual acetic acid in the ether can be removed by one washing with excess 5% sodium bicarbonate solution. If the reaction product

Acids

is a higher acid, for example benzoic acid (C_6H_5COOH), this will stay in the ether layer while acetic acid is being removed by repeated washing with water; the benzoic acid can then be separated from neutral by-products by extraction with bicarbonate solution and acidification of the extract. Acids of high molecular weight are extracted only slowly by sodium bicarbonate and sodium carbonate is used in its place; however carbonate is more prone than bicarbonate to produce emulsions. An emulsion in the lower layer can sometimes be settled by twirling the stem of the funnel, one in the upper layer by grasping the funnel by the neck and swirling it. Since the tendency to emulsify increases with removal of electrolytes and solvents, a little sodium chloride or hydrochloric acid solution is added with each portion of wash water. If the layers largely clear but an emulsion persists at the interface, the clear part of the water layer can be drawn off and the emulsion run into a second funnel and shaken with fresh ether.

At room temperature water dissolves 7.5% of ether (by weight) and ether dissolves 1.5% of water. Equilibration of 100 ml. each of ether and water gives an upper layer of 90 ml. and a lower layer of 105 ml.; if the upper layer is separated and washed with 100-ml. portions of water the volume is reduced about 10 ml. each time. The reduction in volume can be prevented by using wash water saturated with ether, or fresh ether can be added to make up for that lost. In one of the experiments below, an ethereal solution is washed extensively with water with the express purpose of reducing the volume to a desired point. Whereas water dissolves in ether to the extent of 1.5%, water saturated with sodium chloride (36.7 g./100 g.) has no appreciable solubility. Hence the bulk of the water present in a wet ethereal extract can be removed by shaking the extract with saturated sodium chloride solution and drawing off the lower layer. Drying is completed simply by filtering the ethereal solution through a layer of anhydrous sodium sulfate.

When a given substance is partitioned between ether and water the ratio of concentrations in the ether and water layers is a constant defined as the distribution ratio, K, specific to the solute, solvent pair, and temperature in question. If the compound has finite solubility in both solvents, K can be calculated from the ratio of solubilities, since

$$K = \frac{[g./100 \text{ ml.}]^{\text{ Ether layer}}}{[g./100 \text{ ml.}]^{\text{ Water layer}}} = \frac{\text{Solubility, g./100 ml. Ether}}{\text{Solubility, g./100 ml. Water}}$$

Emulsions

Ether-water solubility

Drying an extract

Distribution ratio

49

For a substance such as acetic acid, which is miscible in all proportions with both ether and water, K can be determined by distributing a known weight of acid between measured volumes of the two solvents and determining the concentration in the aqueous layer by titration with standard alkali. Calculation will show that in consequence of the constancy of the ratio of concentrations in the two phases, regardless of the relative volumes, extraction of a substance from an aqueous solution is more efficient if several small portions of ether are used than if the same total volume of ether is employed in one portion. The relation is illustrated by the problem presented in Section 4.

Extraction with a water-immiscible solvent is useful for isolation of natural products that occur in animal and plant tissues having high water content. Diethyl ether, $CH_3CH_2OCH_2CH_3$, has high solvent power for hydrocarbons and for oxygen-containing compounds and is so highly volatile (b.p. $34.6°$) that it is easily removed from an extract at a temperature so low that even highly sensitive compounds are not liable to decompose. Although often preferred for research work because of these properties, ether is avoided in industrial processes because of its fire hazard, high solubility in water, losses in solvent recovery incident to its volatility, and oxidation of ether on long exposure to air to a peroxide, which in a dry state presents the hazard of explosibility. Alternative water-immiscible solvents sometimes preferred even though they do not match all the favorable properties of ether are: petroleum ether, ligroin, benzene, carbon tetrachloride, chloroform, ethylene dichloride, butanol. The chlorinated hydrocarbon solvents are heavier than water rather than lighter and hence, after equilibration of the aqueous and nonaqueous phases, the heavier lower layer is drawn off into a second separatory funnel for washing and the upper aqueous layer is discarded. These solvents have the advantage of freedom from fire hazard, but the higher cost (Table 6.1) mitigates against their general use.

For exhaustive extraction of dried leaves or seeds, the solid is packed into a filter paper thimble placed in a Soxhlet extractor (Fig. 7.2). Solvent vapor rises in the tube on the right and condensed solvent drops onto the solid, leaches out soluble material and carries it to the boiling flask, where nonvolatile extracted material accumulates. The same solvent is used over and over again, and even substances of very slight solubility can be extracted by prolongation of the operation for the necessary period of time.

Extraction solvents

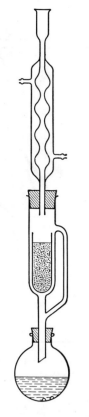

FIG. 7.2 Modified Soxhlet extraction apparatus

1. Equipment

(a) A 125-ml. separatory funnel with the stopcock greased carefully, with avoidance of excess grease that can come in contact with ether and be dissolved. Use a ground-glass stopper if available but do not grease it; otherwise use a rubber stopper. The funnel is conveniently mounted in a dowel stand clip. (b) Saturated sodium chloride solution. Put 130 g. of common salt and 400 ml. of distilled water in a 16-oz. tincture bottle, grease the neck to prevent creeping, and shake occasionally until the solid is dissolved. (c) Calibrated and uncalibrated capillary dropping tubes. (d) Calcutta wash bottle of ether.

2. Acidic and Neutral Substances

A mixture of equal parts of the following substances is to be separated by extraction:[1]

most acidic

	M.p.	pKₐ	Sol. in cold water
Benzoic acid, C_6H_5COOH	123°	4.17	0.2 g./100 g.
β-Naphthol, $C_{10}H_7OH$ — *least acid*	123°	About 8	0.1 g./100 g.
Diphenyl ether, $C_6H_5OC_6H_5$	27°	Neutral	Insoluble

↳ 6.45

pK_a = *acidity constant*
pH = *acidity* = $-\log [H^+]$

Place 3.0 g. of the mixture in a 50-ml. Erlenmeyer flask, add part of 25 ml. of ether, dissolve by swirling, pour the solution into a separatory funnel, and rinse the flask with the remaining ether. Make a wax pencil mark to indicate the original level of the solution and, at the end of each operation that follows, add enough fresh ether to restore the solution to the original volume. Add 10 ml. of water, stopper the funnel, hold it as in Fig. 7.1, shake cautiously, invert the funnel and release the pressure, then shake more vigorously, and continue until you judge the mixture to be equilibrated. Remove the stopper, rinse it and the neck of the flask with a little ether (0.5 ml.), let the layers settle, and run the water layer into an Erlenmeyer flask. Test this solution with blue litmus paper to see if a trace of acid has been distributed into the water and if so return the solution to the funnel along with 20 ml. of 5% sodium bicarbonate solution. Shake, very cautiously at first, test frequently, and continue until you judge that the reaction of the acidic component is complete and the pressure merely that to be expected of a water-ether mixture saturated with carbon dioxide. Record the appearance of the two layers. Run the lower layer into a 125-ml. Erlenmeyer flask

---

[1] Heat a mixture of the components on the steam bath and stir until a homogeneous melt results; then cool with stirring and break up the warm solid with a spatula.

and then, to recover aqueous solution adhering to the funnel, add 10 ml. of water, shake well, run about half of the wash water into the same receiving flask, and test the drop adhering to the stem with blue litmus paper to make sure that extraction is complete. Run the rest of the wash water into the flask and heat the bicarbonate extract on the steam bath until the ether that it contains is expelled (the components of the mixture are all much more soluble in ether than in water). Add 1 ml. of concd. hydrochloric acid cautiously to the hot solution, and if a test with Hydrion paper does not indicate pH 1–2, add more until this end point is reached. Let the hot solution stand for crystallization. [Collect the crystals, wash them with a little water to remove sodium chloride-containing mother liquid, and measure the volume of mother liquor and washings so that you can determine the amount of material lost] Note the crystal form, determine the yield, and identify the product from the melting point and other properties. Test the pH of aqueous solutions of this substance and of acetic acid (pK_a 4.76).

This operation is optional, and can be omitted

For determination of the extent of washing required to remove acetic acid, add $\frac{1}{2}$ ml. of this acid to the ethereal solution in the funnel, shake with successive 25-ml. portions of water until the wash liquor no longer gives a positive test for acid with litmus paper, and record the number of washings required (keep the volume of the ether layer constant by suitable addition of fresh solvent).

The residual ethereal solution is next shaken with 20 ml. of 10% sodium hydroxide solution for extraction of the weakly acidic component. The extract is drawn off and combined with a further portion obtained by washing the ether with 10 ml. of water. If the alkaline extract is colored, filter it by suction through a pad of 150 mg. of Norit. This process may not remove all the color but it serves the further purpose of removing most of the dissolved ether. The component present is sensitive to air oxidation and the solution would become badly discolored if it were heated to drive off the ether. Suction filtration has the advantage of reducing the partial pressure of oxygen to which the solution is exposed. Acidify the filtrate to pH 1–2, cool in ice, and then follow the above prescription for collection, washing, estimating losses, identification. If the melting point of the precipitated material is low, dissolve the sample in a little benzene, filter from a trace of salt if any is present, and add ligroin until the solution is just saturated at the boiling point.

The residual ethereal solution containing the neutral fraction

is worked up as follows. To reduce the water content, shake
with 25 ml. of saturated sodium chloride solution and discard
the lower layer. Rest a 4.2-cm. stemless filter with a folded
paper in a 50-ml. Erlenmeyer flask, fill a dry 10 × 75-mm. test
tube with anhydrous sodium sulfate (a convenient measure of
approximately 5 g.), and pour the drying agent into the cone of

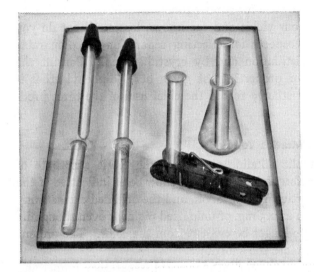

FIG. 7.3

the paper. If a little more salt solution has separated from the
ether, drain it off and then run the solution out of the stem onto
the drying agent in the filter as rapidly as filtration permits.
Note that residual drops of aqueous solution adhere nicely to the
walls and stem of the funnel. If filtration is at all delayed, raise
the filter to see if there is an air lock. Use a Calcutta wash bottle
for rinsing the funnel when it has been emptied and for rinsing
the sodium sulfate and paper. Add a boiling stone and evaporate
on a steam bath with an aspirator tube inserted for entrainment
of vapor until the volume is reduced to 10–15 ml. If the solution
is not perfectly colorless, add an appropriate, small amount of
Norit, filter, and evaporate the ether. To remove traces of solvent from the residual oil, fit the flask with a rubber stopper
carrying a glass tube connected to the suction pump, and pump
out the still warm flask for a few minutes. Cool the flask in ice
and see if the oil will solidify. Prepare to transfer the sample to
a 10 × 75-mm. test tube, in which it is to be turned in. Either
select an oversized test tube in which the barrel of an ordinary
capillary dropping tube will fit and allow the tip to touch the
bottom (Fig. 7.3, right), or make a dropper with a capillary of
suitable length (left). See if your thermometer will fit into the

test tube selected, and if not determine the melting point of the sample before making the transfer. Support the test tube in one of the ways shown in Fig. 7.3, weigh the assembly, melt the sample, transfer it, and weigh again. Insert a thermometer, chill in ice, until the sample has partially solidified, and determine the temperature at which liquid and solid are in equilibrium. Stopper and label the tube for submission.

Summarize your yields and the known losses. What do you think of the prospects for effecting separation of comparable efficiency by distillation and by crystallization? Consult the Merck Index for properties not given here (diphenyl ether is listed as phenyl ether); record the chief uses of the three products.

3. Isolation of Martius Yellow

The methanolic alkaline extract of the Norit adsorbate of Chapter 6, Section 2b had a strong yellow color indicative of the presence of Martius Yellow anion, and the acidified extract may contain as much as 2.5 mg. of unionized pigment even though its presence may no longer be evident from the color. The present problem is to isolate the substance.

Measure 5 ml. of water into a 125-ml. separatory funnel and mark the level of the liquid with a wax pencil. Pour the methanol solution of Martius Yellow into the funnel, add 70 ml. of water and 35 ml. of ether, shake, and see if layers separate; if not try adding more water to dilute the methanol further. After thorough shaking, draw off and discard the lower layer (H_2O, CH_3OH, NaCl, HCl). The ethereal solution is now to be washed repeatedly with water to remove the remaining methanol and to reduce the volume to 5 ml. Use 25-ml. portions of water and to each portion add 1-2 ml. of concd. hydrochloric acid to inhibit formation of emulsions, and continue the washings to a point where, when the water layer is drawn off, the level of the ether layer is at the 5-ml. mark. Then run the ether solution into a 13 × 100-mm. test tube and rinse the funnel with a little ether. Add 0.2 ml. of 10% sodium hydroxide solution, shake well, and let the layers separate. To transfer the yellow aqueous layer to a second test tube, insert the tip of a capillary dropping tube, force out some air, and draw in liquid until the interface is reached. Extract the ether solution further in the same way with three or four 0.2-ml. portions of water until it is practically colorless. If much ether has been carried over into the second tube, remove it with the dropping tube. Then rest the tube containing the yellow alkaline extract in a ring of the steam bath in a slanting position so that it will be heated over nearly the whole length, and heat until the ether is driven off. Acidify with hydrochloric acid, cool in ice, and see if particles of solid are visible with the naked eye or with a magnifying glass. Filter the chilled mixture by gravity on a 2.5-cm. funnel, wash with water, and test the filtrate for Martius Yellow by making it alkaline. Whether or not a yellow solid is clearly detectable on the filter paper, push the paper into a 20 × 150-mm. test tube, add a 3 × 3-cm. square of silk cloth and enough water to cover the contents, heat to boiling, and then heat on the steam bath until no further change is observed. Remove the silk, rinse it in water, and see if it is dyed a strong yellow. If not, rinse it with sodium carbonate solution (to neutralize hydrochloric acid that may not have been washed out of the precipitate). If a good dyeing is obtained see if further squares of silk will take up more dye. When the bath is exhausted remove the filter paper and observe whether cellulose is dyed as the protein silk is.

Silk takes up acidic molecules of Martius Yellow only until all basic sites present are filled, hence the yield of dye recovered from the Norit can be estimated from the amount of silk dyed. One milligram of pure Martius Yellow will dye to full strength three 3 × 3-cm. squares of silk weighing 56 mg. each. Dyed squares entered in a notebook will bear evidence of isolation and yield. Compare the weights of Norit and silk required to bind 1 mg. of Martius Yellow.

4. Problem

Suppose a reaction mixture when diluted with water afforded 300 ml. of an aqueous solution of 30 g. of the reaction product malononitrile, $CH_2(CN)_2$, which is to be isolated by extraction with ether. The solubility of malononitrile in ether at room temperature is 20.0 g. per 100 ml. and that in water is 13.3 g. per 100 ml. What weight of malononitrile would be recovered by extraction with (a) three 100-ml. portions of ether; (b) one 300-ml. portion of ether? Suggestion: For each extraction let x equal the weight extracted into the ether layer. In case (a) the concentration in the ether layer is $x/100$ and that in the water layer $(30 - x)/300$; the ratio of these quantities is equal to $K = 20/13.3$.

CHAPTER 8 | Steam Distillation

The experience of distilling a mixture of benzene and water (Chapter 2.3) will have shown that the boiling point of the mixture is below that of the more volatile component. The mixture containing 91.1% of benzene (b.p. 80.1°) is an azeotrope, b.p. 69.3°. Since the two liquids are essentially insoluble in each other, the benzene molecules in a droplet of benzene are not diluted by water molecules in nearby water droplets and hence the vapor pressure exerted by the benzene is the same as that of benzene alone at the temperature in question. The same is true of the water present. Because they are immiscible, the two liquids independently exert pressures against the common external pressure, and when the sum of the two partial pressures equals the external pressure boiling occurs. Benzene has a vapor pressure of 760 mm. at 80.1°, and if it is mixed with water the combined vapor pressure must equal 760 mm. at some temperature below 80.1°. This temperature, the boiling point of the mixture, can be calculated from known values of the vapor pressures of the separate liquids at various temperatures. Vapor pressures found for water and benzene in the range 50–80° are plotted in Fig. 8.1. The dotted line cuts the two curves at points where the sum of the vapor pressures is 760 mm.; hence this is the boiling point of the mixture (69.3°).

Practical use can sometimes be made of the fact that many water-insoluble liquids and solids behave like benzene and when mixed with water volatilize at temperatures below their boiling points. Thus naphthalene, a solid, boils at 218° but distils with water at a temperature below 100°. Since naphthalene is not very volatile, considerable water is required to entrain it and the conventional way of conducting the operation of steam distilla-

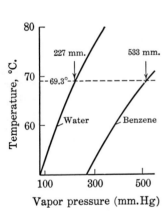

FIG. 8.1 Vapor pressure curves

tion is to pass steam into a boiling flask containing naphthalene and water. With more volatile compounds, or with a small amount of material, the substance can be heated with water in a simple distillation flask and the steam generated *in situ*. The simple procedure is prescribed in the following experiments. Types of apparatus used for conventional steam distillation are illustrated in Figs. 26.1 and 45.3.

Some high-boiling substances decompose at the boiling point, particularly if impure, but can be freed from contaminating substances by steam distillation at a lower temperature at which they are stable. Steam distillation also offers the advantage of selectivity, since some water-insoluble substances are volatile with steam and others are not, and some volatilize so very slowly that sharp separation is possible. The technique is useful in processing natural oils and resins, which can be separated into steam-volatile and nonsteam-volatile fractions. It is useful for recovery of a nonsteam-volatile solid from its solution in a high-boiling solvent such as nitrobenzene, b.p. 210°; all traces of the solvent can be eliminated and the temperature can be kept low.

The boiling point remains constant during a steam distillation so long as adequate amounts of both water and the organic component are present to saturate the vapor space. Determination of the boiling point and correction for any deviation from normal atmospheric pressure permits calculation of the amount of water required for distillation of a given amount of organic substance. According to Dalton's law the molecular proportion of the two components in the distillate is equal to the ratio of their vapor pressures (p) in the boiling mixture; the more volatile component contributes the greater number of molecules to the vapor phase. Thus:

$$\frac{\text{Moles of water}}{\text{Moles of substance}} = \frac{p^{\text{Water}}}{p^{\text{Substance}}}$$

The vapor pressure of water (p^{Water}) at the boiling temperature in question can be found by interpolation of the data of Table 8.1 and that of the organic substance is equal to $760 - p^{\text{Water}}$. Hence the weight of water required per gram of substance is given by the expression

$$\frac{\text{wt. of water per}}{\text{g. of substance}} = \frac{18 \times p^{\text{Water}}}{\text{Mol. wt. of substance} \times (760 - p^{\text{Water}})}$$

From the data given in Fig. 8.1 for benzene–water, and the molecular weight 78.11 for benzene, the water required for steam

TABLE 8.1

VAPOR PRESSURE OF WATER IN MM. OF MERCURY

$t°$	p	$t°$	p	$t°$	p	$t°$	p
60	149.3	70	233.7	80	355.1	90	525.8
61	156.4	71	243.9	81	369.7	91	546.0
62	163.8	72	254.6	82	384.9	92	567.0
63	171.4	73	265.7	83	400.6	93	588.6
64	179.3	74	277.2	84	416.8	94	610.9
65	187.5	75	289.1	85	433.6	95	633.9
66	196.1	76	301.4	86	450.9	96	657.6
67	205.0	77	314.1	87	468.7	97	682.1
68	214.2	78	327.3	88	487.1	98	707.3
69	223.7	79	341.0	89	506.1	99	733.2

distillation of 1 g. of benzene is only $227 \times 18/533 \times 78 = 0.10$ g. Nitrobenzene (b.p. 210°, mol. wt. 123.11) steam distils at 99° and requires 4.0 g. of water per gram. The low molecular weight of water makes this a favorable liquid for two-phase distillation of organic compounds.

EXPERIMENTS

1. Recovery of a Dissolved Substance

Connect a 250-ml. distilling flask to a short condenser set for downward distillation and use a 100-ml. graduate for the receiver. The flask can be heated with a free flame or mounted on a tripod with iron gauze. Introduce through a funnel 50 ml. of a 0.2% solution of anthracene [1] ($C_{14}H_{10}$) in toluene (C_7H_8, sp. gr. 0.866) and 100 ml. of water. View the upper layer from different angles with the eye at the level of the layer and see if you can observe a violet fluorescence. Introduce a boiling stone, see that the cork holding the thermometer is secure, and distil. Note the b.p. as each 10 ml. of distillate collects and remove the flame when approximately 50 ml. has collected. Measure the volumes of the two liquids carefully and calculate the weight of water per gram of toluene. Compare the result with the theoretical value calculated from the average of the boiling points observed. Continue the distillation until the toluene is eliminated (note b.p.) and then until fluorescence appearing in the upper part of the condenser indicates that a trace of anthracene is being carried over. Then stop and let the flask cool.

Anthracene has a vapor pressure of 0.02 mm. at 100°. If the distillation were continued by passing in steam and conducted

Note for the instructor

[1] Pure, fluorescent anthracene should be used. Preparation: Chapter 29.

at the rate of 10 ml. per minute, how long would it take to distil all the anthracene present?

The bulk of the anthracene can be dislodged from the walls and collected on a small suction filter. To recover the rest, add a little acetone to the emptied flask, warm on the steam bath to dissolve the material, add water to precipitate it, and collect the precipitate on the same funnel. About 80% of the hydrocarbon in the original toluene solution should be recoverable. When dry, crystallize the material from about 1 ml. of benzene and observe that the crystals are more intensely fluorescent than the solution or the amorphous solid. The characteristic fluorescence is quenched by mere traces of impurities.

Note the total volume of toluene recovered and decant it into a bottle for wet toluene.

2. Isolation of a Natural Product

Clean the above apparatus and to the distilling flask add 10 ml. of lemon grass oil (sp. gr. 0.89) and 175 ml. of water (boiling stone). Distil rather rapidly and collect the distillate in a 500-ml. Erlenmeyer flask. When about 100 ml. of oily distillate has collected, interrupt the distillation, add 100 ml. of fresh water, and then distil further until droplets of oil no longer appear (total distillate about 250 ml.).

Distillation time about 40 min.

The steam-volatile oil consists very largely of citral, $C_{10}H_{16}O$. Note the odor. The product is separated from the water by ether extraction. Pour 50 ml. of ether into a 125-ml. separatory funnel, add about one third of the distillate, shake and let the layers separate. Discard the lower layer, add another portion of distillate, and repeat. When the last portion of distillate has been added, rinse the flask with a little ether to recover adhering citral. Use the techniques described in Chapter 7.2 for drying the ethereal extract, filtering (into a 125-ml. Erlenmeyer flask), and evaporating the ether. To remove last traces of solvent connect the flask to the water pump by means of a rubber stopper and tube, wrap the flask in a towel as a precaution against a defective flask that might break, and evacuate for a few minutes. Take the tare (empty weight) of a 1-oz. tincture bottle, transfer the citral to it with a capillary dropping tube, and determine the weight and the yield from lemon grass oil. Label the bottle and put it away in a dark place for use in later experiments in which the substance is to be tested for the presence of various functional groups. Clean the dropping tube and flask with a little acetone from a wash bottle.

Fire hazard

1. A mixture of ethyl iodide (C_2H_5I, b.p. 72.3°) and water boils at 63.7°. What weight of ethyl iodide would be carried over by 1 g. of steam?

2. Iodobenzene (C_6H_5I, b.p. 188°) steam distils at a temperature of 98.2°. How many molecules of water are required to carry over one molecule of iodobenzene? How many grams per gram of iodobenzene?

(I)   (II)

Cyclohexene | CHAPTER 9

cis + trans

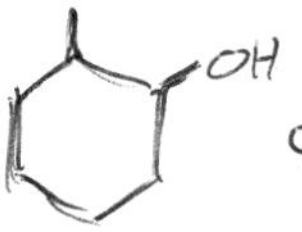

b. 165° 166.5°

n_D^{20} 1.4640 1.4611

(I) – b. 110°/769 mm

$n_D^{18.5}$ 1.4503

d_8^{14} 0.8145

Dehydration of cyclohexanol to cyclohexene can be accomplished by heating the cyclic secondary alcohol with an acid catalyst at a moderate temperature or by distillation over alumina or silica gel. The procedure selected for this experiment

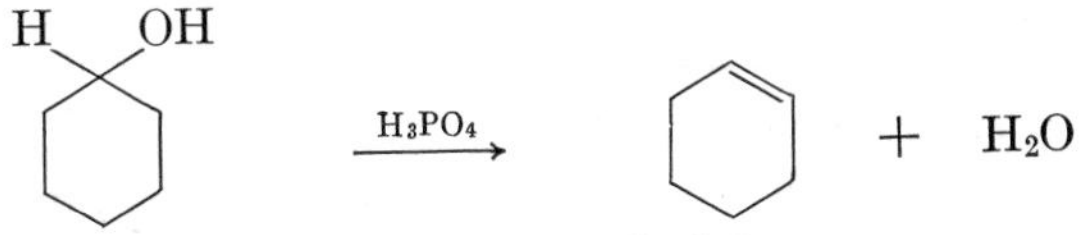

$$\text{Cyclohexanol} \xrightarrow{H_3PO_4} \text{Cyclohexene} + H_2O$$

Cyclohexanol
M.p. 25°, b.p. 161°
Sp. gr. 0.96, mol. wt. 100.16

Cyclohexene
B.p. 83°
Sp. gr. 0.81, mol. wt. 82.14

(II) – b. 104°
[cis]: n_D^{25} 1.4432
d^{25} 0.799

[d]: b. 103–4°
n_D^{14} 1.4459
d^{14} 0.803

involves catalysis by phosphoric acid; sulfuric acid is no more efficient, causes charring, and gives rise to sulfur dioxide. When a mixture of cyclohexanol and phosphoric acid is heated in a flask equipped with a fractionating column, the formation of water is soon evident. On further heating, the water and the cyclohexene formed distil together by the principle of steam distillation, and any high-boiling cyclohexanol that may volatilize is returned to the flask. However, after dehydration is complete and the bulk of the product has distilled, the column remains saturated with water–cyclohexene that merely refluxes and does not distil. Hence for recovery of otherwise lost reaction product, a chaser solvent is added and distillation is continued. A suitable chaser solvent is the water-immiscible s-tetrachloroethane (Cl₂CHCHCl₂, b.p. 147°); as it steam distils it carries over the more volatile cyclohexene. When the total water-insoluble layer is separated, dried, and redistilled through the dried column the chaser again drives the cyclohexene out of the column; the difference in boiling points is such that a sharp separation is possible.

CHAPTER 9

The hold-up in the metal sponge-packed column is so great that if a chaser solvent is not used in the following procedure the yield will be only about one third that reported.

PROCEDURE

Run steam through / Use condenser for column

FIG. 9.1

Add H₂O

If excess chaser was used the organic layer will be the lower one; use of xylene as chaser eliminates this trouble

---

Beilstein test for halogen

Introduce 20.0 g. of cyclohexanol (technical grade), 5 ml. of 85% phosphoric acid, and a boiling stone into a 100-ml. round bottomed boiling flask and shake to mix the layers. The arrangement for fractional distillation can be the same as before (Fig. 3.1) except that evaporation losses are avoided by fitting the condenser with an adapter and cooling the 50-ml. receiver in an ice–water bath (Fig. 9.1). Make sure that the corks all fit tightly. Note the initial effect of heating the mixture, and then distil until the residue in the flask is reduced to a volume of 5–10 ml. and distillation becomes very slow; note the temperature range. Then let the assembly cool a little, remove the thermometer briefly and pour 20 ml. of s-tetrachloroethane into the top of the column through a long-stemmed funnel. Note the size of the upper layer and distil again until the volume of the layer has been reduced by about half. Pour the contents of the receiver into a small separatory funnel and rinse the flask with a little chaser solvent; use more of this solvent for rinsing in subsequent operations. Wash the mixture with an equal volume of saturated sodium chloride solution, separate the water layer, run the upper layer into a clean flask, and add 5 g. of anhydrous sodium sulfate (10 × 75-mm. test tube-full) to dry it. Before the final distillation note the barometric pressure, apply any thermometer corrections necessary, and determine the reading to be expected for a boiling point of 83°. Dry the boiling flask, column, and condenser (acetone wash, evacuation, air through calcium chloride tube), decant the dried liquid into the flask through a stemless funnel plugged with a bit of cotton, and fractionally distil, with all precautions against evaporation losses. The rim of condensate should rise very slowly as it approaches the top in order that the thermometer may record the true boiling point soon after distillation starts. Record both the corrected boiling point of the bulk of the cyclohexene fraction and the range, which should not be more than 2°. Yield, 13.2 g. Note that chaser solvent in the product can be detected by a simple Beilstein test: heat the end of a copper wire to redness in the oxidizing flame of a burner until the flame is no longer colored, let the wire cool and dip it into the liquid (or touch it to a solid) and reheat; a volatile copper halide imparts a green color to the flame.

2-Methylbutene-2 [1]

Pour 36 ml. of water into a 200-ml. round-bottomed flask and cautiously add with shaking 18 ml. of concentrated sulfuric acid. This "1 : 2 acid" is now cooled under the tap and 30 g. (36 ml.) of *tert.*-amyl alcohol is added slowly. The mixture is shaken thoroughly and the flask is connected by means of bent glass tubing to a Liebig condenser fitted with an adapter, and heated on the steam bath. A 125-ml. Erlenmeyer flask packed in an ice bath serves as the receiving flask; to lessen evaporation the space between the adapter and the mouth of the flask may be plugged loosely with cotton. All connections must be tight and a rapid stream of water should be run through the condenser, for the hydrocarbon is very volatile (and also flammable).

For efficient heating use the largest ring that will hold the flask, insert a match stick between the ring and the flask to allow steam to rise around the upper walls of the container, and wrap the flask with a towel to confine the steam. Turn on the steam until there is just a slight escape; an excess does no good and is objectionable. The flask is heated until distillation of the hydrocarbon has practically ceased (1–2 hr.). To remove traces of sulfurous acid from the product the distillate is transferred to a separatory funnel and about 10 ml. of 10% sodium hydroxide solution is added. Note that this aqueous solution sinks to the bottom. Stopper the funnel and shake it well, occasionally releasing the pressure, after inverting the funnel, by turning the stopcock. Now separate and discard the water layer and pour the hydrocarbon layer through the mouth of the funnel into a clean, dry flask. To dry the product add about 2 g. of anhydrous calcium chloride, insert a stopper loosely in the flask, and allow it to stand for about one half hour, with occasional shaking.

Decant the dried hydrocarbon into a distilling flask of suitable size, attach a thermometer and a clean, dry condenser, and distil from a water bath, taking the same precautions as before to avoid evaporation losses. Collect in a weighed bottle the portion boiling at 37–43°. Pure 2-methylbutene-2 boils at 38.4°; the yield reported in the literature is 84%; the average student yield is about 50%.

[1] J. F. Norris and J. M. Joubert, *J. Am. Chem. Soc.*, **49,** 873 (1927).

Cyclohexene

Alternative Preparation of an Alkene

CHAPTER 10 | Alkanes and Alkenes

The following tests demonstrate properties characteristic of saturated and unsaturated hydrocarbons, provide means of distinguishing between compounds of the two types, and distinguish between pure and impure alkanes. Use your own preparation of cyclohexene as a typical alkene, purified 66–75° ligroin (Eastman Kodak Co. No. 513) as a typical alkane mixture, and unpurified ligroin (Eastman No. P513) as an impure alkane. Write equations for all tests that are positive.

1. Bromine Water

Measure 3 ml. of a 3% aqueous solution of bromine into each of three 13 × 100-mm. test tubes, add 1-ml. portions of purified ligroin to two of the tubes and 1 ml. of cyclohexene to the third. Shake each tube and record the initial results. Put one of the ligroin-containing tubes in the desk out of the light and expose the other to bright sunlight or hold it close to a light bulb. When a change is noted compare the appearance with that of the mixture kept in the dark.

2. Bromine in Nonaqueous Solution

Treat 1-ml. samples of purified ligroin, unpurified ligroin, and cyclohexene with 5–6 drops of a 3% solution of bromine in carbon tetrachloride. In case decolorization occurs, breathe across the mouth of the tube to see if hydrogen bromide can be detected. If the bromine color persists illuminate the solution and, if a reaction occurs, test as before for hydrogen bromide.

3. Acid Permanganate Test

To 1-ml. portions of purified ligroin, unpurified ligroin, and cyclohexene add a drop of an aqueous solution containing 1%

potassium permanganate and 10% sulfuric acid and shake. If the initial portion of reagent is decolorized, add further portions.

4. Sulfuric Acid

Cool 1-ml. portions of purified ligroin and cyclohexene in ice, treat each with 3 ml. of concd. sulfuric acid, and shake. Observe and interpret the results. Is any reaction apparent? Any warming? If the mixture separates into two layers, identify them.

Caution: *student-prepared cyclohexene may be wet*

5. Bromination with Pyridinium Bromide Perbromide ($C_5H_5\overset{+}{N}HBr_3{}^-$)[1]

This substance is a crystalline, nonvolatile, odorless complex of high molecular weight (319.85), which, in the presence of a bromine acceptor such as an alkene, dissociates to liberate one mole of bromine. For small-scale experiments it is much more convenient and agreeable to measure and use than free bromine.

Weigh one millimole (320 mg.) of the reagent as accurately as you can on a triple beam balance, put it into a 10-ml. Erlenmeyer flask and add 2 ml. of acetic acid. Swirl the mixture and note that the solid is sparingly soluble. Determine the mg. per micro drop of cyclohexene delivered by a capillary dropping tube and add one millimole of the alkene to the suspension of reagent. Swirl, crush any remaining crystals with a flattened stirring rod, and if after a time, the amount of cyclohexene appears insufficient to exhaust the reagent, add a little more. When the solid is all dissolved, dilute with water and note the character of the product. By what property can you be sure that it is a reaction product and not starting material?

6. Formation of a Bromohydrin

N-Bromosuccinimide in an aqueous solution is in equilibrium with hypobromous acid and may be used to effect addition of this reagent:

$$
\begin{array}{c}
CH_2CO \\
| \quad \quad \rangle NBr + HOH \rightleftharpoons \\
CH_2CO
\end{array}
\quad
\begin{array}{c}
CH_2CO \\
| \quad \quad \rangle NH + HOBr \\
CH_2CO
\end{array}
$$

N-Bromosuccinimide   Succinimide
Mol. wt. 178.00

---

[1] Crystalline material suitable for small-scale experiments is supplied by Arapahoe Chemicals, Inc. Massive crystals commercially available should be recrystallized from acetic acid (4 ml. per g.). Preparation: Mix 15 ml. of pyridine with 30 ml. of 48% hydrobromic acid and cool; add 25 g. of bromine gradually with swirling, cool, collect the product with use of acetic acid for rinsing and washing. Without drying the solid, crystallize it from 100 ml. of acetic acid. Yield of orange needles, 33 g. (69%).

Note for the instructor

Weigh 178 mg. of N-bromosuccinimide approximately (triple beam balance), put it into a 13 × 100-mm. test tube and add 0.5 ml. of dioxane and 1 millimole of cyclohexene. In another tube chill 0.2 ml. of water and add to it 1 millimole of concd. sulfuric acid. Transfer the cold dilute solution to the first tube with the capillary dropper. Note the result and the nature of the product that separates on dilution with water.

7. Tests for Unsaturation

Determine which of the following hydrocarbons are saturated and which are unsaturated or contain unsaturated material. Use any of the above tests that seem appropriate.

Pinene, the principal constituent of turpentine oil

Paraffin oil, a purified petroleum product

Gasoline produced by cracking

Cyclohexane

Rubber (The adhesive Grippit is a solution of unvulcanized rubber in benzene. Squeeze a drop of it onto a stirring rod and dissolve it in more benzene. For tests with permanganate or with bromine in carbon tetrachloride use only a drop of the former and just enough of the latter to produce coloration.)

CHAPTER 11

Cholesterol

This experiment demonstrates purification of a monounsaturated substance by conversion to the dibromide and debromination. The example chosen, cholesterol, is a crystalline substance that is present in all tissues of the animal organism and that is to be isolated from gallstones by solvent extraction. The cholesterol molecule, represented by an abbreviated formula, contains a secondary alcoholic group attached to a cyclohexane ring, as in cyclohexanol. For the purpose of the experiment it is suf-

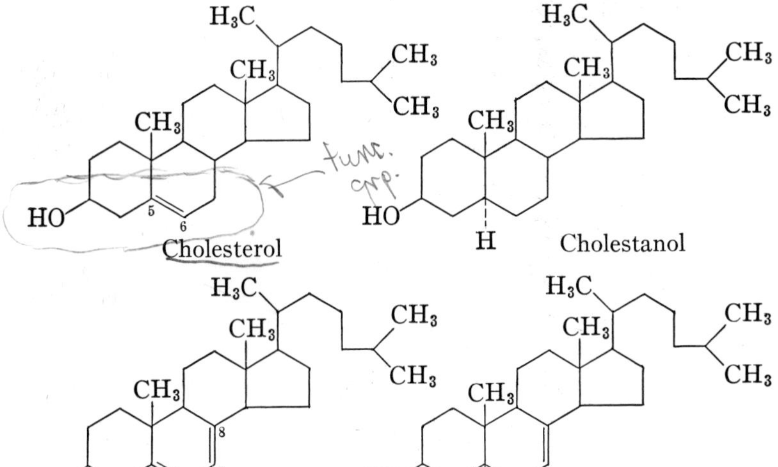

Cholesterol   Cholestanol

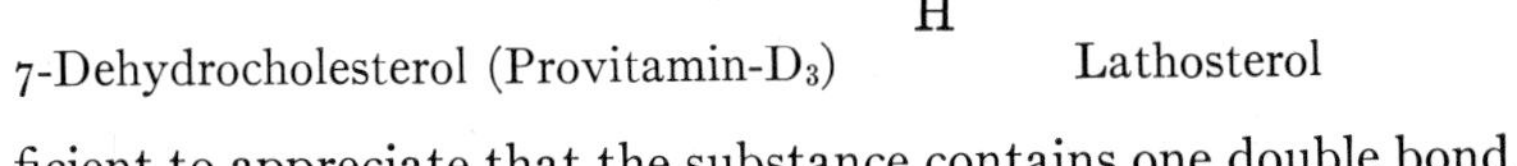

7-Dehydrocholesterol (Provitamin-D_3)   Lathosterol

ficient to appreciate that the substance contains one double bond (between carbon atoms 5 and 6). Cholesterol isolated from gallstones or from body tissues contains small amounts (0.1–3%) of the following companions: cholestanol (saturated), 7-dehydrocholesterol (a diene), and lathosterol (a double-bond isomer).[1] The companions are so very similar to cholesterol in solubility that their removal by crystallization is not feasible. However, complete purification can be accomplished through the sparingly soluble cholesterol dibromide. Cholestanol, being saturated, does not react and remains in the mother liquor. Lathosterol and 7-dehydrocholesterol are dehydrogenated by bromine to dienes and trienes that likewise remain in the mother liquor and are eliminated along with colored by-products.

The cholesterol dibromide that crystallizes from the reaction solution is collected, washed free of the companion substances or their dehydrogenation products, and debrominated with zinc dust, with regeneration of cholesterol in pure form. By specific color tests it is possible to differentiate between pure cholesterol and tissue cholesterol purified by ordinary methods.

EXPERIMENTS

1. Cholesterol from Gallstones

Swirl 2 g. of crushed gallstones[2] in a 25-ml. Erlenmeyer flask with 10 ml. of dioxane on a hot plate for a few minutes until the solid has disintegrated and the cholesterol has dissolved, and filter the dirty yellow solution while hot from a brown residue of bile pigments. Dilute the filtrate with 10 ml. of methanol, clarify by warming the solution with a little Norit for a few minutes, filter through a funnel that has been warmed on the steam bath, reheat the weak greenish-yellow filtrate to the boiling point, add a little water gradually until the solution is saturated at the boiling point, and let the solution stand for crystallization. Collect the crystals, wash, dry, and take the melting point. Typical result: 1.5 g. of large colorless plates, m.p. 146–147.5°. Use 1 g. for purification and save the rest for color tests.

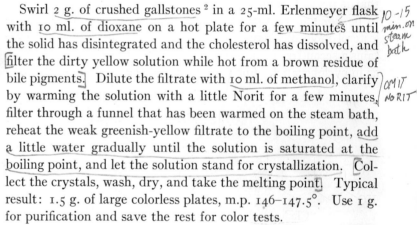

(handwritten margin notes: 10–15 min. on steam bath; OMIT NO RIT)

In a 25-ml. Erlenmeyer flask dissolve 1 g. of gallstone cholesterol or of commercial cholesterol (usually from spinal cord and brain of cattle; lathosterol content about 0.6%) in 7 ml. of ether by gentle warming and add 5 ml. of a solution of bromine and sodium acetate in acetic acid.[3] Cholesterol dibromide begins

FIG. 11.1 Pipetters with steel and glass (Waco) needles (rubber disc pierced with hot awl)

Note for the instructor

---

[1] A fourth companion, cerebrosterol or 24-hydroxycholesterol, is easily eliminated by crystallization from alcohol.

[2] Obtainable from the department of surgery of a hospital. Wrap the stones in a towel and crush by light pounding with a hammer.

[3] Weigh a 125-ml. Erlenmeyer flask on a balance placed in the hood, add 4.5 g. of bromine by a capillary dropping tube (avoid breathing the vapor), and add 50 ml. of acetic acid and 0.4 g. of sodium acetate (anhydrous). It is recommended that the 5-ml. portion of solution be measured with a pipette filled by means of a pipetter made from a rubber bulb, a hypodermic needle, and a disc of Gooch rubber; see S. L. Hood, *Anal. Chem.*, **24**, 2020 (1952); see Fig. 11.1.

to crystallize in a minute or two. Cool in an ice bath and stir the crystalline paste with a stirring rod for about 10 minutes to insure complete crystallization, and at the same time cool a mixture of 3 ml. of ether and 7 ml. of acetic acid in ice. Then collect the crystals on a small suction funnel and wash with the iced ether–acetic acid solution to remove the yellow mother liquor. Finally wash with a little methanol, suck well, and transfer the white solid without drying it (dry weight 1.2 g.) to a 50-ml. Erlenmeyer flask. Add 20 ml. of ether, 5 ml. of acetic acid, and 0.2 g. of zinc dust and swirl. In about 3 min. the dibromide dissolves; after 5–10 min. swirling, zinc acetate usually separates to form a white paste (the dilution sometimes is such that no separation occurs). Stir for 5 min. more and then add water by drops (about 0.5 ml.) until any solid present dissolves to a clear solution. Decant the solution from the zinc into a separatory funnel, wash the ethereal solution twice with water and then with 10% sodium hydroxide (to remove traces of acetic acid). Then shake the solution with an equal volume of saturated sodium chloride solution to reduce the water content, filter it by gravity through a paper containing anhydrous sodium sulfate, add 10 ml. of methanol (and a boiling stone), and evaporate the solution on the steam bath to the point where most of the ether is removed and the purified cholesterol begins to crystallize. Remove the solution, let crystallization proceed at room temperature, and then in an ice bath, and collect and wash with methanol; yield 0.6–0.7 g., m.p. 149–150°. Save material not required for the following tests for later use (Chapter 15).

Aspirator tube

2. Liebermann-Burchard Color Test

Cholesterol reacts with acetic anhydride containing sulfuric acid to give a transient purple color changing to blue and then green. The color, though highly intense, develops slowly. Lathosterol and 7-dehydrocholesterol give colors of comparable shade and intensity but react much more rapidly. The fully saturated cholestanol gives no color. The test is particularly sensitive when carried out by the following microtechnique. First test purified cholesterol; then compare pure material with unpurified gallstone cholesterol. Introduce a few very small particles of pure cholesterol into a melting point capillary and shake and tamp it down to the bottom. The amount should be no more than enough to cover the bottom of the tube and form a layer about 0.5 mm. thick (Fig. 11.2a). Make a pipette (b) by drawing down the end of another capillary to a fine tip, dip it into chloroform in a specimen vial until it takes up solvent, then insert the tip into the mouth of the first tube (c) so that it touches the wall, and let a 3–4 mm. column of chloroform flow in (d). Shake down the solvent by a whipping motion, the way the thread of a clinical thermometer is shaken down, and introduce more solvent until the sample is dissolved in a 10-mm. column of liquid (e). The test reagent is made by chilling 1 ml. of acetic anhydride in

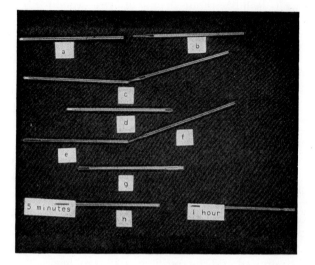

FIG. 11.2 Color test in a capillary tube

a 10-ml. Erlenmeyer flask in an ice bath and adding one drop of concd. sulfuric acid (the solution is stable for 3–4 hrs. if kept iced). With a second pipette (f) introduce a 3-mm. column of this reagent into the open end of the tube held in a horizontal position (g). Now grasp the tube at the open end and give it a quick whip to mix the two solutions (h) and note the time to the nearest second. Place the tube on a piece of white paper and note the time at which you can first detect color. A faint color is most easily detected by viewing the tube in a line close to the axis.

After testing pure cholesterol make parallel tests of pure cholesterol and gallstone cholesterol in tubes marked for identification with one and two dots. Try to use the same amounts of samples and reagents and process each test to the point (g) just prior to mixing. Then grasp the ends of the two tubes together, whip down the reagent, watch the two test solutions together until one develops color, and then note which tube this is. Pure lathosterol reacts very rapidly to give an initial blue color changing to green; pure cholesterol reacts more slowly and the initial transient color is purplish. Gallstone cholesterol, which contains

2–3% lathosterol, should be distinguishable from the purified material in the comparative test.

The test is still more sensitive when conducted at 0° because at this temperature lathosterol reacts to the point of maximum color density in 5 min. whereas cholesterol is negative indefinitely. See if, by this modified test, you can differentiate between pure cholesterol and commercial cholesterol, which contains about 0.6% lathosterol. The only change necessary is to cool the chloroform solution in an ice bath and keep the tube in ice while introducing the acid reagent into the open end; whip the tube and return it to the ice bath.

A 3-mm. column of cholesterol in a melting point capillary weighs approximately 1 mg. (1000γ). Estimate the weight in γ of the amount of lathosterol that you are just able to detect.

3. Selenium Dioxide Test

Selenium dioxide in acetic acid oxidizes lathosterol at 25° (or even at 0°) to an acetoxy derivative with liberation of selenium, detectable first as a yellow colloidal solution and then as a red precipitate. Cholesterol is oxidized only at 50–60°. Cholesterol containing as much as 3% of lathosterol gives a faint yellow color in about 5 minutes and red selenium in 15–20 minutes.

Introduce a 3-mm. column (tamped down; about 1 mg.) of gallstone cholesterol in one capillary tube and of pure cholesterol in another. Add enough toluene to each tube to extend the column to 6 mm., and heat on the steam bath until all the solid is dissolved. Now introduce 0.1 M selenium dioxide solution[4] to give a total column of 10 mm., place the tubes on a piece of white paper, and note the time and the ultimate result.

4. Tetranitromethane Test

Whereas the two tests above are specific to sterols, the test with tetranitromethane $[C(NO_2)_4$, b.p. 126°] is a generally applicable method of detecting unsaturation. Compounds containing one or more ethylenic double bonds, providing these are not conjugated with carbonyl groups, give a yellow color with the reagent, probably as the result of complex formation (compare the picric acid complex, Chapter 6.3). The microtechnique is particularly appropriate because the reagent is costly and must be used sparingly. It is conveniently mixed with an equal vol-

[4] Dissolve 1.29 g. of selenious acid or 1.11 g. of selenium dioxide in 2 ml. of water by heating and dilute with acetic acid to a volume of 100 ml.

ume of chloroform and kept in a specimen vial with a capillary pipette sealed (liquid solder) into a hole drilled through the Bakelite screw cap.

To a 0.5-mm. layer of cholesterol in a melting point capillary introduce a 5-mm. column of tetranitromethane solution and view the tube against white paper. Test your samples of cyclohexene and citral for unsaturation, and for comparison, test purified ligroin.

$$CH_3CH_2CH_2CH_2OH \xrightarrow{\text{NaBr, H}_2\text{SO}_4} CH_3CH_2CH_2CH_2Br + NaHSO_4 + H_2O$$

n-Butyl alcohol n-Butyl bromide
B.p. 118°   B.p. 101.6°
Sp. gr. 0.810   Sp. gr. 1.275
Mol. wt. 74.12   Mol. wt. 137.03

A primary alkyl bromide can be prepared by heating the corresponding alcohol with (a) constant-boiling hydrobromic acid (47% HBr), (b) an aqueous solution of sodium bromide and excess sulfuric acid, which is an equilibrium mixture containing hydrobromic acid, or (c) with a solution of hydrobromic acid produced by bubbling sulfur dioxide into a suspension of bromine in water. Reagents (b) and (c) contain sulfuric acid at a concentration high enough to dehydrate secondary and tertiary alcohols to undesirable by-products, alkenes and ethers, and hence the HBr method (a) is preferred for preparation of halides of the types R_2CHBr and R_3CBr. Primary alcohols are more resistant to dehydration and can be converted efficiently into the bromides by the more economical methods (b) and (c) unless they are of such high molecular weight as to lack adequate solubility in the aqueous mixtures. The $NaBr$-H_2SO_4 method is preferred to the Br_2-SO_2 method because of the unpleasant, choking property of sulfur dioxide. The overall equation is given in the flow sheet above along with key properties of the starting material and principal product.

The procedure that follows specifies a certain proportion of n-butyl alcohol, sodium bromide, sulfuric acid, and water, defines the reaction temperature and time, and describes operations to be performed in working up the reaction mixture. The prescription of quantities is based upon considerations of stoichi-

ometry as modified by the results of experimentation. Before
undertaking a preparative experiment you should analyze the
directions and calculate the molecular properties of the reagents.
Construction of tables of properties of starting material, reagents,
products, and by-products provides guidance in regulation of
temperature and in separation and purification of the product.

REAGENTS

Reagent	Mol. wt.	Sp. gr.	B.p.	Wt. used	Moles	
					Theory	Used
n-C_4H_9OH	74.12	0.810	118°	16.2	0.22	0.22
NaBr	102.91	—	—	27.0	.22	.26
H_2SO_4	98.08	1.84	—	42.3	.22	.44

PRODUCT AND BY-PRODUCTS

Compound	Mol. wt.	Sp. gr.	B.p.		Yield	
			Given	Found	Theory	%
n-C_4H_9Br	137.03	1.275	101.6°		30.0	
$CH_3CH_2CH{=}CH_2$			$-18°$			
$C_4H_9OC_4H_9$			141°			

One mole of butyl alcohol theoretically requires one mole each of
sodium bromide and sulfuric acid, but the prescription calls for
use of a slight excess of the bromide and twice the theoretical
amount of the acid. Excess acid is used to shift the equilibrium
in favor of a high concentration of hydrobromic acid. The
amount of sodium bromide taken, arbitrarily set at 1.2 times
the theory as an insurance measure, is calculated as follows:

$$\frac{16.2 \text{ (g. of } C_4H_9OH)}{} \left| \frac{102.91 \text{ (mol. wt. of NaBr)}}{74.12 \text{ (mol. wt. of } C_4H_9OH)} \right| \frac{1.2}{} = 27.0 \text{ g. of NaBr}$$

The theoretical yield is 0.22 mole of product, corresponding to
the 0.22 mole of butyl alcohol taken; the maximal weight of
product is calculated thus:

0.22 (mole of alcohol) $\times$ 137.03 (mol. wt. of product)

$$= 30.0 \text{ g. butyl bromide}$$

The probable by-products are butylene, dibutyl ether, and
starting material. The alkene is easily separable by distillation,
but the other substances are in the same boiling point range as
the product. However, all three possible by-products can be
eliminated by extraction with concentrated sulfuric acid.

PROCEDURE

Put 27.0 g. of sodium bromide, 30 ml. of water, and 20 ml. of *n*-butyl alcohol into a 200-ml. round bottomed boiling flask, cool the mixture in an ice-water bath, and add 23 ml. of concd. sulfuric acid slowly with swirling and cooling. The flask is then equipped with a vertically mounted long reflux condenser and supported on an asbestos-covered wire gauze resting on a tripod in the manner shown in Fig. 12.1. The condenser should not protrude very far through the stopper into the flask. The clamp supporting the reflux condenser is mounted high on the ring stand and is screwed only to a loose fit so that the flask may be grasped and swirled if desired. In the present experiment adequate agitation is provided by introducing a boiling stone and adjusting the flame of the burner to a point of brisk refluxing, which is continued for a period of 2 hrs. The butyl bromide is in the upper layer since the aqueous solution of inorganic salts has a higher specific gravity. Let the mixture cool and the condenser drain for about 5 min. and then disconnect the flask and arrange for downward distillation by connecting the flask to the condenser through an adapter made by bending a short piece of 8-mm. glass tubing to an angle of about 70°. Add a boiling stone and distil until no more water-insoluble material comes over (collect a few drops in a test tube and see if it is water soluble); butyl bromide distils along with water (steam distillation).

FIG. 12.1 Refluxing a reaction mixture

Prepare the adapter before the 2-hr. reflux period is over

Pour the distillate into a separatory funnel, shake with about 20 ml. of water, and note that the butyl bromide now constitutes the lower layer, in accordance with its specific gravity of 1.275. A pink coloration due to a trace of bromine in the lower layer can be discharged by adding a pinch of sodium bisulfite and shaking again. Drain the lower layer of butyl bromide into a clean flask, clean and dry the separatory funnel, and return the butyl bromide to it. Then cool 20 ml. of concd. sulfuric acid thoroughly in an ice bath and add it to the funnel, shake well, and allow 5 min. for settling of the layers. The relative specific gravities given in the tables above identify the two layers; an empirical method of telling the layers apart is to draw off a few drops of the lower layer into a test tube and see whether the material is soluble in water (H_2SO_4) or insoluble (butyl bromide). Separate the layers, allow 5 min. for further drainage, and separate again. Then wash the butyl bromide with 20 ml. of 10% sodium hydroxide solution to remove traces of acid, separate, and be careful to save the proper layer. *Save all layers until end of expt*

Dry the cloudy butyl bromide by adding 5 g. of calcium chloride and warming the mixture gently on the steam bath with swirling until the liquid clears. Decant the dried liquid into a distilling flask through a funnel fitted with a small loose plug of cotton, add a boiling stone, distil, and collect material boiling in the range 99–103°. Yield 21–27 g. Note the approximate volumes of forerun and residue.

Distil slowly

Put the sample in a narrow-mouth bottle of appropriate size, make a neatly printed label giving the name and formula of the product, the boiling point range, the yield in weight and in per cent, e.g., 21 g. (70%), and your name. Press the label onto the bottle under a piece of filter paper for a full minute and make sure that it is secure. After all the time spent on the preparation, the final product should be worthy of a carefully executed and secured label.

QUESTIONS

1. What experimental method would you recommend for the preparation of *n*-octyl bromide? *tert.*-Butyl bromide?

2. Explain why the crude product is likely to contain certain definite organic impurities.

3. How does each of these impurities react with sulfuric acid when the butyl bromide is shaken with this reagent?

4.

Triphenylcarbinol CHAPTER 13

$$C_6H_5CO_2H \xrightarrow{CH_3OH(H_2SO_4)} C_6H_5CO_2CH_3 \xrightarrow{2C_6H_5MgBr} (C_6H_5)_3COMgBr$$

Benzoic acid   Methyl benzoate
M.p. 122°   B.p. 199°
Mol. wt. 122.12   Mol. wt. 136.14

$$\xrightarrow{H_2O} (C_6H_5)_3COH$$

Triphenylcarbinol
M.p. 162°
Mol. wt. 260.32

Benzoic acid, the carboxylic acid derivative of benzene, is esterified by the Fischer method, and the methyl benzoate produced is used for the Grignard synthesis of triphenylcarbinol by interaction with two equivalents of phenylmagnesium bromide.

In the Fischer esterification, methanol is used in excess both to shift the equilibrium in favor of the product and to serve as solvent for the solid acid component. Of the Lewis acid catalysts commonly employed, sulfuric acid is preferred to gaseous hydrochloric acid because of greater convenience and to boron fluoride etherate because it is a more effective catalyst. In case either the alcohol or the acid involved in an esterification contains reactive double bonds or is sensitive to dehydration, boron fluoride etherate becomes the catalyst of choice.

In this two-step synthesis directions are given for the Grignard reaction of 5.0 g. (0.037 mole) of pure methyl benzoate and you are to adjust the quantities of reagents according to the amount of intermediate available. Satisfactory yield and quality of the final product require care in the preparation and purification of the intermediate ester as well as in the second step. The chief impurity in the Grignard reaction mixture is diphenyl, formed by the coupling reaction:

$$C_6H_5MgBr + C_6H_5Br \rightarrow C_6H_5 \cdot C_6H_5 + MgBr_2$$

CHAPTER 13

The hydrocarbon by-product is easily eliminated, however, since it is much more soluble in hydrocarbon solvents than the hydroxylic major product.

EXPERIMENTS

1. Methyl Benzoate

Place 10.0 g. of benzoic acid and 25 ml. of methanol in a 100-ml. round bottomed flask, and pour 3 ml. of concd. sulfuric acid slowly and carefully down the walls of the flask and then swirl to mix the components. Add a boiling stone, attach a reflux condenser, and reflux the mixture gently on the steam bath for 1 hr. Cool the solution and decant it into a separatory funnel containing 50 ml. of water, with care to avoid entrance of the boiling stone, for this may prevent operation of the stopcock. Add 35 ml. of ether for extraction of the product, using part to rinse the flask. Shake, and drain off the water, which removes the sulfuric acid and the bulk of the methanol. Wash with a second portion of water (25 ml.), drain, and then wash with 25 ml. of 5% sodium bicarbonate to remove unreacted benzoic acid. Shake, with frequent release of pressure, until no further reaction is apparent; then drain off and acidify the water layer. Any benzoic acid that precipitates is collected and the amount recovered allowed for in calculation of the percentage yield. Repeat the washing with bicarbonate until no precipitate forms on acidification of the aqueous layer. Wash with saturated salt solution and drain off the salt solution, then filter the ether solution through sodium sulfate into an Erlenmeyer flask.

Remove the ether by distillation through a condenser from a 125-ml. distilling flask heated on the steam bath, and collect the flammable solvent in a receiver chilled in ice. When distillation ceases, add 2–3 g. of anhydrous sodium sulfate to the residual oil and continue the heating for a few minutes longer. Then decant the methyl benzoate into a 50-ml. distilling flask and distil with a free flame through a short air condenser, that is, either the inner tube of an ordinary condenser or the complete condenser with no water in the jacket. The boiling point is so high (199°, corr.) that a water-cooled condenser is liable to crack. Use a tared 25-ml. Erlenmeyer flask as the receiver, collect material boiling above 190°, most of which should boil over a 2° range. Yield 8 g. Add a drop of the ester to a few drops of concd. sulfuric acid and see if it dissolves, as an oxygen-containing compound should, and if the solution is colorless; a yellow coloration indicates lack of purity. Keep the flask stoppered until the ester is to be used.

See page 75

1-Hr. reflux period; this can be done in advance and the mixture let stand

78

The Grignard reagent is prepared in a 100-ml. round bottomed flask fitted by means of a well cut cork stopper with a long reflux condenser. A calcium chloride drying tube inserted in a cork that will fit either the flask or the top of the condenser is also made ready. The flask and condenser should be as dry as possible to begin with and then, as a further precaution to eliminate a possible film of moisture, the magnesium to be used (2 g. = 0.082 mole of magnesium turnings) is placed in the flask, the calcium chloride tube is attached directly, and the flask is heated gently but thoroughly either on the steam bath or, better, by carefully brushing the bottom with a luminous flame. The flask on cooling sucks in dry air through the calcium chloride. Cool to room temperature before proceeding! Extinguish all flames!

Make an ice bath ready in case control of the reaction becomes necessary, remove the drying tube and fit it to the top of the condenser. Then pour into the flask 15 ml. of *absolute* ether and 9 ml. (13.5 g. = 0.086 mole) of bromobenzene. More ether is to be added as soon as the reaction starts but at the outset the concentration of bromobenzene is kept high to promote easy starting. If there is no immediate change, insert a dry stirring rod with a flattened end and crush a piece of magnesium firmly against the bottom of the flask under the surface of the liquid, giving a twisting motion to the rod. When this is done properly the liquid suddenly becomes slightly cloudy and ebullition commences at the surface of the turning that has been compressed. Attach the condenser at once, swirl the flask to provide fresh surfaces for contact and as soon as you are sure that the reaction has started add 25 ml. more absolute ether through the top of the condenser before spontaneous boiling becomes too vigorous (replace the drying tube). (If difficulty is experienced in initiating the reaction, try in succession the expedients described in the note.[1]) Cool in ice if necessary. If spontaneous boiling in the diluted mixture is slow or becomes slow, mount the flask and condenser on the steam bath and reflux gently until the magnesium has disintegrated and the solution has acquired a cloudy or brownish appearance. The reaction is complete when only a few small

Specially dried ether is required

Use minimum steam to avoid condensation on condenser

---

[1] (a) Warm on the steam bath with swirling. Then see if boiling continues when the flask (condenser attached) is removed from the heating bath. (b) Try further mashing of the metal with a stirring rod. (c) Add a tiny crystal of iodine as a starter (in this case the ethereal solution of the final reaction product should be washed with sodium bisulfite solution in order to remove the yellow color). (d) Add a few drops of a solution of phenylmagnesium bromide or of methylmagnesium iodide. (e) Start in afresh, taking greater care for the dryness of apparatus and reagents.

remnants of metal (or metal contaminants) remain. Since the solution deteriorates on standing, the next step should be started at once.

3. Triphenylcarbinol

Put 5 g. (0.037 mole) of methyl benzoate and 15 ml. of absolute ether into a separatory funnel, cool the flask containing phenylmagnesium bromide solution briefly in an ice bath, remove the drying tube, and insert the stem of the separatory funnel into the top of the condenser. Then run in the solution slowly with only such cooling as is required to control the mildly exothermic reaction, which affords an intermediate addition compound which separates as a white solid. Replace the calcium chloride tube, swirl the flask until it is at room temperature and the reaction has subsided. The reaction is then completed by either refluxing the mixture for one half hour, or stoppering the flask with the calcium chloride tube and letting the mixture stand overnight (subsequent refluxing is then unnecessary).

This is a suitable stopping point

Pour the reaction mixture into a 250-ml. Erlenmeyer flask containing 50 ml. of 10% sulfuric acid and about 25 g. of ice and use both ordinary ether and 10% sulfuric acid to rinse the flask. Swirl well to promote hydrolysis of the addition compound; basic magnesium salts are converted into water-soluble neutral salts and triphenylcarbinol is distributed into the ether layer. An additional amount of ether (ordinary) may be required. Pour the mixture into a separatory funnel (rinse), shake, and draw off the aqueous layer. Shake the ethereal solution with 10% sulfuric acid to further remove magnesium salts, wash it with saturated salt solution, and filter the solution through anhydrous sodium sulfate. If this solution is evaporated to dryness the residue will be found to be a solid (9.5 g.) of low and wide melting range (110–115°), since it contains considerable diphenyl. The by-product can be removed by crystallization from ligroin, but instead of removing the ether and dissolving the residue in ligroin it is simpler to add the ligroin to the ethereal solution, distil, and so displace the ether by the less volatile crystallization solvent. Use 25 ml. of 66–77° ligroin and concentrate the ether–ligroin solution (steam bath) either in a distilling flask fitted with condenser and iced receiver, as in the preparation of methyl benzoate, or in an Erlenmeyer flask under an aspirator tube. Evaporate slowly until crystals of triphenylcarbinol just begin to separate and then let crystallization proceed, first at room temperature and then at 0°. The product should be colorless

Wash with ether — ligroin

and should melt not lower than 160°. Concentration of the mother liquor may yield a second crop. Total yield 5.0 g. Evaporate the mother liquors to dryness and save the residue for later isolation of the components by chromatography.

4. Reactions of Triphenylcarbinol

(a) Dissolve the sample in 20 ml. of acetic acid (50-ml. Erlenmeyer, steam bath), add 2 ml. of 47% hydrobromic acid, heat for 5 min. on the steam bath, cool in ice, collect the product (0.8 g.) and wash it with petroleum ether.

Treat 1-g. samples as described and identify each product

(b) Prepare a solution as in (a), then add 2 ml. of an acetic acid solution containing 5% of chloroacetic acid and 1% of sulfuric acid, heat 5 min., add water (5–6 ml.) to produce a saturated solution, and let it stand for crystallization. Wash solvent: 1 : 1 methanol-water; yield 0.8 g.

(c) As in (a), then add 2 ml. of 47% hydriodic acid, heat for 1 hr., cool, add 1 g. of sodium bisulfite in 20 ml. of water, collect the precipitate, wash well with water, and crystallize the moist solid from methanol (15–20 ml.).

Fit one flask (c) into a ring of the steam bath and place the other (d) beside it

(d) As in (a), then add a hot solution of 2 g. of stannous chloride in 5 ml. of concd. hydrochloric acid, heat for 1 hr., cool, collect, and wash well with methanol; yield 0.8 g.

(e) Dissolve 1 g. of the carbinol in 25 ml. of methanol, add 1 ml. of 47% hydrobromic acid, heat gently for 15 min. and let cool. Crystallization can be hastened by scratching. Wash the product (1.0 g.) with methanol.

(f) Weigh 1 g. of the carbinol and 2 g. of malonic acid (crush any lumps) into a 25-ml. Erlenmeyer flask, and heat the mixture for 7 min. on the hot plate (about 150°) under an aspirator tube (p. 46) for removal of fumes. Cool, dissolve in 2 ml. of benzene, add 10 ml. of ligroin (60–90°) and set the solution aside. Wash solvent: ligroin; yield 0.8 g.

	M.p.
$(C_6H_5)_3CCl$	113°
$(C_6H_5)_3CBr$ [2]	152°
$(C_6H_5)_3CI$	132°
$CH_3COOC(C_6H_5)_3$	97°
$CH_2ClCOOC(C_6H_5)_3$	144°
$(C_6H_5)_3CH$	94°
$(C_6H_5)_3CC(C_6H_5)_3$	147°
$(C_6H_5)_3COOC(C_6H_5)_3$	186°
9-Phenylfluorene	148°
p-$(C_6H_5)_2CHC_6H_4C$-$(C_6H_5)_3$	224°
$(C_6H_5)_3COCH_3$	97°
$(C_6H_5)_3COC(C_6H_5)_3$	237°
$(C_6H_5)_3CCH_2CO_2H$	176°

Identification

Identify each product, and present some reason for your conclusion in addition to correspondence in m.p. Halogen can be detected by the Beilstein test (bottom of p. 62). Some of the possible products are listed in the margin.

[2] Put a small spatulaful of product in a 13 × 100-mm. test tube, dissolve in benzene and cool, add a few mg. of zinc dust and stir with a rod to produce a yellow solution containing triphenylmethyl. Decant into a clean tube and shake with air; the cloudy precipitate is the peroxide, $(C_6H_5)_3COOC(C_6H_5)_3$.

Aldehydes and Ketones

Sections 1–5 present orienting experiments in preparation for the identification of unknowns (Section 6). First a test is described for recognizing a carbonyl compound by its reaction with phenylhydrazine in the presence of acetic acid as catalyst. All aldehydes and nearly all ketones rapidly form phenylhydrazones, and the increase in molecular weight of 90 units attending the

$$R_2C{=}O + H_2NNHC_6H_5 \rightarrow R_2C{=}NNHC_6H_5$$

conversion renders the derivative so much less soluble than the starting material that it precipitates or crystallizes and thus gives evidence that a reaction has occurred. The phenylhydrazine test given below is a generally applicable method of distinguishing carbonyl compounds from substances of other classes.

Many phenylhydrazones are crystalline compounds suitable for characterization by melting point and mixed melting point determination, but some are oils and some are unstable. 2,4-Dinitrophenylhydrazones, prepared with 2,4-dinitrophenylhydrazine, $(NO_2)_2C_6H_3NHNH_2$, are often preferable for characterization because they are higher melting, less soluble, and more stable than the corresponding phenylhydrazones; the molecular weight change on conversion to the derivative is 180 units. Semicarbazones have comparable advantageous properties. Oximes are less useful for characterization, for many are liquids at

$$R_2C{=}O + H_2NNHCONH_2 \rightarrow R_2C{=}NNHCONH_2$$

Semicarbazide   Semicarbazone

room temperature and those that are solids are often obtainable in crystalline form only with difficulty (the preparation of an oxime is described in Chapter 18.3). If a substance under study is to be compared with a compound that is known but not available for mixed melting point determination, probable identity can be established by showing that several derivatives of the substance in question all correspond in melting point with known derivatives. After the experience of preparing the phenylhydrazone, 2,4-dinitrophenylhydrazone, and semicarbazone derivatives of known compounds, you may find similar derivatives useful in characterization of your unknowns.

Of the methods available for distinguishing between aldehydes and ketones, that recommended is the reaction with aqueous sodium bisulfite solution. Nearly all aldehydes and most methyl ketones afford solid, water-soluble addition compounds, and the iodoform test distinguishes a methyl ketone from all aldehydes but acetaldehyde. Methyl aryl ketones such as acetophenone, $C_6H_5COCH_3$, fail to give bisulfite addition compounds but are recognizable by the iodoform test.

EXPERIMENTS

1. Phenylhydrazones

To prepare a stock solution of the reagent, measure 1.0 ml. of phenylhydrazine with a calibrated capillary dropper into a 25-ml. Erlenmeyer flask, add 5 ml. of acetic acid from a 10-ml. graduate, swirl and note the heat of neutralization, dilute the solution with 2–3 ml. of water, pour it into a 10-ml. graduate, and make up the volume to 10.0 ml.; then return the solution to the Erlenmeyer flask for storage. The molecular weight and specific gravity of phenylhydrazine are such that 1 ml. of the stock solution contains 1 millimole of phenylhydrazine acetate, the amine salt of acetic acid. Excess acetic acid is used both as condensation catalyst and as solvent for the reagent.

Reagent: $C_6H_5NHNH_2$
Mol. wt. 108.14
Sp. gr. 1.10

A substance to be tested for the presence of a carbonyl function should first be examined to see whether or not it is soluble in water; if 8–10 micro drops dissolve in 1 ml. of water at room temperature, the test is conducted by dissolving one millimole of sample in 1 ml. of water and adding 1 ml. of the stock solution containing 1 millimole of phenylhydrazine acetate; separation of an oil or solid constitutes a positive indication that the substance has a carbonyl function. Test acetone (5 micro drops) in this way.

*(a) Water-soluble
substances*

Diethyl ketone (mol. wt. 86.13) is soluble to the extent of about 4 micro drops (47 mg.) in 1 ml. of water. Calibrate a capillary dropping tube for this substance by counting 30–40 micro drops delivered into a tared container, which is then weighed. Calculate the number of micro drops required to give 1 millimole of the ketone (about 8; record the figure for future use), measure this amount into 1 ml. of water in a small flask or test tube, and note that the first few drops dissolve but that an oily layer eventually appears. Add a few drops of methanol to just bring the oil into solution and then add 1 ml. of stock phenylhydrazine solution. Rub the oil with a stirring rod briefly to see if it will crystallize easily and if not discard it.

A typical water-insoluble liquid is acetophenone, $C_6H_5COCH_3$, mol. wt. 120.66. Calibrate the same capillary dropper for delivery of this substance, dissolve 1 millimole of substance in 1 ml. of methanol, and add 1 ml. of phenylhydrazine solution. Let the mixture stand for 5 min., collect the product, and see how the melting point corresponds with the value 105° reported for the pure derivative. A water-insoluble solid is likewise tested in methanol solution.

(b) Water-insoluble sample

Save the residual stock solution for testing unknowns.

2. 2,4-Dinitrophenylhydrazones

The reagent is a red solid of high melting point and low solubility in methanol.[1] It forms a yellow hydrochloride that is much more soluble, and a solution of this salt in a small volume of ethanol is used in the general application of the reaction, as in the following experiment.

Reagent: $(NO_2)_2C_6H_3NHNH_2$
Mol. wt. 198.14
M.p. 197°

Calibrate a 5-mm. measuring tube for delivery of 2,4-dinitrophenylhydrazine, measure 1 millimole of the reagent into a 25-ml. Erlenmeyer flask, add 10 ml. of 95% ethanol, and heat to boiling. Then add 6–8 micro drops of concd. hydrochloric acid, boil gently, and rub the solid with a flattened stirring rod until solution is complete. Then add 1 millimole of diethyl ketone (see calibration of 1a), warm on the steam bath for a few minutes and let crystallization proceed. The melting point reported is 156°; note the contrast between this derivative and the phenylhydrazone of the same ketone.

Procedure for unknowns

A second experiment illustrates an alternative procedure applicable where the 2,4-dinitrophenylhydrazone is known to be sparingly soluble in ethanol. The test substance is cinnamaldehyde ($C_6H_5CH{=}CHCHO$, mol. wt. 132.15), an α,β-unsaturated aldehyde. Determine the number of micro drops cor-

[1] *Preparation.* Dissolve 100 g. of 2,4-dinitrochlorobenzene (m.p. 50–52°) in 200 ml. of triethyleneglycol, stir mechanically in a salt–ice bath to 15° (or until crystallization starts), and add 28 ml. of 64% hydrazine solution by drops at a temperature of $20 \pm 3°$ (25 min.). When the strongly exothermal reaction is over, digest the paste on the steam bath, add 100 ml. of methanol and digest further, then cool, collect, and wash with methanol. Yield 98 g. (100%), m.p. 190–192°.

Note for the instructor

responding to 1 millimole of the liquid. Measure 1 millimole of 2,4-dinitrophenylhydrazine into a 125-ml. Erlenmeyer flask, add 30 ml. of 95% ethanol and digest on the steam bath until all particles of solid are dissolved, and then add 1 millimole of cinnamaldehyde and continue warming. If there is no immediate change, add 6–8 micro drops of concd. hydrochloric acid as catalyst and note the result. Warm for a few minutes, then cool and collect the product. Note that the derivative is more intensely colored than that of diethyl ketone; this is because it contains an α,β-double bond conjugated with the carbon-nitrogen double bond.

The second procedure strikingly demonstrates the catalytic effect of hydrochloric acid but is not applicable to a substance like diethyl ketone, whose 2,4-dinitrophenylhydrazone is much too soluble to crystallize from the large volume of ethanol. The first procedure is obviously the one to use for an unknown.

3. Semicarbazones

Semicarbazide (m.p. 96°) is not very stable in the free form and is used as the crystalline hydrochloride (m.p. 173°). Since this salt is insoluble in methanol or ethanol and does not react readily with typical carbonyl compounds in alcohol-water mixtures, a basic reagent is added to liberate free semicarbazide. In one procedure a suspension of semicarbazide hydrochloride and sodium carbonate in methanol is digested, filtered from the sodium chloride formed, and the carbonyl compound added to the filtrate. In another a mixture of semicarbazide hydrochloride and sodium acetate in methanol-water is employed. The procedure that follows utilizes the aromatic amine pyridine as the basic reagent.

Prepare a stock solution by dissolving 1.11 g. of semicarbazide hydrochloride in 5 ml. of water; 0.5 ml. of this solution contains 1 millimole of reagent. To 0.5 ml. of the solution add 1 millimole of acetophenone and enough methanol (1 ml.) to produce a clear solution; then add 10 micro drops of pyridine (a two-fold excess) and warm the solution gently on the steam bath for a few minutes until crystals begin to separate. The melting point of the pure product is 198°.

Repeat the reaction with cinnamaldehyde and see if you can observe a difference. Cinnamaldehyde semicarbazone melts at 215°.

4. Bisulfite Test

Prepare a stock solution by dissolving 5 g. of sodium bisulfite in 20 ml. of water by brief swirling. Put 1 ml. of the solution into

Reagent: $H_2NCONHNH_3{}^+Cl^-$
Mol. wt. 111.54

each of five 13×100-mm. test tubes and to each tube then add 5 micro drops of the following substances: acetone, butyraldehyde, cinnamaldehyde, diethyl ketone, and acetophenone. Shake occasionally for about 10 min. and note the results.

If the test is applied to a liquid or solid that is very sparingly soluble in water, formation of the addition product is facilitated by adding a small amount of methanol before addition of bisulfite solution.

5. Iodoform Test

The reagent contains iodine in potassium iodide solution [2] at a concentration such that 2 ml. of solution, on reaction with excess methyl ketone, will yield 174 mg. of iodoform. If the substance is water-soluble, dissolve 4 micro drops of a liquid or an estimated 50 mg. of a solid in 2 ml. of water in a 20×150-mm. test tube, add 2 ml. of 10% sodium hydroxide, and then slowly add 3 ml. of the iodine solution. In a positive test the brown color disappears and yellow iodoform separates. If the substance tested is insoluble in water, dissolve it in 2 ml. of dioxane, proceed as above, and at the end dilute with 10 ml. of water.

Test hexane-2,5-dione (water-soluble), *n*-butyraldehyde (water-soluble), and acetophenone (water-insoluble).

Iodoform can be recognized by its odor and yellow color and, more securely, from the melting point ($119°$). The substance can be isolated by suction filtration of the test suspension or by adding 2 ml. of chloroform, shaking the stoppered test tube to extract the iodoform into the small lower layer, withdrawing the clear part of this layer with a capillary dropping tube, and evaporating it in a small tube on the steam bath. The crude solid is crystallized from methanol–water.

6. Unknowns

An unknown may be any of the aldehydes or ketones listed in Table 14.1 or it may be a noncarbonyl compound. Hence the first test should be that with phenylhydrazine; if this test is negative report accordingly and proceed to another unknown. At least one derivative of the unknown is to be submitted, but if you first do the characterizing tests 4 and 5 the results may suggest derivatives whose melting points will be particularly revealing.

---

[2] Dissolve 25 g. of iodine in a solution of 50 g. of potassium iodide in 200 ml. of water.

TABLE 14.1

LIQUID UNKNOWNS AND MELTING POINTS OF DERIVATIVES (°C.)

Compound	Formula	Mol. wt.	Sp. gr.	Water solubility	Phenyl-hydrazone	2,4-DNP	Semi-carbazone
Acetone	CH₃COCH₃	58.08	0.79	4 g./100 g.	42	128	190
n-Butyraldehyde	CH₃CH₂CH₂CHO	72.10	0.82	4.7 g./100 g.	Oil	123	106
Diethyl ketone	CH₃CH₂COCH₂CH₃	86.13	0.81		Oil	156	139
Furfural	C₄H₃O·CHO	96.08	1.16	9 g./100 g.	97	229	202
Benzaldehyde	C₆H₅CHO	106.12	1.05	Insol.	158	237	222
Hexane-2,5-dione	CH₃COCH₂CH₂COCH₃	114.14	0.97	∞	120 ª	256 ª	222 ª
Heptanone-2	CH₃(CH₂)₄COCH₃	114.18	0.83	Insol.	Oil	89	123
Heptanone-3	CH₃(CH₂)₃COCH₂CH₃	114.18		Insol.	Oil	81	102
n-Heptaldehyde	n-C₆H₁₃CHO	114.18	0.82	Insol.	Oil	108	109
Acetophenone	C₆H₅COCH₃	120.66	1.03	Insol.	105	250	198
Octanone-2	CH₃(CH₂)₅COCH₃	128.21	0.82	Insol.	Oil	58	123
Cinnamaldehyde	C₆H₅CH=CHCHO	132.15	1.10	Insol.	168	255	215
Propiophenone	C₆H₅COCH₂CH₃	134.17	1.01	Insol.	about 48°	191	177

ª Diderivative

CHAPTER 14

Fluorene: $C_6H_4CH_2C_6H_4$

|_____|

M.p. 114°, mol. wt. 166.21

and

Fluorenone: $C_6H_4COC_6H_4$

|_____|

M.p. 83°, mol. wt. 180.19

**One half hour
unattended heating**

---

7. Citral

Prepare the 2,4-dinitrophenylhydrazone of the material isolated from lemon grass oil (Chapter 8.2) and extend your previous characterization of the functional groups present (Chapter 11.4).

8. Preparation of a Ketone–Hydrocarbon Mixture

This mixture is required for separation with Girard's reagent (next section) and separation by chromatography (Chapter 15). The hydrocarbon component fluorene is inexpensive, but the yellow ketone derived from it by dichromate oxidation is very costly because of difficulty in pushing the oxidation to completion. Hence you are to prepare your own mixture by brief, partial oxidation of fluorene.

In a 250-ml. Erlenmeyer flask dissolve 5.0 g. of practical fluorene in 25 ml. of acetic acid by heating the flask over a hole on the hot plate with occasional swirling. In a 125-ml. Erlenmeyer dissolve 15 g. of sodium dichromate dihydrate in 50 ml. of acetic acid by swirling on a hot plate. Adjust the temperature of the dichromate solution to 80°, transfer the thermometer and adjust the other solution to 80°, and then, under the hood, pour in the dichromate solution. Note the time and temperature, and heat the flask over a hole on the steam bath for 30 min. Observe the maximum and final temperature, and then cool the solution and add 150 ml. of water. Swirl the mixture for a full two minutes to coagulate the product and promote rapid filtration, and collect the yellow solid on an 8.5-cm. Büchner funnel (in case filtration is slow, empty the funnel and flask into a beaker and stir vigorously for a few minutes). Wash well with water and then suck the filter cake as dry as possible. Either let the product dry overnight, or dry it quickly as follows. Put the moist solid into a 50-ml. Erlenmeyer, add ether (20 ml.) and swirl to dissolve, and add anhydrous sodium sulfate (10 g.) to retain the water. Decant the ethereal solution through a cone of anhydrous sodium sulfate into a 125-ml. Erlenmeyer, and use a Calcutta wash bottle for rinsing the flask and funnel with ether. Evaporate on the steam bath under an aspirator, heat until the ether is all removed, and pour the hot oil into a 50-ml. beaker to cool and solidify. Scrape out the yellow solid; yield 4.0 g.

9. Girard Separation of a Fluorene–Fluorenone Mixture

Girard's reagent, trimethylaminoacetohydrazide chloride, of structure similar to that of semicarbazide, condenses with carbonyl compounds in ethanol containing a little acetic acid as catalyst to give derivatives of the type $Cl^-[(CH_3)_3\overset{+}{N}CH_2CONHN=CR_2]$, which are soluble in water because of the presence of the dipolar ionic grouping. A Girard derivative, once formed and extracted from a water–ether mixture into the aqueous phase, is hydrolyzed easily with excess water under catalysis by mineral acid, with regeneration of the carbonyl compound.

In a 25×150-mm. test tube place o.5 g. of the fluorene-fluorenone mixture, o.25 g. of Girard's reagent, o.5 ml. of acetic acid, and 5 ml. of 95% ethanol. Add a boiling stone and reflux the mixture for 1 hr. under a cold-finger condenser, made from a 20×150-mm. test tube with side-arm and conveniently supported at any height desired by a No. 3 Neoprene adapter (Fig. 14.1). Then cool the solution and pour it into a separatory funnel containing 25 ml. of ether, 25 ml. of water, and 10 ml. of saturated sodium chloride solution (to help break a possible emulsion). Rinse the test tube with both water and ether, shake, and when the layers separate, drain the lower layer into a clean flask (or a second separatory funnel), wash the ethereal solution with 10 ml. of water, and add the water to the main water extract. Then wash the ethereal solution in turn with 5% sodium bicarbonate solution and saturated salt solution and filter it through sodium sulfate drying agent. This ethereal solution of nonketonic material may be colored from impurities present in the technical fluorene, hence it should be shaken briefly with Norit, filtered, and then evaporated to dryness under an aspirator tube. Dissolve the residue in the least amount of methanol required (about 5 ml.), let crystallization proceed at room temperature, and then at 0°, collect the product and wash it with chilled methanol. The resulting fluorene should be colorless and the melting point close to 114°; yield 140 mg.

The aqueous layer resulting from treatment with Girard's reagent should be shaken with fresh ether to remove hydrocarbon contaminant, separated, treated with 1 ml. of concd. hydrochloric acid, and heated for 10 min. on the steam bath to hydrolyze the Girard derivative and drive off the dissolved ether. A faintly yellowish oil separates, and when the mixture is cooled fully in ice the oil solidifies and the solid when collected on a filter is seen to be bright yellow. Let the crude fluorenone dry (170 mg., m.p. 75–78°), and crystallize it from a very small volume of 66–75° ligroin; it forms beautiful, large, bright yellow spars, m.p. 82–83°.

Aldehydes and Ketones

Girard's reagent:
$Cl^-[(CH_3)_3\overset{+}{N}CH_2CONHNH_2]$
Mol. wt. 153.64

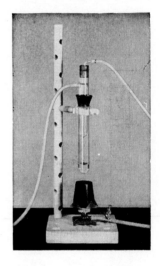

FIG. 14.1 Cold-finger reflux condenser

CHAPTER 15 | Elution Chromatography

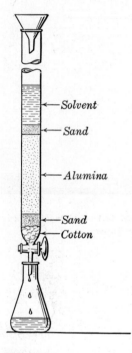

—Solvent

—Sand

—Alumina

—Sand
—Cotton

FIG. 15.1

Mixtures of organic substances often can be separated by adsorbing the material from a small volume of solvent onto a column of alumina and then leaching the column with a sequence of solvents of increasing eluant power, that is, of increasing ability to dislodge the adsorbed substances from the adsorbate (Fig. 15.1). The eluant liquid is collected in numbered fractions, each of which is evaporated for examination of the residue. If the components of the mixture are of different chemical types, some will be eluted at an early stage of the process and others in intermediate or late fractions. The usual order of elution is:

Alkanes	Esters, acetates
Alkenes	Ketones
Dienes	Alcohols
Aromatic hydrocarbons	Diols
Ethers	Acids

Solvents employed for elution, listed in the order of increasing eluant power, are: petroleum ether, benzene, ether, methanol. In an investigation of an unknown mixture one elutes first with petroleum ether, then with petroleum ether–benzene mixtures varying from 4:1 to 1:4, then with benzene, benzene–ether mixtures, ether, and ether-methanol mixtures.

Directions are given below for the preparation of a column and for three applications of the technique. In the first an alcohol is partially acetylated and the extent of reaction determined by separation of the easily eluted acetate from the strongly adsorbed alcohol; start the acetylation and let it run while you are preparing the column. The second experiment is separation of yellow fluorenone from the colorless hydrocarbon from which it is obtained by oxidation, and the third is an investigation of the triphenylcarbinol mother liquor of Chapter 13.3. Ordinarily 25 g. of alumina is taken per gram of substance, and this is the ratio specified in the first two experiments. In the third experiment the difference in adsorbability is sufficient to permit a decrease in the proportion of alumina. In all three experiments the transition from solvents of low to high solvent power is done more rapidly than in an unknown case.

EXPERIMENTS

1. Preparation of the Chromatograph Column [1]

Weigh out the required amount of alumina (12.5 g. in the first experiment), close the stopper of an ungreased 50-ml. burrette (or the tube, Fig. 15.3) and fill it half full with 30–60° petroleum ether. With a dowel push a cotton plug through the solvent to the bottom of the burette, and dust in through a funnel enough sand to form a 1-cm. layer over the cotton, and level the surface by tapping. Unclamp the burette and with the right hand grasp both the top of the burette and the funnel so that the whole assembly can be shaken to dislodge alumina that may stick to the walls, and with the left hand pour in the alumina from the paper (Fig. 15.2). When the fine powder has settled, add a little sand to provide a protective layer at the top. Open the stopcock, let the solvent level fall until it is just a little above the upper layer of sand, and then stop the flow. The column is then ready for use. Prepare a few 50-ml. Erlenmeyer flasks as receivers by marking numbers on the etched circle.

After use the burette is conveniently emptied by pointing the open end into a beaker, opening the stopcock and holding it in place, and applying gentle air pressure to the tip. If the plug of cotton remains in the tube, wet it with acetone and apply air pressure again.

FIG. 15.2   Filling an alumina column

2. Acetylation of Cholesterol

Cover 0.5 g. of cholesterol (Chapter 11.1) with 5 ml. of acetic acid, swirl, and note that the initially thin slurry soon sets to a stiff paste of the molecular compound $C_{27}H_{45}OH \cdot CH_3CO_2H$. Add 1 ml. of acetic anhydride and heat the mixture on the steam bath for any convenient period of time from 15 min. to 1 hr.; record the actual heating period. Cool, add water, and extract with ether. Wash the ethereal extract twice with water and once

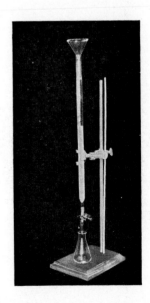

FIG. 15.3   Waco tube 3387

[1] Aluminum oxide Merck (acid-washed) is suitable. Purified sand is supplied by J. T. Baker Chemical Co. A dowel ($\frac{3}{16}''$ or $\frac{1}{4}''$) is preferred to a fragile glass rod.

Aspirator for
entrainment of
solvent vapor

[handwritten marginal notes:]
for 3/30
Have: (1) Boiling Stones
(2) Petrol. ether, 50ml.
(3) Benzene, 50 ml.
(4) Benzene-ether, 1:1 77-100 ml.

with 10% sodium hydroxide, dry, filter, and evaporate the ether. Dissolve the residue in 3–4 ml. of benzene, pour the solution onto a column of 12.5 g. of alumina and rinse the flask with another 3–4 ml. portion of benzene.[2] Open the stopcock, run the eluant solution into a 50-ml. Erlenmeyer flask, and as soon as the solvent in the burette has fallen to the level of the upper layer of sand fill the burette with a part of a measured 50 ml. of petroleum ether. When about 25 ml. of eluate has collected in the flask (fraction 1), change to a fresh flask, add a boiling stone to the first flask, and evaporate to dryness on the steam bath; evacuation at the water pump helps to remove last traces of benzene. If this fraction 1 is negative (no residue), use the flask for collecting further fractions. Continue adding petroleum ether until the 50-ml. portion is exhausted and then use 50 ml. of benzene, followed by 75–100 ml. of a 1:1 mixture of benzene and ether. Collect and evaporate successive 25-ml. fractions of eluate. Evaporation of the solutions, particularly those rich in benzene, can be hastened by use of the water-pump vacuum.

Cholesteryl acetate (m.p. 115°) and cholesterol (m.p. 149°) should appear, respectively, in early and late fractions with one or two negative fractions in between. If so, combine consecutive fractions of early and of late material and determine the weights and melting points. Calculate the percentage of the acetylated material to the total recovered and compare your result with those of others employing different reaction periods. The total recovery is about 80%.

3. Separation of Fluorene and Fluorenone

Prepare a column of 12.5 g. of alumina, run out excess solvent, and pour onto the column a solution of 0.5 g. of the fluorene-fluorenone mixture previously separated with Girard's reagent (Chapter 14.9). See if you can better the yields by chromatography. Elute at first with petroleum ether and use tared 50-ml. flasks as receivers. The yellow color of fluorenone provides one index of the course of the fractionation, and separation of solid around the tip of the burette provides another. Wash the solid frequently into the receiver with ether delivered from a Calcutta wash bottle. When you think that one component has been eluted completely, change to another receiver until you judge that the second component is beginning to appear. Then,

---

[2] Ideally, the material to be adsorbed is dissolved in petroleum ether, the solvent of least eluant power. The present mixture is not soluble enough in petroleum ether and so benzene is used, but the volume is kept to a minimum.

when you are sure the second component is being eluted, change to a 1:1 petroleum ether-benzene mixture and continue until the column is exhausted. It is possible to collect practically all the two components in each of two receiving flasks, with only a negligible intermediate fraction. After evaporation of solvent, pump out each flask at the suction pump and determine the weights and melting points of the products. Compare the outcome of the separation with that obtained with Girard's reagent.

4. Examination of a Mother Liquor

Dissolve the residues from the purification of triphenylcarbinol in a little ether, pour the solution into a tared flask, evaporate and evacuate at the water pump, and weigh. Digest 2 g. of the oil or semisolid with 15–20 ml. of 30–60° petroleum ether and prepare a column of 12.5 g. of alumina. If solid has separated from the solution of sample, filter the mixture through a paper into the column and save the crystals for possible combination with more of the same material. Since the early eluates are liable to contain mixtures, the first five fractions should be limited to 5 ml. each and collected in small Erlenmeyer flasks (10- or 25-ml.). When the fifth fraction has been collected, close the stopcock and defer further chromatography until the early eluates have been evaporated, pumped out, and examined (appearance and odor, particularly when warm). Let these fractions stand to see if, in time, crystals appear, and continue with the chromatogram. If fraction 5 afforded only a trace of oil, eluate with 20 ml. of petroleum ether and collect the liquid in a 50-ml. flask, as fraction 6. Then collect three fractions eluted by 20-ml. portions of benzene, stop the chromatogram, and take stock of the results.

Late fractions consisting of oils usually crystallize readily when scratched. If so, add a little petroleum ether, digest briefly on the steam bath, rub the material off the walls with a stirring rod, cool, collect, and take the melting point. If one or more of the early fractions crystallizes the crystals will probably be contaminated with oil, which can be separated as follows. Make ready a Hirsch funnel and paper, chill a mixture of 2 ml. of water and 8 ml. of methanol in ice and cool the flask as well, introduce solvent and stir to loosen the crystals, and then collect the product and wash it with chilled solvent.

Identify all crystalline products encountered and account for their presence. Review the steps in the Grignard synthesis and see if you can suggest substances that may have been present in oils that failed to crystallize.

CHAPTER 16 | Adipic Acid

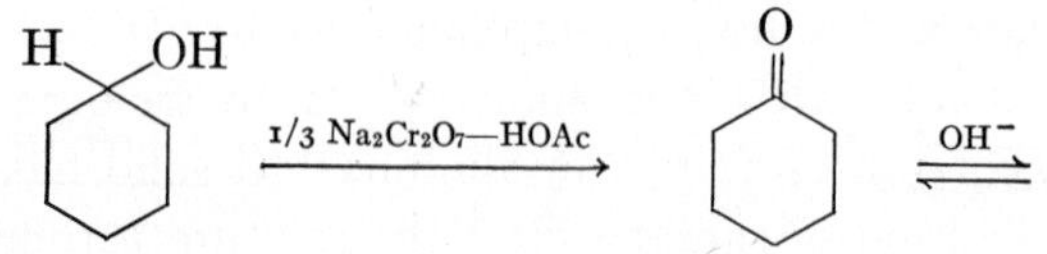

Cyclohexanol
B.p. 161.5°, sp. gr. 0.96
Mol. wt. 100.16

Cyclohexanone
B.p. 157°, sp. gr. 0.95
Mol. wt. 98.14, 1.5 g./100 ml. $H_2O^{10°}$

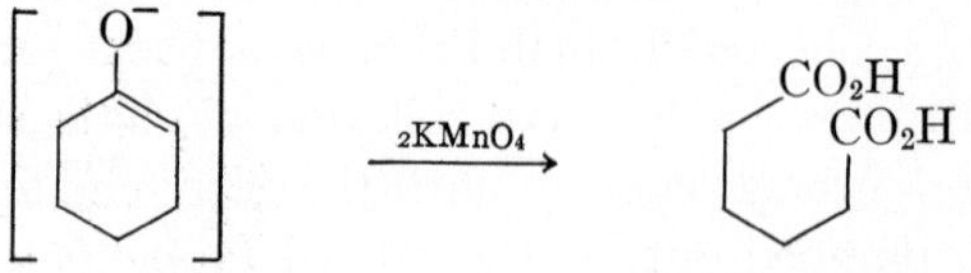

1/3 Na₂Cr₂O₇—HOAc

OH^-

2KMnO₄

Enolate

Adipic acid
M.p. 153°, 1.4 g./100 g. $H_2O^{15°}$
Mol. wt. 146.14

Cyclohexanol can be oxidized directly to adipic acid by nitric acid in about 50% yield, but a stirring motor is required and toxic fumes have to be disposed of. Direct oxidation with permanganate is free from these limitations but takes several days. Since the first step in the permanganate reaction is the slow one, the overall reaction time is greatly reduced by oxidation of cyclohexanol to cyclohexanone with dichromate in acetic acid followed by permanganate oxidation of cyclohexanone catalyzed by alkali to promote formation of the intermediate enolate.

1. Cyclohexanone

In a 125-ml. Erlenmeyer flask dissolve 15 g. of sodium dichromate dihydrate in 25 ml. of acetic acid by heating the mixture, and then cool in ice to 15°. In a second flask chill a mixture of 15.0 g. of cyclohexanol and 10 ml. of acetic acid in ice. After the first solution is cooled to 15°, transfer the thermometer and adjust the temperature in the second flask to 15° or below. Wipe the flask containing the dichromate solution, pour it in, rinse the flask with a little solvent, note the time, and take the initially light orange solution from the ice bath, but keep the ice bath ready for use when required. The exothermic reaction that is soon evident can get out of hand unless controlled. When the temperature rises to 60° cool in ice just enough to prevent a further rise and then, by intermittent brief cooling, keep the temperature close to 60° for 15 min. No further cooling is needed, but the flask should be swirled occasionally and the temperature watched. The usual maximal temperature is 65° (25–30 min.). When the temperature begins to drop and the solution becomes pure green, the reaction is over. Allow 5–10 min. more and then pour the green solution into a 250-ml. distilling flask, rinse the Erlenmeyer flask with 100 ml. of water, and add the solution to the flask for steam distillation of the product. Distil as long as any oil passes over with the water, and since cyclohexanone is appreciably soluble in water, continue somewhat beyond this point. After 50 ml. of distillate has collected add an equal volume of water to the flask before further distillation.

To salt out the cyclohexanone add to the distillate 0.2 g. of sodium chloride per ml. of water present and swirl to dissolve it. Then pour the mixture into a separatory funnel, rinse the flask with ether, add more ether to a total volume of 25–30 ml., shake, and draw off the water layer. Then wash the ether layer with 25 ml. of 10% sodium hydroxide solution to remove acetic acid, test a drop of the wash liquor to make sure it contains excess alkali, and draw off the aqueous layer. Wash with salt solution and dry the ethereal extract over sodium sulfate, decant it into a tared 125-ml. Erlenmeyer flask, and then either decant the solution into a 125-ml. distilling flask and distil off the ether from the steam bath through a condenser into an ice-cooled receiver or evaporate the ether under an aspirator. Cool to room temperature, evacuate the residual cyclohexanone at the water pump to remove a further amount of ether, and weigh the crude product; yield 11–12.5 g.[1]

[1] When the acetic acid solutions of cyclohexanol and dichromate were mixed at 25° rather than at 10° the yield of crude cyclohexanone was only 6.9 g. A clue to the evident importance of the initial temperature is suggested by an experiment in which the cyclohexanol was dissolved in 12.5 ml. of benzene instead of in 10 ml. of acetic acid and the two solutions were mixed at 15°. Within a few minutes orange-yellow crystals separated and soon filled the flask; the substance probably is the chromate ester, $(C_6H_{11}O)_2CrO_2$. When the crystal magma was let stand at room temperature the crystals soon dissolved, exothermic oxidation proceeded, and cyclohexanone was formed in high yield. Perhaps a low initial temperature insures complete conversion of the alcohol into the chromate ester before side reactions set in.

Adipic Acid

=swirl

Reaction time 45 min.

Prepare 2,4-DNP (handwritten margin note)

You have the choice of using the crude cyclohexanone for the next step or of purifying it by distillation. One way of judging the suitability of the crude product is to prepare a carbonyl derivative such as the oxime (m.p. 89°), 2,4-dinitrophenylhydrazone (m.p. 160°), or semicarbazone (m.p. 166°).

2. Adipic Acid

To a 500-ml. Erlenmeyer flask add 10 g. of cyclohexanone, 30.5 g. of potassium permanganate, and 250 ml. of water. While swirling on the hot plate to promote solution of the permanganate, adjust the temperature to exactly 35° and discontinue the heating. Add 5 ml. of 10% sodium hydroxide solution, swirl frequently, probe the bottom of the flask with the thermometer for undissolved permanganate, and swirl until it is all dissolved. The temperature rises and reaches a maximum of 80–82° in 15–20 min. and then begins to fall (in case of a temperature surge to 90°, cool quickly to 80°). When the exothermic reaction is over and the temperature begins to fall, heat the flask gently over a hole on the steam bath to complete the oxidation and to coagulate the manganese dioxide (5 min.). Prepare for filtration of the mixture on an 8.5-cm. Büchner funnel and for evaporation of the alkaline filtrate in a 400-ml. beaker; measure 70 ml. of water into the beaker, note the level, and discard the water. When the purple color of the oxidation mixture is no longer grossly evident, make a spot test by touching a drop of solution from the end of the thermometer onto a filter paper; permanganate, if present, will appear in a pink ring around the spot of manganese dioxide. When the test is negative, filter the hot mixture; to avoid frothing, turn the suction pump on only part way. If a 250-ml. filter flask is used, empty it into the beaker when it is about half full and then filter the remaining mixture and wash the manganese dioxide well with water. Transfer the filtrate and rinse the flask, add a boiling stone, and boil the alkaline filtrate in the beaker supported on a wire gauze and heated over a burner. Evaporate to a volume estimated to be 70 ml. Rinse down the salt deposited on the walls of the beaker, acidify the hot solution with concd. hydrochloric acid to pH 1–2, add 10 ml. acid in excess, and let the solution stand to crystallize.

The yield of adipic acid, m.p. 152–153°, is 7–8 g. To clean the reaction flask and thermometer, add water and a little sodium bisulfite, and rub stained spots with a test tube brush.

Reaction period about 30 min.

Avoid excess steam

$$C_6H_5CHO \xrightarrow{\text{NaHSO}_3} C_6H_5CH(OH)SO_3Na \xrightarrow{\text{KCN}} C_6H_5CH(OH)CN$$

Benzaldehyde   Mandelonitrile
Mol. wt. 106.12
Sp. gr. 1.05

$$\xrightarrow{\text{H}_2\text{O-HCl}} C_6H_5CH(OH)CO_2H$$

Mandelic acid
M.p. 118.5, mol. wt. 152.14
16.0 g./100 g. $H_2O^{20°}$, pK_a 3.4

This α-hydroxy acid is prepared from benzaldehyde through the cyanohydrin, which is produced by interaction of the benzaldehyde bisulfite addition compound with potassium cyanide. This interchange reaction eliminates the hazard of working with volatile, toxic hydrogen cyanide, but even potassium cyanide is dangerous if safety measures are not observed. The interchange reaction is reversible and excess cyanide is used to shift the equilibrium in favor of the cyanohydrin. Mandelonitrile, a liquid, undergoes changes on standing and hence should be processed further without delay; it is extracted with ether, the solution is carefully washed free of cyanide ion, and the nitrile is then hydrolyzed with hydrochloric acid. An intermediate mandelic acid amide, $C_6H_5CHOHC(\!\!=\!\!O)NH_2$, soon gives way to mandelic acid and ammonium chloride, both of which are soluble in the aqueous acid. The solution is cooled and extracted with ether, and the ether is then displaced by benzene for crystallization, since mandelic acid is much less soluble in this solvent than in ether.

EXPERIMENT

1. Caution

Potassium cyanide is extremely poisonous if it gets into the blood through a cut, if transferred from the hand to the mouth, or if it comes into contact with acid and liberates hydrogen cyanide. Never touch the solid with the fingers; be very careful not to spill it and if you do clean it up at once. Take care not to spill a solution or reaction mixture containing the substance, and discard the waste solution directly into the drain and wash down the sink with excess water.

2. Procedure

In a 125-ml. Erlenmeyer flask dissolve 11 g. of sodium bisulfite in 30 ml. of water by brief swirling, add 10 ml. of benzaldehyde [1] and swirl vigorously and stir until the oily aldehyde is all converted into the crystalline bisulfite addition compound. Cool to room temperature but not below, add 14 g. of potassium cyanide (*caution*) and 25 ml. of water (rinse down the walls), and take the mixture to a hood. Swirl and stir for about 10 min. until all but a trace of solid has dissolved (break up lumps with the rod). Mandelonitrile separates as a thick oil. Pour the mixture into a separatory funnel, rinse the flask with small amounts of ether and water (and at once wash the flask free of cyanide), and then shake the mixture vigorously for a full minute to insure complete reaction. Add 20 ml. of ether, shake, and run the aqueous solution down the drain. Wash the ether extract with 25 ml. of water and then with 25 ml. of saturated salt solution (note and account for the difference in appearance of the ether layer). Then run the solution into a 125-ml. distilling flask containing 15 ml. each of concd. hydrochloric acid and water. Add a boiling stone, stopper the flask, and mount it on a steam bath for distillation through a condenser into an ice-cooled receiver. Distil off the ether and then disconnect the condenser, note the time, and continue heating on the steam bath with frequent swirling to mix the layers and promote hydrolysis. Note that the initially lighter-than-water layer of mandelonitrile gradually changes to an oil of density greater than that of the aqueous acid. In a little less than 1 hr. the oil dissolves to a clear solution; however if the solution is cooled at this point it will become cloudy from separation of unhydrolyzed oil still present. Hence continue heating for one half hour more to complete the reaction and then cool to room temperature. Measure 100 ml. of benzene into a 250-ml. distilling flask and make a mark at the level of the liquid. Transfer the acid solution to a separatory funnel and rinse the flask with a little ether (5 ml.). Then add 20 ml. of ether, shake

---

[1] As a safety measure, the benzaldehyde should be tested to make sure it does not contain an appreciable amount of benzoic acid.

Note for the instructor

well, let the layers separate, and draw off the aqueous layer into a second separatory funnel or a dry flask, and wait a few minutes for separation of a little more aqueous solution. Run the ethereal extract into the flask containing benzene, and reextract the aqueous solution with two further 20-ml. portions of ether, and add the extracts to the flask containing benzene. Add a boiling stone, connect the flask to a condenser and an ice-cooled receiver, put a thermometer in place, and distil the solvent, cautiously at first since the flask is very full. Water is eliminated gradually by azeotropic distillation and the boiling point rises as ether and water are eliminated. Continue the distillation until the solution has cleared, water is no longer evident in the neck of the distilling flask, and the volume of the solution has been reduced to the 100-ml. mark. Disconnect the flask and inspect the bottom to see if a trace of ammonium chloride has separated, as either a solid or a gum, make sure that no flames are near, and decant the hot solution into a 250-ml. Erlenmeyer flask. Crystallization usually starts soon; yield 10.0 g., m.p. 118–119°.[2] In case no crystals appear, pour the solution into a 250-ml. distilling flask, evaporate the solvent, scratch to induce crystallization, and digest the solid with benzene.[2]

Note. When mandelic acid that has been crystallized from benzene is allowed to stand in contact with the mother liquor for several days, the needles gradually change into granular, sugar-like crystals of a molecular compound containing one molecule each of mandelic acid and benzene. These crystals are stable only in contact with benzene and at temperatures below 32.6°; on exposure to the air the benzene of crystallization evaporates and the mandelic acid is left as a white powder.

[2] A special experiment that provides starting material for use in Chapter 31 is reduction of mandelic acid to phenylacetic acid by the method of Miescher and Billeter, *Helv. Chim. Acta,* **22,** 601 (1939). The product can be distilled in vacuum in an apparatus such as that of Fig. 39.1.

Note for the instructor

CHAPTER 18 | Pinacol and Pinacolone

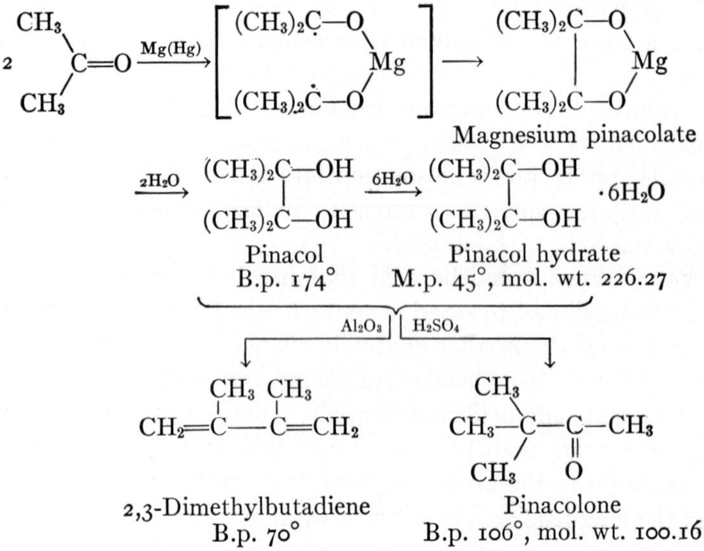

$$2 \underset{CH_3}{\overset{CH_3}{>}} C=O \xrightarrow{Mg(Hg)} \left[\begin{array}{c} (CH_3)_2\overset{\cdot}{C}-O \\ \\ (CH_3)_2\overset{\cdot}{C}-O \end{array} Mg \right] \longrightarrow \begin{array}{c} (CH_3)_2C-O \\ | \quad\quad Mg \\ (CH_3)_2C-O \end{array}$$

Magnesium pinacolate

$$\xrightarrow{2H_2O} \begin{array}{c} (CH_3)_2C-OH \\ | \\ (CH_3)_2C-OH \end{array} \xrightarrow{6H_2O} \begin{array}{c} (CH_3)_2C-OH \\ | \\ (CH_3)_2C-OH \end{array} \cdot 6H_2O$$

Pinacol
B.p. 174°

Pinacol hydrate
M.p. 45°, mol. wt. 226.27

$\xrightarrow{Al_2O_3}$ | $\xrightarrow{H_2SO_4}$

$$\begin{array}{cc} CH_3 & CH_3 \\ | & | \\ CH_2=C\!-\!\!-\!C=CH_2 \end{array} \qquad\qquad \begin{array}{c} CH_3 \\ | \\ CH_3\!-\!C\!-\!C\!-\!CH_3 \\ | \quad\; \| \\ CH_3 \quad O \end{array}$$

2,3-Dimethylbutadiene
B.p. 70°

Pinacolone
B.p. 106°, mol. wt. 100.16

Acetone on treatment with metallic reducing agents is converted to a considerable extent into the product of bimolecular reduction, pinacol. The diol is a liquid but can be isolated as the crystalline hexahydrate. In the procedure given below dry acetone is treated under Grignard conditions with magnesium that has been amalgamated with 0.02 mole of mercury by reaction with mercuric chloride in the presence of a portion of the acetone: $HgCl_2 + Mg \rightarrow Hg + MgCl_2$. Bimolecular reduction probably proceeds through a bi-radical and affords magnesium pinacolate as a voluminous precipitate, which on treatment with water affords pinacol and then pinacol hydrate. This crystalline solid is easily separated from unreacted acetone and isopropyl alcohol, the product of normal, unimolecular reduction.

Pinacol on catalytic dehydration over alumina undergoes normal dehydration to 2,3-dimethylbutadiene-1,3, but on dehydration with sulfuric acid the ditertiary glycol largely undergoes rearrangement and affords pinacolone in 70% yield. Fully purified pinacolone, as well as its oxime, has a fine camphor-like odor, and a similarity in structure is evident from the formulas.

Camphor   Pinacolone

You are to prepare pinacol, purify it as the hydrate, and use this for preparation of pinacolone, which is to be characterized as the crystalline oxime. As a special experiment pinacolone can be further converted by the haloform reaction into trimethylacetic acid.[1]

EXPERIMENTS

1. Pinacol Hydrate

In a 500-ml. round bottomed flask equipped with a long reflux condenser place 8 g. of magnesium turnings and 100 ml. of dry benzene. The apparatus should be thoroughly dry, as in a Grignard reaction. A solution of 9 g. of mercuric chloride in 75 ml. of dry acetone is placed in a small dropping funnel fitted into the top of the condenser by means of a grooved cork. Add about one fourth of this solution, and if the reaction does not start in a few minutes (vigorous ebullition) warm the flask gently on the steam bath, but make ready to plunge it into cold water if moderation of the reaction becomes necessary. Once started, the reaction will proceed vigorously at this stage without further heating. Run in the remainder of the acetone solution at such a rate as to keep the reaction in progress. The boiling should be vigorous, but some cooling may be necessary in order to prevent escape of uncondensed acetone. After 5–10 min. the reaction slows down, and heat is then applied from the steam bath to keep the mixture boiling briskly for one hour longer. The flask should be shaken occasionally during this period and if the magnesium pinacolate forms a mass too stiff for shaking this should be broken up after the first half hour of boiling (cool slightly, disconnect the flask and use a stirring rod).

[1] *Org. Synth., Coll. Vol.,* **1,** 526 (1941).

At the end of the one-hour period pour in 20 ml. of water through the condenser and boil the mixture for one half hour with frequent shaking. This converts the pinacolate into pinacol (soluble in benzene) and a precipitate of magnesium hydroxide. Filter the hot solution by suction, return the solid magnesium hydroxide to the flask and reflux it with 50 ml. of ordinary benzene for 5–10 min., and filter this solution as before. Pour the combined filtrates into an Erlenmeyer flask and evaporate the solution on a steam bath under an aspirator tube to one third the original volume. Then add 15 ml. of water, cool well in an ice bath, and scratch the walls of the flask with a stirring rod. The pinacol hydrate separates as an oil which soon solidifies; it should be collected only after thorough cooling and stirring for maximum crystallization. Scrape the crude material onto a suction funnel, wash it with a little cold benzene, press it well with a spatula, and let it drain for about 5 min. in order to remove as much benzene as possible.

The crude material is purified by crystallization from water, in which it is very soluble. Transfer the product to a small Erlenmeyer flask, dissolve it in 25 ml. of water by heating, and boil the solution gently for about 5 min. in order to remove traces of benzene. If the solution is appreciably colored it should be clarified with Norit. Filter the hot solution through a rather large funnel, which has been warmed on the steam bath, into a second flask and set it aside to crystallize. Cool in ice before collecting the large crystals of pinacol hydrate. The purified product should be dried in a cool place since it sublimes easily. The yield is 18–20 g.; m.p. 46–47°. Calculate the theoretical yield from the amount of magnesium employed, for acetone is taken in considerable excess.

2. Pinacolone

Into a 200-ml. round bottomed flask pour 80 ml. of water, then 20 ml. of concentrated sulfuric acid, and dissolve 20 g. of pinacol hydrate in the warm solution. Attach a reflux condenser, boil the mixture for 15 min., and observe carefully the changes that take place. Cool until the boiling ceases, pour the solution into a distilling flask, and distil until no more pinacolone comes over. Separate the upper layer of crude pinacolone, dry it with calcium chloride, and purify the material by distillation. Use a fractionating column with tetrachloroethane as chaser and see if you can detect and remove a small forerun containing dimethylbutadiene.

3. Oxime

Measure into a test tube provided with a cold-finger condenser 1 ml. of pinacolone and 3 ml. each of 5 M hydroxylamine hydrochloride solution and 5 M sodium acetate solution, and add 5 ml. of 95% ethanol in order to bring the oil completely into solution. Reflux the solution gently on the steam bath for 2 hrs., when sufficient of the oxime should be formed for purposes of identification. The oxime usually separates as an oily layer; on very thorough cooling and by rubbing the walls of the tube with a stirring rod the material can be caused to solidify. Collect the product on a suction funnel, dry a portion on a filter paper, and determine the melting point. Pure pinacolone oxime melts at 77–78°. It is soluble in cold, dilute hydrochloric acid, and the fine odor becomes particularly apparent on boiling the solution. The oxime evaporates rapidly, even at room temperature, and it should not be left exposed to the air for more than a few hours.

Succinic Anhydride

Acetic anhydride can be prepared by the interaction of sodium acetate and acetyl chloride or by the addition of acetic acid to ketene:

$$CH_3COONa + CH_3COCl \longrightarrow (CH_3CO)_2O + NaCl$$
$$CH_2{=}C{=}O + CH_3COOH \longrightarrow (CH_3CO)_2O$$

The acid also can be treated with a dehydrating agent, and in the case of a dibasic acid of the type of succinic acid this direct method is the only one applicable. The dehydration can be accomplished with the use of either acetic anhydride or acetyl chloride:

$$\begin{matrix} CH_2COOH \\ | \\ CH_2COOH \end{matrix} + \begin{Bmatrix} (CH_3CO)_2O \\ \text{or} \\ CH_3COCl \end{Bmatrix} \longrightarrow \begin{matrix} CH_2CO \\ | \quad \diagdown \\ \quad \quad O \\ | \quad \diagup \\ CH_2CO \end{matrix} + \begin{Bmatrix} 2CH_3COOH \\ \text{or} \\ CH_3COOH + HCl \end{Bmatrix}$$

M.p. 120°
Mol. wt. 100.07

The cyclic anhydride formed is not contaminated with inorganic reagents and the acetic acid produced serves as a solvent for crystallization. The procedure may be used for preparing the anhydrides of glutaric, maleic, and phthalic acid.

Succinic anhydride is useful in affording routes to derivatives not available directly from the acid. On alcoholysis it yields the monomethyl ester, I; the acid amide, II, is formed on ammonol-

$$\begin{matrix} CH_2COOCH_3 \\ | \\ CH_2COOH \end{matrix} \qquad \begin{matrix} CH_2CONH_2 \\ | \\ CH_2COOH \end{matrix} \qquad \begin{matrix} CH_2CO \\ | \quad \diagdown \\ \quad \quad O \\ | \quad \diagup \\ CH_2CH_2 \end{matrix}$$

I   II   III

ysis of the anhydride; reduction gives butyrolactone, III, a typical γ-lactone. The reaction of the anhydride with aniline

$$\begin{array}{c} CH_2CO \\ | \qquad \diagdown \\ \qquad \qquad O + H_2NC_6H_5 \longrightarrow \\ | \qquad \diagup \\ CH_2CO \end{array} \quad \begin{array}{l} CH_2CONHC_6H_5 \\ | \\ CH_2COOH \end{array}$$

Succinanilic acid

can be used for the identification of this primary amine, for the product is a crystalline substance of sharp melting point. On treatment with acetyl chloride, succinanilic acid is cyclized to succinanil.

$$\begin{array}{l} CH_2CONHC_6H_5 \\ | \qquad \qquad \qquad + CH_3COCl \longrightarrow \\ CH_2COOH \end{array} \quad \begin{array}{c} CH_2CO \\ | \qquad \diagdown \\ \qquad \qquad NC_6H_5 + CH_3COOH + HCl \\ | \qquad \diagup \\ CH_2CO \end{array}$$

Succinanil

EXPERIMENTS

1. Succinic Anhydride

In a 100-ml. round bottomed flask fitted with a reflux condenser closed with a calcium chloride tube place 15 g. of succinic acid and 25 ml. of acetic anhydride. Heat the mixture gently on the steam bath with occasional shaking until a clear solution is obtained and then for one half hour longer to insure completion of the reaction (total time of heating about 1 hr.). Remove the flask from the steam bath with the condenser and drying tube still attached and allow it to cool for a time undisturbed, and observe the crystallization. Finally cool in an ice bath and collect the crystals on a dry suction funnel, using ether (several small portions) to rinse the reaction flask and wash the crystalline anhydride. The yield is 10–11 g.; m.p. 119–120°. Test the product with cold sodium bicarbonate solution for the presence of unchanged acid.

Reaction time 1 hr.

2. Succinanilic Acid

Dissolve 1 g. of succinic anhydride in 30 ml. of benzene on the steam bath and to the boiling solution add all at once a solution of 0.9 ml. of aniline in about 5 ml. of benzene. The separation of the reaction product occurs in a striking manner. Cool the mixture, collect the crystalline product, and wash it with benzene. Determine the yield and melting point and note the action on the substance of cold sodium bicarbonate solution. Pure succinanilic acid melts at 150°.

105

The reaction can be carried out rapidly and with very small amounts of material. Dissolve a few small crystals of succinic anhydride in 1 ml. of hot benzene in a 10 × 75-mm. test tube, add one small crystal of *p*-toluidine (another primary amine), and observe the result.

3. Succinanil

Convert the remainder of the succinanilic acid into this cyclization product (apparatus as in Section 1). Cover the material (about 1.8 g.) with 5 ml. of acetyl chloride and heat on the steam bath until the reaction is complete (10 min.). Allow crystallization to take place, collect the product, and wash it with ether as before. Test the solubility in bicarbonate solution. The pure material melts at 154°.

QUESTIONS

1. How could succinic acid be converted into β-aminopropionic acid?

2. Devise a method for the resolution of a *dl*-alcohol, assuming that an optically active derivative of aniline is available, and noting that the succinanilic acid, like other acids, can be esterified without difficulty.

Amines, whether primary, secondary, or tertiary, are distinguished from compounds of other classes, including other nitrogen-containing substances, in being basic. Some are not soluble enough in water to give a basic response to test paper but nevertheless combine with mineral acids to form salts, and hence the basic character can be recognized by a simple test with acid that distinguishes amines from neutral substances such as amides ($RCONH_2$), N-acylamines ($RNHCOCH_3$), and nitriles (RCN). An amine salt can be recognized by its reaction with base. Procedures for the tests for basicity are given in Section 1. The next section presents a test for distinguishing between primary, secondary, and tertiary amines, and Section 3 gives procedures for preparing solid derivatives for melting point characterizations. After applying the procedures to known substances you are to identify a series of unknowns.

EXPERIMENTS

1. Basicity

First see if the substance has a fishy, ammonia-like odor, for if so it probably is an amine of low molecular weight. Then test the solubility in water by putting 2 micro drops of a liquid or an estimated 20 mg. of a solid into a 10 × 75-mm. test tube, adding 0.2 ml. of water (a 5-mm. column) and first seeing if the substance dissolves in the cold. If the substance is a solid rub it well with a stirring rod and break up any lumps before drawing a conclusion.

If the substance is *readily soluble in cold water* and if the odor is suggestive of an amine, test the solution with Hydrion paper and further determine if the odor disappears on addition of a few drops of 10% hydrochloric acid. If the properties are more like those of a salt, add a few drops of 10% sodium hydroxide solution. If the solution remains clear, addition of a little sodium chloride may cause separation of a liquid or solid amine.

If the substance is not soluble in cold water, see if it will dissolve on heating; be careful not to mistake melting of a substance for dissolving. If it *dissolves in hot water*, add a few drops of 10% alkali and see if an amine precipitates. (If you are in doubt as to whether a salt has dissolved partially or not at all, pour off supernatant liquid and basify it.)

If the substance is *insoluble in hot water*, add 10% hydrochloric acid, heat if necessary, and see if it dissolves. If so make the solution basic and see if an amine precipitates.

Substances to be tested:

Aniline, $C_6H_5NH_2$, b.p. 184°
p-Toluidine, $CH_3 \cdot C_6H_4NH_2$, m.p. 43°
Pyridine, C_5H_5N, b.p. 115° (a tertiary amine)
Methylamine hydrochloride (salt of CH_3NH_2, b.p. −6.7°)
Aniline hydrochloride (salt of $C_6H_5NH_2$, b.p. 184°)
β-Naphthylamine hydrochloride (salt of $C_{10}H_7NH_2$, m.p. 112°)

2. Hinsberg Test

Primary and secondary amines react in the presence of alkali with benzenesulfonyl chloride, $C_6H_5SO_2Cl$, to give sulfonamides

1. $C_6H_5SO_2Cl + H—NHR + NaOH \longrightarrow C_6H_5SO_2NHR + NaCl + H_2O$
2. $C_6H_5SO_2Cl + H—NR_2 + NaOH \longrightarrow C_6H_5SO_2NR_2 + NaCl + H_2O$

that are distinguishable because the derivative from a primary amine has an acidic hydrogen atom rendering the product of reaction (1) soluble in alkali, whereas that from a secondary amine (2) is insoluble. Tertiary amines lack the necessary re-

$$C_6H_5—\overset{\overset{O}{\|}}{\underset{\underset{O}{\|}}{S}}—\underset{\underset{H}{|}}{N}—R + NaOH \longrightarrow C_6H_5—\overset{\overset{O}{\|}}{\underset{\underset{O}{\|}}{S}}—\underset{\underset{Na}{|}}{N}—R + H_2O$$

placeable hydrogen atom for formation of benzenesulfonyl derivatives.

To about 4 ml. of water in a 13 × 100-mm. test tube (4-cm. column) add 4 micro drops of a liquid amine or an estimated 100 mg. of an amine salt, 1 ml. of 10% sodium hydroxide solution, and 7 micro drops of benzenesulfonyl chloride. Stopper the tube, shake for 5 min., note if there is any heat effect and if a solid separates. Warm the tube slightly, shake for a few minutes longer until the odor of benzenesulfonyl chloride is no longer apparent, and cool the mixture. If an oil separates at this point cool the tube in an ice bath, rub the oil against the walls with a stirring rod, and see if this is a product which will solidify or if it is unreacted amine. Make sure that the solution is still alkaline, and if there is a precipitate at this point it should be collected by suction filtration and a portion tested with dilute alkali to prove that it is actually insoluble in alkali. (An alkali-soluble product may precipitate at this point as the sodium salt if too much alkali is used.) If there is no precipitate the alkaline solution may contain an alkali-soluble sulfonamide. Acidify with concd. hydrochloric acid and if a precipitate forms collect it and confirm the solubility in alkali.

Run tests in parallel on the following substances:

> Aniline, $C_6H_5NH_2$ (b.p. 184°)
> N-Methylaniline, $C_6H_5NHCH_3$ (b.p. 194°)
> Triethylamine, $(CH_3CH_2)_3N$ (b.p. 90°)

3. Solid Derivatives

Acetyl derivatives of primary and secondary amines are usually solids suitable for melting point characterization and are readily prepared by reaction with acetic anhydride, even in the presence of water. Benzoyl and benzenesulfonyl derivatives are made by reaction of the amine with the acid chloride in the presence of alkali, as in Section 2 (the benzenesulfonamides of aniline and of N-methylaniline melt at 110° and 79°).

Solid derivatives suitable for characterization of tertiary amines are the methiodides and picrates:

$$R_3N + CH_3I \longrightarrow R_3\overset{+}{N}(CH_3)\overset{-}{I}$$
$$C_6H_2O_6N_3OH + NR_3 \longrightarrow C_6H_2O_6N_3O\overset{-}{\overset{+}{N}}HR_3$$

Typical derivatives are to be prepared, and although determination of melting points is not necessary since the values are given, the samples should be saved for possible identification of unknowns.

(a) Measure 4–5 micro drops (about 1 millimole) of aniline into a 13 × 100-ml. test tube and add 5 micro drops of acetic anhydride. Note the heat effect, allow 2–3 min. for completion of the reaction, and then cool and add water. The oily precipitate soon solidifies, m.p. 114°. Test its solubility in dilute hydrochloric acid.

(b) Dissolve about 100 mg. of aniline hydrochloride in 1 ml. of water, add 5 micro drops of acetic anhydride, and then (at once) about 100 mg. of sodium acetate.

(c) Dissolve about 100 mg. of picric acid in 1 ml. of methanol and to the warm solution add 4 micro drops of triethylamine and let the solution stand. The picrate melts at 171°.

4. Unknowns

Determine first if an unknown is an amine or an amine salt and then the class to which it belongs. Complete identification may be tried but is not required.

QUESTIONS

1. How could you most easily distinguish between samples of β-naphthylamine and of acetanilide?

2. Would you expect the reaction product from benzene-sulfonyl chloride and ammonia to be soluble or insoluble in alkali?

3. Is it safe to conclude that a substance is a tertiary amine because it forms a picrate?

4. Why is it usually true that amines that are insoluble in water are odorless?

5. Technical dimethylaniline contains traces of aniline and of methylaniline. Suggest a method of freeing it completely from these impurities.

6. How would you prepare aniline from aniline hydrochloride?

Sugars | CHAPTER **21**

The term sugar applies to mono-, di-, and oligosaccharides, which are all soluble in water and thereby distinguished from polysaccharides. Many natural sugars are sweet, but some are not. Table 21.1 shows that this form of physiological activity varies greatly with stereochemical configuration and that activity is exhibited by compounds of widely differing structural type.

Sugars are neutral, combustible substances, and these prop-

TABLE 21.1

RELATIVE SWEETNESS

Compound	Sweetness	
	To man	To bees
Monosaccharides		
D-Fructose	1.5	+
D-Glucose	0.55	+
D-Mannose	Sweet, then bitter	−
D-Galactose	0.55	−
D-Arabinose	0.70	−
Disaccharides		
Sucrose (glucose, fructose)	1	+
Maltose (2 glucose)	0.3	+
α-Lactose (glucose, galactose)	0.2	−
Cellobiose (2 glucose)	Indifferent	−
Gentiobiose (2 glucose)	Bitter	−
Synthetic sugar substitutes		
Saccharin	550	
2-Amino-1-*n*-propoxy-4-nitrobenzene	4000	

erties distinguish them from other water-soluble compounds. Some polycarboxylic acids and some lower amines are soluble in water, but the solutions are acidic or basic. Water-soluble amine salts react with alkali with liberation of the amine, and sodium salts of acids are noncombustible.

One gram of sucrose dissolves in 0.5 ml. of water at 25° and in 0.2 ml. at the boiling point, but the substance has such marked crystallizing power that in spite of the high solubility it can be obtained in beautiful, large crystals (rock candy). More typical sugars are obtainable in crystalline form only with difficulty, particularly in the presence of a trace of impurity, and even then give small and not well-formed crystals. Alcohol is often added to a water solution to decrease solubility and induce crystallization. The amounts of 95% ethanol required to dissolve 1-g. samples at 25° are: sucrose, 170 ml.; glucose, 60 ml.; fructose, 15 ml. Some sugars have never been obtained in crystalline condition and are known only as viscous syrups. Osazones are much less soluble in water than the parent sugars, since the molecular weight is increased by 178 units and the number of hydroxyl groups reduced from five to four. It is easier to isolate an osazone than to isolate the sugar, and sugars that are syrups often give crystalline osazones. Osazones of the more highly hydroxylic disaccharides are notably more soluble than those of monosaccharides.

Some disaccharides do not form osazones, but a test for formation or nonformation of the derivative is ambiguous because the glycosidic linkage may suffer hydrolysis in a boiling solution of phenylhydrazine and acetic acid with formation of an osazone derived from a component sugar and not from the disaccharide. If a sugar has reducing properties it is also capable of osazone formation; hence an unknown is tested for reducing properties before preparation of an osazone is attempted. Three tests for differentiation between reducing and nonreducing sugars are described below; two are classical and the third modern.

1. Fehling's Solution [1]

The reagent is made just prior to use by mixing equal volumes of Fehling's solution I, containing copper sulfate, with solution II, containing tartaric acid and alkali. The copper, present as a deep blue complex anion, is reduced by glucose from the cupric to the cuprous state and precipitates as red cuprous oxide. If the

---

[1] *Solution I:* 34.64 g. of $CuSO_4 \cdot 5H_2O$ dissolved in water and diluted to 500 ml. *Solution II:* 173 g. of sodium potassium tartrate (Rochelle salt) and 65 g. of sodium hydroxide dissolved in water and diluted to 500 ml.

initial step in the reaction involved oxidation of the aldehydic group of the aldose to a carboxyl group, a ketose should not reduce Fehling's solution, or at least should react less rapidly than an aldose, but the comparative experiment given below will show that this is not the case. Hence the point of attack by an alkaline oxidizing agent must be the activated hydroxyl group of the α-ketol grouping common to aldoses and hexoses, and perhaps proceeds through an enediol, the formation of which is

$$
\begin{array}{ccc}
\overset{|}{\underset{|}{C}}{=}O & \overset{|}{\underset{|}{C}}{-}OH & \overset{|}{\underset{|}{C}}{=}O \\
\overset{|}{\underset{|}{C}}HOH & \overset{\|}{\underset{|}{C}}{-}OH \xrightarrow{\text{[O]}} \overset{|}{\underset{|}{C}}{=}O \\
\overset{|}{\underset{|}{C}}HOH & \overset{|}{\underset{|}{C}}HOH & \overset{|}{\underset{|}{C}}HOH \\
\alpha\text{-Ketol} & \text{Enediol} & \alpha\text{-Ketol}
\end{array}
$$

favored by alkali. A new α-ketol grouping is produced and thus oxidation proceeds down the carbon chain. One milliliter of mixed solution is equivalent to 5 mg. of glucose; the empirically determined ratio is the basis for quantitative determination of the sugar. Fehling's test is not specific to reducing sugars, since ordinary aldehydes reduce the reagent, if by a different mechanism and, as will be observed in the experiments, at a different rate.

To be tested: 0.1 *M* solutions of glucose, fructose, lactose, maltose, *n*-butyraldehyde.[2]

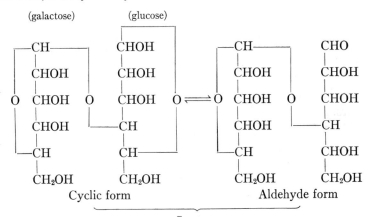

Lactose

4-O-β-*d*-Galactopyranosyl-α-*d*-glucopyranose

[2] Dissolve the following amounts of substance in 100 ml. of water each: D-glucose monohydrate, 1.98 g.; fructose, 1.80 g.; α-lactose monohydrate, 3.60 g.; maltose monohydrate, 3.60 g.; *n*-butyraldehyde, 0.72 g.

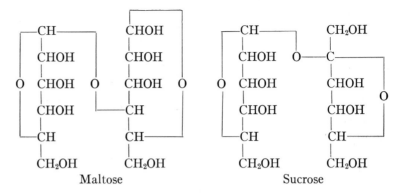

Maltose   Sucrose

Introduce 10 micro drops of the 0.1 M solutions to each of five 13 × 100-mm. test tubes carrying some form of serial numbers resistant to heat and water (see Fig. 0.6), and prepare a beaker of hot water in which all the tubes can be heated at once. Measure 5 ml. of solution I into a small flask and wash the graduate before using it to measure 5 ml. of solution II into the same flask. Mix until all precipitate dissolves, measure 2 ml. of mixed solution into each of the five test tubes, shake, put the tubes in the heating bath, and observe the results. If the tube containing *n*-butyraldehyde shows no change in 5 min., add a drop of the pure aldehyde and continue heating. Wash the tubes with water and then with dilute acid (leave the markers in place and continue heating the beaker of water).

2. Tollens' Reagent

The reagent, a solution of silver ammonium hydroxide and sodium hydroxide, is reduced by aldoses and ketoses and also by simple aldehydes with deposition of metallic silver, partly in the form of a mirror. The test is more sensitive than that of Fehling and better able to reveal small differences in reactivity, but it is less reliable in distinguishing between reducing and nonreducing sugars.

Add a few ml. of 10% sodium hydroxide to each of the five marked test tubes and heat the tubes in the water bath (for thorough cleaning) while preparing reagent sufficient for five tests. Measure 2 ml. of 5% silver nitrate solution and 1 ml. of 10% sodium hydroxide into a test tube, and make a dilute solution of ammonia by mixing 1 ml. of concd. ammonia solution with 10 ml. of distilled water. Add 0.5 ml. of this solution to the precipitated silver oxide, stopper the tube, and shake. Repeat the process until the precipitate just dissolves (3 ml., avoid an excess) and then dilute the solution to a volume of 10 ml. Empty

Procedure

the five tubes and rinse them with distilled water, and into each tube put one micro drop of a 0.1 M solution of glucose, fructose, lactose, maltose, and *n*-butyraldehyde. Add 1 ml. of Tollens' reagent to each tube and let the reactions proceed at room temperature at first. Watch closely and try to define the order of reactivity as measured not by the color of a solution but by the time of appearance of the first precipitate of metal. After a few minutes put the tubes in the heating bath.

3. Red Tetrazolium [3]

The reagent (RT) is a nearly colorless, water-soluble substance that oxidizes aldoses and ketoses, as well as other α-ketols, and is thereby reduced to a water-insoluble, intensely colored pig-

Red tetrazolium   RT-Diformazan

ment, a diformazan. It affords a highly sensitive test for reducing sugars and distinguishes between α-ketols and simple aldehydes more sharply than the above tests.

Procedure

Put one micro drop of each of the five 0.1 M test solutions in the marked test tubes, and to each tube add 1 ml. of a 0.5% aqueous solution of red tetrazolium and one drop of 10% sodium hydroxide solution. Put the tubes in the beaker of hot water and note the order of development of color.

For estimation of the sensitivity of the test use the substance that you regard as the most reactive of the five studied. Dilute 1 ml. of the 0.1 M solution with water to a volume of 100 ml., and run a test on 0.2 ml. of the diluted solution.

Questions. What, do you conclude, is the order of relative reactivity of the five compounds studied? Which test do you regard as the most reliable for distinguishing reducing from non-reducing sugars, and which for differentiating an α-ketol from a simple aldehyde?

4. Phenylosazones

Prepare 10 ml. of stock phenylhydrazine reagent as in Chapter 14.1 and put 1-ml. (1-millimole) portions of it into four of the

[3] 2,3,5-Triphenyltetrazolium chloride. Available from Monomer-Polymer, Inc., Leominster, Mass. Fresh solution should be used and the excess acidified and discarded.

numbered test tubes. Add 3.3-ml. (0.3-millimole) portions of 0.1 M solutions of glucose, fructose, lactose, and maltose and heat the tubes in a beaker of boiling water for 20 min. Shake the tubes occasionally to relieve supersaturation and note the times at which osazones separate. If, at the end of 20 min., no product has separated, cool and scratch to induce crystallization. (Save unused reagent.)

Collect and save the products for possible later use in identification of unknowns. Since osazones melt with decomposition, the melting point bath should be heated at a standard rate (0.5° per sec.).

5. Hydrolysis of a Disaccharide

The object of this experiment is to determine conditions suitable for hydrolysis of a typical disaccharide. Put 1-ml. portions of a 0.1 M solution of sucrose (3.42 g. of cane sugar in 100 ml. of water) in each of five numbered test tubes and add 5 micro drops of concd. hydrochloric acid to tubes 2–5. Let tube 2 stand at room temperature and heat the other four tubes in the hot water bath for the following periods of time: tube 3, 2.5 min.; tube 4, 5 min.; tubes 1 and 5, 15 min. As each tube is removed from the bath, it is cooled to room temperature, and if it contains acid, adjusted to approximate neutrality by addition of 15 micro drops of 10% sodium hydroxide. The solution is then stored in a small test tube placed in a filter block adjacent to the numbered one, which is washed with water and returned to its place. At the end of the 15-min. period tube 2 is similarly neutralized and the solution stored in a small tube. Measure one micro drop of each solution into the appropriate numbered test tube, add 1 ml. of red tetrazolium solution and a drop of 10% sodium hydroxide, and heat the tubes together for 2 min. and watch them closely.

In which of the tubes was hydrolysis negligible, incomplete, and extensive? Does the comparison indicate the minimum heating period required for complete hydrolysis? If not, return the stored solutions to the numbered test tubes, treat each with 1 ml. of stock phenylhydrazine reagent and heat the tubes together for 5 min. On the basis of your results, decide upon a hydrolysis procedure to use in studying unknowns; the same method is applicable to the hydrolysis of methyl glycosides.

6. Evaporation Test

Few solid derivatives suitable for identification of sugars are available. Osazones present the difficulty that the same osazone can form from more than one sugar. Acetylation, in the case of a reducing sugar, is complicated by the possibility of formation of the α- or the β-anomeric form, or a mixture of both. The unknown (next section) is supplied in 0.1 M aqueous solution, and if this is evaporated and the residue acetylated the ratio of α to β acetates may not be the same as that reported from a crystalline starting material. In the case of glucose, acetylation after evaporation, and crystallization of the product from water gives β-glucose pentaacetate (two polymorphic forms, m.p. 111° and 135°), but the yield is only 36% (α-pentaacetate, m.p. 114°). The other sugars give less favorable results.

Triphenylmethyl, or trityl, ethers can be made by reaction of an anhydrous sugar in pyridine solution with trityl chloride, $(C_6H_5)_3CCl$. Primary alcoholic groups are attacked in preference to secondary, and hence the amount of reagent required varies: glucose requires one mole, fructose, lactose, and maltose require two, and sucrose three. 6-Trityl glucose forms solvated crystals of indefinite m.p. Acetylation of this product gives tetraacetyl trityl-α-glucose, m.p. 130°, whereas if glucose is tritylated in pyridine, and the product then acetylated in the same solution without being isolated, the substance formed is tetraacetyl trityl-β-glucose, m.p. 163°.

Although preparation of the above derivatives is not recommended, the first step in the preparation, evaporation of the aqueous solution of the sugar, provides useful guidance in identification. On thorough evaporation of all the water from a solution of glucose, fructose, mannose, or galactose, the sugar is left as a syrup that appears as a glassy film on the walls of the container. Evaporation of solutions of lactose or maltose gives white solid products which are distinguishable because the temperature ranges at which they decompose differ by about 100°.

Procedure

Measure 2 ml. of a 0.1 M solution of either lactose or maltose into a 25 × 150-mm. test tube, and add an equal volume of benzene (to hasten the evaporation). Connect the test tube through a filter trap to the suction pump with a rubber stopper that fits the test tube snugly, or with one that is larger than the flared mouth of the test tube and is held in place by the vacuum. Make sure that the pressure-gauge of the filter trap is adjusted correctly so that it will show whether or not all connections are tight and the suction pump is operating efficiently. Then turn the pump on at full force and rest the tube horizontally in the steam bath with all but the largest ring removed, so that the whole tube will be heated strongly. If evaporation does not occur rapidly, check the connections and trap to see what is wrong. If a water layer persists for long, disconnect and add 1–2 ml. of benzene to hasten evaporation. When evaporation appears to be complete, disconnect, rinse the walls of the tube down with 1–2 ml. of methanol, and evaporate again, when a solid should separate on the walls. Rinse this down with methanol and evaporate again to produce a thoroughly anhydrous product. Then scrape out the solid and determine the melting point, or actually the temperature range of decomposition.

Anhydrous α-maltose decomposes at about 100–120°, and anhydrous α-lactose at 200–220°. Note that in the case of an unknown a point of decomposition in one range or the other is valid as an index of identity only if the substance has been characterized as a reducing sugar. Before applying the test to an unknown, perform a comparable evaporation of a 0.1 M solution of glucose, fructose, galactose, or mannose.

7. Unknowns

The unknown, supplied as a 0.1 M solution, may be any one of the following substances:

D-Glucose	Maltose
D-Fructose	Sucrose
D-Galactose	Methyl α-D-glucoside
Lactose	

You are to devise your own procedure of identification.

Enzymatic Resolution of DL-Alanine

Resolution of DL-alanine (I) is accomplished by subjecting the N-acetyl derivative (II) in weakly alkaline solution to the action of acylase, a proteinoid preparation from hog kidney containing an enzyme that promotes rapid hydrolysis of N-acyl derivatives of natural L-amino acids but acts only immeasurably slowly on the unnatural D-isomers.[1] N-Acetyl DL-alanine (II) can thus be

$$DL\text{-}CH_3CHCO_2H \longrightarrow DL\text{-}CH_3CHCO_2H \longrightarrow H_2N\overset{\displaystyle CO_2H}{\underset{\displaystyle CH_3}{\overset{|}{C}H}} \quad + \quad HC\overset{\displaystyle CO_2H}{\underset{\displaystyle CH_3}{\overset{|}{N}HCOCH_3}}$$

I	II	III	IV
NH$_2$	NHCOCH$_3$	CH$_3$	CH$_3$
M.p. 295°	M.p. 137°	M.p. 297°	M.p. 125°
Mol. wt. 89.05	Mol. wt. 131.13	αD +14.4°	αD +66.5°

converted into a mixture of L(+)-alanine (III) and N-acetyl D-alanine (IV). The mixture is easily separable into the components, since the free amino acid III is insoluble in ethanol whereas the

$$
\underset{\textbf{IV}}{CH_3CHCO_2H \atop \underset{COCH_3}{NH}}
\rightleftharpoons
\underset{\textbf{V}}{CH_3CHCO_2H \atop \underset{\underset{CH_3}{C}}{N \quad OH}}
\xrightarrow{-H_2O}
\underset{\textbf{VI}}{CH_3CH-C=O \atop \underset{\underset{CH_3}{C}}{N \quad O}}
$$

N-acetyl derivative IV is readily soluble in this solvent. Note that, in contrast to the weakly levorotatory D(−)-alanine (−14.4°), its acetyl derivative is strongly dextrorotatory.

The acetylation of an α-amino acid presents the difficulty that

[1] J. P. Greenstein, and others, *J. Biol. Chem.*, **175**, 969 (1948); **194**, 455 (1952).

if the conditions are too drastic the N-acetyl derivative (IV) is converted in part through the enol V to the azlactone VI.[2] However, under critically controlled conditions of concentration, temperature, and reaction time, N-acetyl DL-alanine can be prepared easily in high yield.

Procedure

Place 2 g. of DL-alanine and 5 ml. of acetic acid in a 20 × 150-mm. test tube, insert a thermometer, clamp the tube in a vertical position, heat it with a small flame until the temperature has risen a little above 100°, and then remove the burner. Stir the suspension, let the temperature gradually fall, and when it reaches 100° add 3 ml. of acetic anhydride and note the time. After one minute, during which time the temperature falls (95°), rises (103°; the acetylation is exothermic), and begins to fall, cool to 50–60° under the tap and pour the solution into a 200-ml. round bottomed flask. Use a part of 40 ml. of distilled water[3] to rinse the tube into the flask and add the rest. Add a boiling stone, put the flask *inside* the rings of the steam bath, evacuate at the suction pump, and evaporate until the water and acid are largely removed and a thick syrup remains (10 min.). Use 10 ml. of acetone to rinse the stopper and walls of the flask, add 10 ml. of benzene, and again evaporate at the suction pump and remove as much solvent as possible (benzene removes water by azeotropic distillation); this time the product should consist in part of a white solid. Add 10 ml. of benzene and repeat the evaporation. If the product has now separated on the walls as a solid or semisolid crust, add acetone (50–75 ml.) and warm on the steam bath until the product is dissolved, transfer the solution to a 250-ml. Erlenmeyer flask, add a boiling stone, and evaporate to a volume of 20–25 ml. Cool in ice and scratch the walls of the flask well to induce maximum separation of acetyl DL-alanine as a microcrystalline powder.[4] The product is collected, washed, and dried; yield 2.0 g., m.p. 134–136°.

Put the acetyl DL-alanine in a 20 × 150-mm. test tube, add 10 ml. of 1.5 N ammonia solution,[5] check the pH, and add more of the dilute ammonia (1–3 ml.) until the solution is weakly basic (pH 8). Add 100 mg. of commercial acylase powder or

Use a rubber stopper; check pressure gauge for maximum suction

Flammable vapor; use aspirator tube

Working time to this point 30–40 min.

---

[2] The azlactone of DL-alanine is known only as a partially purified liquid.
[3] Tap water may contain sufficient heavy metal ion to deactivate the enzyme.
[4] Note that the substance is prone to remain in supersaturated solution even though the amount of solvent is only about one third that required to dissolve it.
[5] Dilute 2 ml. of concd. ammonia solution to 20 ml. with water.

2 ml. of fresh acylase solution,[6] mix with a stirring rod, rinse the rod with distilled water and make up the volume until the tube is about half full. Then stopper the tube, mark it for identification (Fig. 22.1), and let the mixture stand at room temperature overnight or at $37°$ [7] for 4 hrs.

At the end of the incubation add 3 ml. of acetic acid to deactivate (denature) the enzyme and if the solution is not as acidic as pH 5 add more acid. Rinse the cloudy solution into a 125-ml. Erlenmeyer flask, add 100 mg. of decolorizing carbon (0.5-cm. column in a 13 × 100-mm. test tube), heat and swirl over a free flame for a few moments to coagulate the protein, and filter the solution by suction. Transfer the solution to a 200-ml. round bottomed flask, add 25 ml. of benzene (to prevent frothing) and a boiling stone, and evaporate on the steam bath under vacuum to remove water and acetic acid as fully as possible. Remove the last traces by adding 15 ml. of benzene and evaporating again. The mixture of L-alanine and acetyl D-alanine separates as a white scum on the walls. Add 15 ml. of 95% ethanol, digest on the steam bath, and dislodge some of the solid with a spatula. Cool well in ice for a few minutes, collect the crude L-alanine on a suction funnel and wash it with ethanol. Save the ethanol mother liquor.[8] To recover the L-alanine retained by the emptied flask, add 2 ml. of water and warm on the steam bath until the solid is all dissolved, then transfer the solution to a 25-ml. Erlenmeyer flask by means of a capillary dropping tube, rinse the flask with 2 ml. more water and transfer in the same way.

Enzymatic Resolution of DL-Alanine

Name
Tues. 4:10
p. 83

FIG. 22.1 Filter paper marker

Work-up time $\frac{1}{2}-\frac{3}{4}$ hr.

---

[6] The preparation should be started on the day of the week that fresh pork kidneys are available at a slaughter house. The fat is sliced off two kidneys (about 150 g.) and the kidneys cut into small pieces and either (a) ground in a mortar with sand and suspended in 300 ml. of distilled water or (b) placed in a Waring blender with 300 ml. of water and spun for 2 min. The homogenate prepared by either method is centrifuged in the cold until the supernatant liquid is clear (3000 × g. for 30 min. or 2000 × g. for 3 hrs.). An 18″-length of cellulose sausage casing (1″ in diameter) is wetted so that it can be opened, and tied off at one end. The enzyme solution is carefully decanted into the sack, the other end is tied off, and the sack is let soak overnight in a pan of running tap water (dialysis removes soluble kidney components that would interfere with isolation of the amino acid; colored impurities are removed in the course of the isolation and do not interfere). The enzyme solution is centrifuged again to remove debris and stored at 5° until required; the volume is about 150 ml.

[7] A simple thermostat that will hold 15 tubes is made by filling a 1-liter beaker with water, adjusting to 37°, and maintaining this temperature by the heat of a 250-watt infrared drying lamp shining horizontally on the beaker from a distance of about 40 cm. The capacity can be tripled by placing other beakers on each side of the first one and a few cm. closer to the lamp.

[8] In case the yield of L-alanine is low, evaporation of this mother liquor may reveal the reason. If the residue solidifies readily and crystallizes from acetone to give acetyl DL-alanine, m.p. 130° or higher, the acylase preparation is recognized as inadequate in activity or amount. Acetyl D-alanine is much more soluble and slow to crystallize.

121

Add the filtered L-alanine, dissolve by warming, and filter the solution by gravity into a 50-ml. Erlenmeyer flask (use the dropping tube to effect the transfer). Rinse the flask and funnel with 1 ml. of water and then with 5 ml. of warm 95% ethanol. Then heat the filtrate on the steam bath and add more 95% ethanol (10–15 ml.) in portions until crystals of L-alanine begin to separate from the hot solution and let crystallization proceed. Collect and wash with ethanol. The yield of colorless needles of L-alanine, α_D +13.7 to +14.4° [9] (in 1 N hydrochloric acid) varies from 0.40 to 0.56 g., depending on the activity of the enzyme.

[9] Determination of optical activity can be made in the student laboratory with a Zeiss Pocket Polarimeter, which requires no monochromatic light source and no light shield. For construction of a very inexpensive polarimeter, see W. H. R. Shaw, *J. Chem. Ed.*, **32**, 10, (1955).

Ninhydrin

CHAPTER 23

Ninhydrin (VIII), an expensive reagent widely used for identification of amino acids by paper-strip chromatography (Chapter 24), can be prepared by a six-step synthesis starting with a double ester condensation of dimethyl phthalate (I) with ethyl acetate under the influence of sodium to give the yellow sodium enolate II. Ester interchange occurs during the process and the product is largely the methyl ester, sodio-2-carbomethoxyindane-1,3-dione (II). Dimethyl phthalate is preferable to the diethyl or

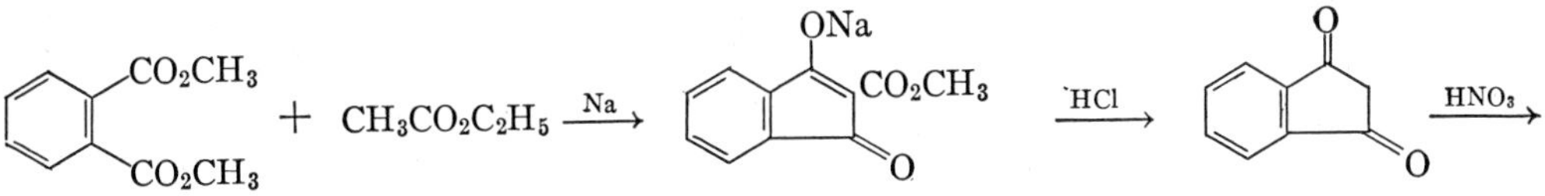

I — B.p. 280°, sp. gr. 1.19; Mol. wt. 194.18

II — Mol. wt. 226.17

III — M.p. 133°; Mol. wt. 146.14

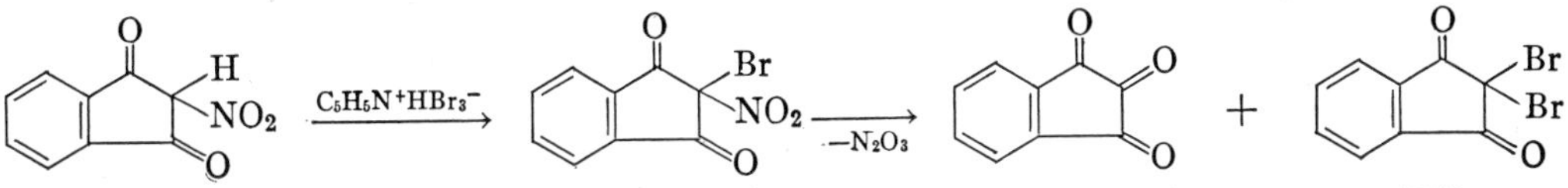

IV — Dec. 115-125°; Mol. wt. 191.14

V — M.p. 116°; Mol. wt. 270.05

VI — M.p. 255°; Mol. wt. 160.12

VII — M.p. 180°; Mol. wt. 303.97

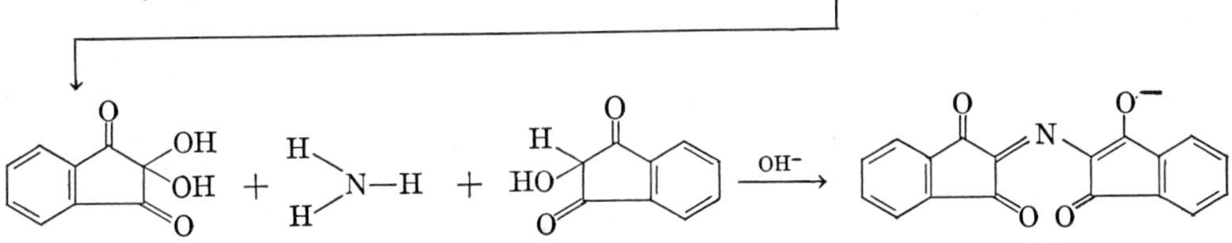

VIII — Ninhydrin, dec. 125°; Mol. wt. 178.14

IX

X

dibutyl ester both because the reaction proceeds best with the lowest homolog and because, since the cost per pound is about the same for the three esters, the one of lowest molecular weight is the most economical. The yield is limited by the side reaction of ester condensation of ethyl acetate to ethyl acetoacetate, $CH_3COCH_2CO_2C_2H_5$.

In the next step the sodium enolate II is heated with dilute hydrochloric acid; the initially formed free enol of the β-keto ester undergoes ready hydrolysis and decarboxylation to indane-1,3-dione (III). This substance is largely enolic and highly sensitive; it has a doubly activated methylene group that is prone to enter into aldol-type condensation with a carbonyl group of a second molecule of dione. Nitration under critically controlled conditions affords 2-nitroindane-1,3-dione (IV), a yellow substance that is strongly acidic and appears to exist largely in the acinitro form: $R_2CHNO_2 \rightarrow R_2C\!=\!N(O)OH$. It forms sparingly soluble salts with amines and has been suggested as a reagent for their characterization.

Bromination of 2-nitroindane-1,3-dione in aqueous solution affords the colorless 2-nitro-2-bromo dione (V), which when heated in o-dichlorobenzene solution at 175° decomposes smoothly to dinitrogen trioxide and equal parts of indane-1,2,3-trione (VI) and 2,2-dibromoindane-1,3-dione (VII). Indane-1,2,3-trione, a beautifully crystalline red substance, is converted into the colorless 2-hydrate, ninhydrin (VIII) by crystallization from water.

The reaction of ninhydrin with amino acids of the type $RCH(NH_2)CO_2H$ involves partial reduction of the ninhydrin to the 1,3-dione-2-ol (IX) and conversion of the amino acid to $RCHO$, NH_3, and CO_2. The blue (or purple) pigment results from condensation of ninhydrin and its reduction product IX with ammonia; the anion (X) offers opportunity for distribution of the charge among four resonance structures. The degradation of the amino acid apparently occurs through an intermediate product of condensation of the acid with ninhydrin.

EXPERIMENTS

Sodio-2-carbomethoxyindane-1,3-dione (II)

Preparation of powdered sodium. CAUTION. Read the whole of this paragraph and be prepared to do the shaking immediately after the sodium has been melted

The ester condensation does not proceed satisfactorily if the sodium used is in the form of chunks or slices, and hence the first operation is preparation of powdered sodium, a mixture of fine particles and globules the size of bird shot. Remove a piece of sodium from a bottle in which it is stored under kerosene by impaling it on the tip of a knife or with a forceps, remove the solvent by pressing the piece in the folds of a *dry* towel (filter paper is less efficient), and by manipulating the material with a combination of knife and forceps and without touching the sodium with the fingers, cut off slices totalling a weight of 2 g. (1.4 times the theoretical amount). Transfer these slices to a 20 × 150-mm. test tube and add 5 ml. of xylene. Clamp the tube in a vertical position at a height convenient for heating with a very small burner flame, insert an aspirator tube (dry) at the top for safety, heat the mixture gently until the xylene (b.p.

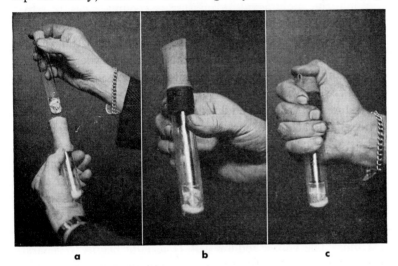

a   b   c

FIG. 23.1 Preparation of pow-dered sodium

140°) just begins to boil, and turn off the flame when the rim of condensate rises about 1 inch above the surface of the liquid. The sodium is then in a molten state (m.p. 97°), even though the pieces roughly retain their original shape. The tube is to be stoppered and the contents shaken vigorously while the sodium is still molten, an operation that can be done efficiently and safely with use of a protective 25 × 150-mm. test tube with a wad of cotton at the bottom and to the top of which is taped a section of $1\frac{3}{4}''$ Gooch tubing (Fig. 23.1b; the rubber tubing should extend 6 cm. beyond the rim of the test tube [1]). Before the sodium is melted under xylene, the protective rubber tubing of the longer tube should be skinned back as in (a); the stoppered tube containing hot xylene–sodium is then inserted, the Gooch rubber is extended as in (b), folded over (c), and the tube grasped firmly in the hand with the thumb pressing the stopper under the protective rubber. The tube assembly is then given a sharp whip-

[1] A few sodium stations, each equipped with a supply of sodium, xylene, 5-ml. pipette, knife, tweezers, dry towel, protective tube, ring stand with clamp, burner, and a bottle for xylene-sodium residues should service a large class.

ping shake in the direction of its length, which should produce large globules of sodium. Successive sharp shakes, made deliberately and each time followed by inspection of the result, further reduce the particle size until, after five or six shakes, the sodium is reduced to fine particles and small globules (c). Shaking beyond this point may cause the particles to coalesce. The rubber is then skinned back from the protective tube and the smaller tube removed, let cool, and the bulk of the xylene decanted into a xylene–sodium bottle.

While the sodium–xylene mixture is cooling, measure into a 50-ml. Erlenmeyer flask 10 ml. of dimethyl phthalate and 20 ml. of ethyl acetate, and mix the liquids by swirling. Add 3 ml. of the mixture to the test tube containing the powdered sodium, shake, and pour the suspension into a dry 100-ml. round bottomed flask. Rinse the test tube with another 3-ml. portion of the ester mixture, and add 5 drops of 95% ethanol. A reflux condenser is attached, and can be provided with a shield, consisting of a No. 2 and a No. 3 Neoprene adapter, to prevent water that collects on the outside of the condenser from running onto the stopper and neck of the flask (Fig. 23.2). Then heat the reaction mixture on the steam bath for 10 min.,[2] add the rest of the ester mixture through the top of the condenser, and continue refluxing, either continuously, or on separate days, for a total of 3–4 hrs. The yellow sodium salt II usually begins to separate in about 1 hr.; then the paste gradually thickens and may become an immobile mass. Even though there may only be time on the first day for refluxing for a few minutes, the operation is advantageous since the reaction will then proceed to a significant extent at room temperature in the course of 1–2 days.

If the refluxing is interrupted, either attach a calcium chloride tube to the flask or fill the mouth with a plug of dry absorbent cotton.

At the end of the reflux period, break up the yellow cake with a spatula, add a little ethyl acetate for thinning, and collect the product on a Büchner funnel. For efficient removal of dark-colored mother liquor, release the suction, cover the cake with ethyl acetate, scrape the solid and liquid together with a spatula to an even paste, and then apply suction. Press and suck the cake well, then spread the product out to dry (to constant weight). The yield varies from 5–10 g.; the average is closer to the lower limit than to the upper. The variability is probably

FIG. 23.2 Stopper shield

Reflux time 3–4 hrs. either continuously or, more advantageously, on separate days

After washing the salt on the filter, remove it to a beaker, stir it with ethyl acetate, and refilter

[2] Addition of ethanol helps to get the reaction started, and the maximal effect is obtained when only a small amount of ester mixture is present.

due to differences in the particle size of the sodium.[3] However, 5 g. of product is ample for the synthesis.

While the salt is drying dissolve a small sample (10 mg.) in water, add a drop of acetic acid (pK_a 4.8), and then a drop of hydrochloric acid. Is the pK_a of the free enol larger or smaller than 4.8?

Indane-1,3-dione (III)

Place 7 g. of finely crushed sodium salt (II) in one 250-ml. Erlenmeyer flask and 100 ml. of water in another. Pour 10 ml. of concd. hydrochloric acid into the water, heat the solution to 80°, pour it onto the salt, and keep the temperature close to 70° for 5–6 min. The salt is converted to the free enol (yellow) and this loses carbon dioxide and affords the dione III, which separates as an almost colorless solid. Cool to 15–20°, collect the solid on a small filter, and wash it with water weakly acidified with a little hydrochloric acid. To keep the drying time at a minimum, press the filter cake firmly under a spatula and let it drain until the drip of filtrate has completely stopped. Note the weight of the wet cake (5–5.6 g.), spread it out on a filter paper, scrape and respread it occasionally, and note the weight after 1 hr., $1\frac{1}{2}$ hr. (4.1 g.), and 2 hr. (4.1 g.). The crude light cream-colored solid, m.p. 131–132°, can be nitrated directly if it is thoroughly dry. It crystallizes from benzene in long, fine needles, m.p. 132–133°.

Swirl vigorously while heating

The substance stains the skin

For quick drying heat in an evacuated Erlenmeyer on the steam bath

2-Nitroindane-1,3-dione (IV)

Indane-1,3-dione is nitrated with 4 ml. of acetic acid and 1 ml. of fuming nitric acid per gram of dione at a temperature not to exceed 35°. Thus, place 3.5 g. of indane-1,3-dione in a 125-ml. Erlenmeyer flask, add 14 ml. of acetic acid, insert a thermometer, make an ice bath ready, and to the suspension at 25° add 3.5 ml. of fuming nitric acid.[4] The temperature usually rises rapidly and should be checked at 35° by brief cooling sufficient to prevent

Total time about 20 min.

Alternative procedure using concd. HNO_3

[3] In industrial practice the reaction time can be shortened and the yield materially improved by use of highly reactive colloidally dispersed sodium.

[4] 90% HNO_3; sp. gr. 1.48. The acid should be pipetted from a freshly opened bottle or one that has been sealed with paraffin after each period of use; use a pipetter (Chapter 11.1, Note 3). *Alternative procedure.* Mix 15 ml. of acetic acid with 10 ml. of acetic anhydride, make an ice bath ready, measure 5 ml. of concd. nitric acid and add it with a dropper in 1-ml. portions. After each addition let the temperature rise (for reaction of the anhydride with the water in the acid) but not above 60°. When the heat effect is over, adjust to **exactly** 35° and pour the solution onto 3.5 g. of dione-III. The temperature drops to 27–28° and then (2 min.) begins to rise slowly. When it rises to 35° control to 34–35° by a quick dip in the ice bath. Control to 33–35° min. for a total of 20 min., cool to 5°, collect and wash the product well with ether. Yield 3.8 g.

a rise above 35° but not enough to cause much drop in temperature. The yellow nitro compound soon begins to separate, and after about 5 min. at 35° the temperature begins to drop. After 15 min. more the mixture can be cooled and the product collected and washed with a little ether (to remove acetic acid). The nitro compound can be dried in a few minutes and is then ready for the next step; set aside an estimated 100 mg. for the following tests.

Dissolve 100 mg. of nitroindanedione in 10 ml. of water and treat 1-ml. portions as follows: (a) with 0.5 ml. of concd. hydrochloric acid and let stand undisturbed, (b) with 1 ml. of 1% aniline hydrochloride and let stand (the salt melts at 209°); (c) with 5 ml. of water and then 1 ml. of 1% aniline hydrochloride solution, cool and scratch; (d) with one drop of 20% copper sulfate solution and scratch.

2-Bromo-2-nitroindane-1,3-dione (V)

Total time about 30 min.

Place a 50-ml. Erlenmeyer flask containing 5 g. of pyridinium bromide perbromide and 25 ml. of acetic acid inside the rings of a steam bath and let the mixture warm while dissolving 3 g. of nitroindanedione in 50 ml. of water in a 250-ml. beaker by stirring. When the perbromide has all dissolved, grasp the flask with a towel and pour the hot solution into the aqueous solution with stirring. The color is discharged and the bromonitrodione separates at once as a white precipitate. Collect this, press the filter cake thoroughly with a spatula and suck it well. Then dissolve the slightly moist product in ether, add 3–4 g. of anhydrous sodium sulfate, swirl for a minute or two, filter, and

Remove the ether vapor with an aspirator tube

evaporate the filtrate to dryness. The solid residue, scraped out of the flask, is suitable for the next step; yield 3.1 g.[5]

Indane-1,2,3-trione (VI)

Operating time 5 min.

Place 3 g. of bromonitroindanedione and 3 ml. of *o*-dichlorobenzene (b.p. 180°) in a 20 × 150-mm. test tube, clamp the tube in a vertical position over a burner, insert a thermometer and an aspirator tube (Fig. 23.3), and heat over a small flame to a temperature of 170°, when the solution turns green and oxides of nitrogen are evolved. By intermittent heating, maintain a temperature of 170–180° for 3 min. and then remove the thermometer and let the solution stand undisturbed to cool, when the indanetrione separates as deep red needles. When crystallization ap-

[5] The substance crystallizes well from 1:1 benzene-ligroin. It is unstable in hydroxylic solvents and reacts with water with liberation of HOBr, which characterizes it as having positive bromine.

pears to be complete at room temperature, cool the mixture well in an ice bath, which may cause separation of a little white hydrate. The crystals are collected on a Hirsch funnel, and since the trione and its hydrate are both insoluble in ether, this solvent is used to rinse the tube and wash the crystals free of o-dichlorobenzene (save the filtrate). The yield of crystalline product is 0.7 g.

If the o-dichlorobenzene–ether filtrate is warmed on the steam bath to evaporate the ether and the residual solution is let stand for several hours, crystals of 2,2-dibromoindane-1,3-dione (VII) separate.[6]

Ninhydrin (VIII)

In a 10-ml. flask heat 0.7 g. of indane-1,2,3-trione with 2 ml. of water until the solid is dissolved (with disappearance of the color), add 2 ml. of concd. hydrochloric acid, and place the flask in a small beaker of ice and water for crystallization. The hydrate separates as colorless prisms, which are collected, washed with a little ice-cold 1:1 hydrochloric acid–water, and dried; yield 0.5 g.

Tests

Dissolve 30 mg. of ninhydrin in 3 ml. of water and distribute the solution into three 13 × 100-mm. test tubes. Add 1-ml. portions of 1% solutions of glycine, DL-alanine, and DL-aspartic acid to the three tubes, heat the solutions together in the rings of a steam bath for 5 min., and note any differences in the speed of color development. Dilute 1 ml. of the solution derived from glycine to 100 ml., note the shade and intensity of color, and test the effect of adding hydrochloric acid to one portion and alkali to another. Reaction with a protein can be demonstrated by pouring a few drops of the ninhydrin solution into a freshly opened eggshell.

[6] By steam distillation of the mother liquor a total of 0.6 g. of VII can be recovered.

Ninhydrin

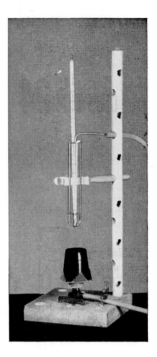

FIG. 23.3

Paper Chromatography of Amino Acids

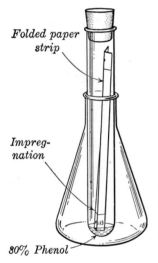

Folded paper strip

Impreg- nation

80% Phenol

FIG. 24.1

Filter paper as ordinarily stored consists of cellulose containing 22% of adsorbed water (hydrogen-bonded; about two molecules per $C_6H_{10}O_5$ unit). When a folded strip of filter paper is inserted into a slightly slanting test tube (Fig. 24.1) with the lower end dipping into phenol, an organic solvent which is only partially miscible with water, the phenol ascends the strip by capillary flow without material disturbance of the adsorbed water. In paper partition chromatography the adsorbed water is the stationary phase and the organic solvent the moving phase. Before the folded strip is inserted, the paper is impregnated with minute amounts of an amino acid solution at the two ends of a starting line (Fig. 24.2a) that will be a little above the level of the phenol. As the phenol rises toward the top of the strip the amino acids are subjected to innumerable partitions between the moving lipid phase and the stationary water phase. The highly lipophilic amino acids travel almost as fast as the organic solvent, whereas the very hydrophilic ones are largely retained by the adsorbed water and make little progress. When the easily discernible solvent front has reached the finish line, 10 cm. from the starting line (Fig. 24.2), the chromatogram is terminated and the strip removed and hung on a hook. The amino acids are all colorless and the strip bears no indication of their distribution until it is sprayed with a solution of ninhydrin. The oxidation-reduction reaction between ninhydrin and an amino acid (Chapter 23) produces a pigment that appears as a small spot (b). The position of the front (top) of the spot is noted and its distance from the starting line measured with a ruler. The rate of flow, or *Rf* value, of a particular amino acid is the ratio of the distance travelled by the acid to the distance travelled by the solvent. In the example of Fig. 24.2b, $Rf = (4.6/10) = 0.46$. The acids having primary α-amino groups give pink to purple spots; the secondary amines proline and hydroxyproline give yellow spots.

Rf values vary with the solvent system and type of filter paper used; those reported in Table 24.1 were determined by the procedure specified below. In the series glycine, alanine, valine, and leucine, Rf increases with increasing molecular weight; the larger the alkyl group the more the acid tends to move along with the organic solvent. Fig. 24.3 includes Rf values for three rarer, straight-chain acids that are the higher n-alkyl homologs of alanine; that the five points for the n-alkyl series fall on a smooth curve demonstrates a regular relationship, if not a strict proportionality, between Rf and molecular weight. The structure of the alkyl group is of minor but noticeable influence, since the isoalkyl compounds valine and leucine do not travel quite as fast, and hence are slightly more hydrophilic than the n-isomers.

The balance between the hydrophilic and lipophilic character of a given acid is expressed by a quantity defined as the molecular flow (Mf), calculated thus:

$$Mf = \text{Mol. wt.}/100 \; Rf$$

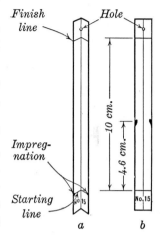

FIG. 24.2

Inspection of the fifth column of the table shows that structurally related compounds have Mf values in a range characteristic of the acid type. For the seven n- and i-alkyl acids plotted in Fig. 24.3 the average Mf is 1.6. That the values for methionine (1.9) and

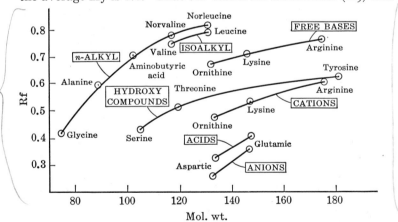

FIG. 24.3   Amino acids

phenylalanine (2.0) are slightly higher means that the sulfur atoms and the phenyl group render the substances a little more hydrophilic, weight for weight, than the alkyl acids. Proline is distinctive in being a cyclic secondary amine; it has the lowest

TABLE 24.1

Rf VALUES OF AMINO ACIDS

Acid	Formula	Rf	Mol. wt.	$Mf = \dfrac{\text{Mol. wt.}}{100\,Rf}$	Cost [a]	Yield:[b] mg. per 100 mg. of Hair	Silk	Gelatin
Cystine	$HO_2CCH(NH_2)CH_2SSCH_2CH(NH_2)CO_2H$	0.16	240.30	15	low	18.0		0.1
Glycine	$CH_2(NH_2)CO_2H$	.42	75.07	1.8	v. low	4.1	42.3	25.5
Alanine	$CH_3CH(NH_2)CO_2H$	.59	89.09	1.5	low	2.8	24.5	8.7
Valine	$(CH_3)_2CHCH(NH_2)CO_2H$	.75	117.15	1.6	mod.	5.5	3.2	2.5
Leucine	$(CH_3)_2CHCH_2CH(NH_2)CO_2H$	.79	131.17	1.7	mod.	11.2	0.8	4.6
Methionine	$CH_3SCH_2CH_2CH(NH_2)CO_2H$	.77	149.21	1.9	v. low	0.7		1.0
Phenylalanine	$C_6H_5CH_2CH(NH_2)CO_2H$	.82	165.19	2.0	mod.	2.4		2.2
Proline	$HNCH_2CH_2CH_2CHCO_2H$	.85	115.13	1.4	v. high	4.3	1.5	18.0
Ornithine cation	$H_2NCH_2CH_2CH_2CH(NH_2)CO_2H$	0.67	132.16	2.0	v. high			
	$^{+}H_3NCH_2CH_2CH_2CH(NH_2)CO_2H$	.47	133.17	2.8				
Lysine cation	$H_2NCH_2CH_2CH_2CH_2CH(NH_2)CO_2H$	.71	146.19	2.1	mod.	1.9	0.4	4.1
	$^{+}H_3NCH_2CH_2CH_2CH_2CH(NH_2)CO_2H$	.53	147.20	2.8				
Arginine cation	$HN{=}C(NH_2)NHCH_2CH_2CH_2CH(NH_2)CO_2H$	.76	174.20	2.3	mod.	8.9	1.1	8.0
	$^{+}H_2N{=}C(NH_2)NHCH_2CH_2CH_2CH(NH_2)CO_2H$	.60	175.21	2.9				
Serine	$HOCH_2CH(NH_2)CO_2H$	0.43	105.09	2.4	high	10.6	12.6	0.4
Threonine	$HOCH(CH_3)CH(NH_2)CO_2H$	.51	119.12	2.3	v. high	8.5	1.5	1.9
Tyrosine	$HOC_6H_4CH_2CH(NH_2)CO_2H$	.62	181.19	2.9	low	2.2	10.6	0.4
Aspartic acid anion	$HO_2CCH_2CH(NH_2)CO_2H$	0.32	133.10	4.2	v. low	3.9		6.7
	$HO_2CCH_2CH(NH_2)CO_2^{-}$	.25	132.09	5.3				
Glutamic acid anion	$HO_2CCH_2CH_2CH(NH_2)CO_2H$	.40	147.13	3.7	v. low	13.1		11.5
	$HO_2CCH_2CH_2CH(NH_2)CO_2^{-}$	.35	146.12	4.0				

[a] Either the L- or DL-form is used, whichever is cheaper. Some of the acids are available in the free form, others only as the hydrochlorides.

[b] Present estimates; subject to revision.

Mf value (1.4) of all the acids. For reasons unknown, cystine is anomalous in both *Mf* and solubility. The high molecular weight would seem to be offset by the presence of two hydrophilic dipolar ion groupings, but the *Rf* is very low and the solubility in water (25°) is only 0.112 g./l., as compared to 24.3 g./l. for leucine.

Introduction of polar groups into the side chains of the alkyl acids (av. *Mf* = 1.6) produces successive hydrophilic shifts as follows: basic group, *Mf* = 2.1; hydroxyl group, *Mf* = 2.5; carboxyl group, *Mf* = 4.0. Fig. 24.3 shows that the curves are of

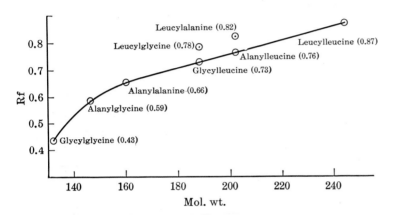

FIG. 24.4 Dipeptides
(Mf = 2.6, av.)

similar types but displaced to lower *Rf* values. The average *Mf* value of 2.6 found for dipeptides (Fig. 24.4) indicates that the lipophilic effect of the peptide link is intermediate between those of the hydroxyl and carboxyl groups. If ornithine, lysine, or glutamic acid is chromatographed not as the free base but as the monohydrochloride, the ionic group provides better retention by the stationary water phase and in each case *Rf* is about 0.2 unit lower than found for the free base. Since lysine perchlorate gives the same *Rf* as the hydrochloride, the rate of flow is determined by the lysine cation alone. A smaller hydrophilic displacement results when aspartic and glutamic acid are chromatographed as anions. The displacements are sometimes useful aids in the identification of unknowns, which is the major objective of the present experiment.

Sections 1–3 describe general procedures, and Section 4 lists five chromatograms that are to be run on known acids and mixtures; these should be started at the very beginning of the period so that they can be carried to a stopping point by the end of the day. As soon as they are under way the protein hydrolysis should be started; during the 1-hr. reflux period the characteriz-

133

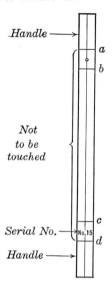

Handle →

a
b

Not
to be
touched

Serial No. →No,15

c
d

Handle →

FIG. 24.5

ing tests of sections 5–8 can be carried out. The protein hydrolyzate should be worked up on the first day and an overnight
chromatogram started.

EXPERIMENTS

1. Procedure of Chromatography

A strip of paper 13 cm. long and 1.3 cm. wide is to be cut from
a roll of half-inch Eaton-Dikeman No. 613 filter paper,[1] marked,
punched, folded, and impregnated as shown in Fig. 24.2a without
being touched with the fingers, since contact with skin protein
can give rise to false spots. This can be done by initially cutting
a strip about 4 cm. longer than required and using the 2-cm.
section at each end as a handle that is to be cut off after all other
operations have been completed. Fig. 24.5 shows such a strip
marked with starting and finish lines (c and b, 10 cm. apart) and
boundary lines (a and d); it is also punched and marked with a
serial number. A strip dispenser (Fig. 24.6) protects the paper
and expedites the preparation of strips. Grasp the end of the

FIG. 24.6 Strip dispenser

This dispenser, which will hold
any of the rolls mentioned in
Footnote 1, can be made from a
$1\frac{1}{4}'' \times 9'' \times 12''$ cardboard box;
for accommodation of the $9\frac{5}{8}''$
roll, the lower edge is mounted
on blocks as shown and its
middle section cut away. The
slot is 8 cm. from the top, marking line a is 1.3 cm. from the
edge, and the other lines are at
the following distances from a:
b, 1.5 cm.; c, 11.5 cm.; d,
13 cm.; e, 26.5 cm.; f, 28 cm.
A small hole centered between
a and b is punched with an awl
through both layers of cardboard.

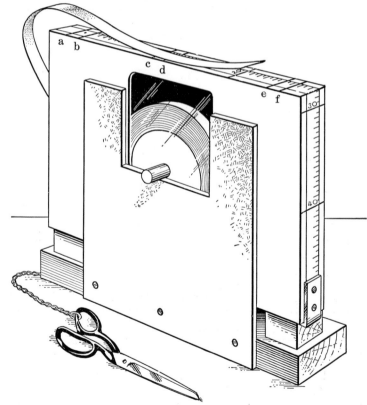

[1] Supplied in rolls $7\frac{1}{4}$ and $9\frac{5}{8}$ in. in diameter. Half-inch Whatman No. 1 paper
($8\frac{3}{8}$-in. roll, 600 ft.) can be used but gives slightly lower *Rf* values.

paper tape and pull out enough to give a 10-cm. (or a 25-cm.) strip, mark pencil lines at a, b, c, and d (or, for a 25-cm. strip at a, b, e, and f), punch a hole centered between a and b with the point of a sharp pencil, and then cut off the strip cleanly at a right angle at a point about 2 cm. above a. Record the serial number of the experiment in the space between c and d, and then fold the strip down the center. A convenient technique of folding (without contact of the fingers in the vital area) is to place the strip with the markings down on a clean, smooth surface, such as the back of a notebook or writing pad, place a transparent 30–60°

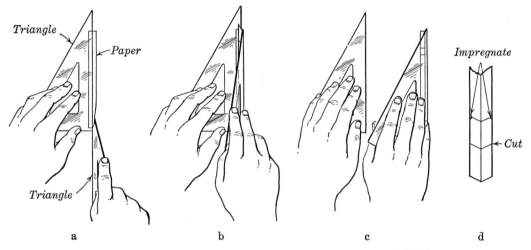

FIG. 24.7

triangle so that it covers exactly one half of the paper (Fig. 24.7a), press it down firmly, insert under the paper the tip of a second triangle, fold the paper up against and over the first one (b), and then withdraw the first triangle while flattening the strip on the crease (c).

Now grasp the folded strip by the lower handle and apply a tiny spot of amino acid solution to each edge of the strip at the ends of the starting line (d). The wetted area should be no more than 1–2 mm. in diameter and may be visible only from the under side. The application is conveniently made with the smaller end of a toothpick that has been soaked in the solution until the wood is saturated.[2] To remove excess solution, touch the end first to the neck of the bottle and then to the strip handle; make practice spots on the handle and then make the actual applica-

[2] In the amino acid dispenser shown in frontispiece Fig. 0.8 a toothpick is inserted through a hole drilled in the plastic cap of a specimen vial containing each amino acid solution. Matching colors on the base board, the vial, and the cap help to insure return to the proper place.

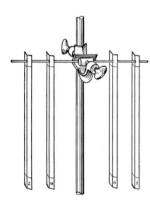

FIG. 24.8

(The ends of the applicator stick can be pointed in a pencil sharpener)

Note for the instructor

Note for the instructor

tions and let the spots dry (1–2 min.). About 0.2 ml. of 80% phenol is to be withdrawn from a bottle in which the solution is overlayered with 90–120° ligroin to prevent oxidation [3] and introduced to the bottom of a 20 × 150-mm. test tube without getting it on the walls of the tube. This can be done by inserting the capillary tip of an 8-mm. dropping tube through the ligroin layer while exerting a slight pressure, drawing up phenol solution, inserting the dropper carefully into the test tube until the tip is at the bottom, and running in an 8-mm. column of liquid. Mount the tube in a stand, an Erlenmeyer flask, or beaker in a slightly slanting position, cut off both handles of the impregnated strip, and with a forceps, lower the strip carefully into the test tube so that it touches only the top and bottom, as in Fig. 24.1. Make sure that the hole is up and the amino acid spots down,[4] cork the tube, and note the time. It takes 2–3 hrs. for the solvent front to complete the travel of 10 cm. and reach the finish line. When this point is reached (note the time) withdraw the strip with a forceps while rinsing it well with a stream of acetone (Calcutta wash bottle) to remove phenol and promote rapid drying. Hang the strip on an applicator stick (Fig. 24.8), a hook, or a pin. When it is dry grasp the lower end with a forceps and spray the strip uniformly but lightly with ninhydrin solution [5] (the paper should become moist but not dripping). Spots usually begin to appear within 5–10 min.; with aspartic acid there may be an induction period of several hours. Each application of test solution should give rise to a separate spot, not more than 3–4 mm. in diameter, on each side of the strip, but one may appear better defined and more reliable than the other. Outline the boundary of each spot in pencil, measure the distance of spot front from the starting line, and calculate the *Rf*.

It is not imperative that the chromatogram be extended to the point where the solvent has exactly reached the finish line. If you wish to stop it either somewhat short of or somewhat beyond

[3] Either (a) warm a mixture of 80 g. of analytical grade phenol with 20 g. of distilled water until dissolved and cool, or (b) pour 114 ml. of boiling water into a 1-lb. bottle of phenol and shake for a few minutes; the solid soon dissolves (and the temperature drops to about 13°). The solution is at once covered with a generous layer of 90–120° ligroin and shaken to effect saturation (very little ligroin dissolves). If the solution is not protected from air it soon turns pink and then brown and eventually acquires capacity for destroying amino acids by oxidation.
[4] If you notice soon enough that the strip is upside down you may be able to withdraw it with a forceps, cut off the wetted section, and insert it in the correct way.
[5] Dissolve 400 mg. of ninhydrin and 1.5 ml. of *s*-collidine in 100 ml. of 95% ethanol. A basic solution is required since the test solutions are acidic; pyridine can be substituted for collidine but gives less range in the color of the spots. Ethanol is superior to the frequently used butanol because it evaporates more rapidly and promotes quick development of spots at room temperature.

this point, withdraw the strip and *mark the position of the solvent front*, and then rinse it with acetone and proceed as above.

2. Overnight Chromatograms

Fig. 24.9 shows that the rate of solvent flow decreases markedly with time.[6] Hence use of a longer strip gives much greater flexibility in the time of terminating the chromatogram. With a 25-cm. strip, the chromatograms can be run for 3–5 hrs., 15 hrs., or any time up to 24 hrs. Such a strip can be measured on the same dispenser (Fig. 24.6), marked with lines at a, b, e, and f, and folded as before. The amino acid sample is doubled by making one pair of applications, drying, and repeating the process. The amount of phenol is increased to 1 ml. (4-cm. column in the dropper); it is introduced as before into a 20 × 150-mm. test tube and this is slid into a 250-ml. graduate and adjusted to a slanting position (see frontispiece Fig. 0.8). The strip is lowered into place and the graduate stoppered.

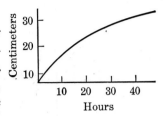

FIG. 24.9   Rate of solvent travel

3. Basification

For either conversion of lysine or arginine hydrochloride to the free base or conversion of aspartic or glutamic acid to the anion, the test solution is spotted onto a strip and let dry and then 10% sodium hydroxide is applied at the same spots (use a fresh toothpick and discard it) and let dry.

4. Knowns

Prepare five 10-cm. strips; impregnate them with 0.1 M solutions [7] of the following acids or pairs. In the case of a pair, apply one acid in two spots, dry, and then apply the other.

Arginine hydrochloride   Phenylalanine and glycine
Arginine (see Section 3)   Alanine and aspartic acid
Leucine and glutamic acid

See if you can effect good separation of spots, and compare your *Rf* values with those of Table 24.1. You may note a general displacement of values which will be of guidance in studying unknowns.

[6] The curve conforms to the equation:

$$\log T \text{ (minutes)} = \sqrt{0.42 \times \text{Distance (cm.)}}$$

[7] The solutions are made by dissolving 0.01 mole of a hydrochloride in 100 ml. of water, or dissolving 0.01 mole of a free amino acid and 1 ml. of concd. hydrochloric acid in 100 ml. of water (cystine and tyrosine require 4 ml. of acid). In the case of the compounds of higher molecular weight the acid is required to effect solution; in other cases it is required to prevent growth of microorganisms.

Note for the instructor

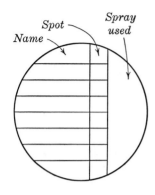

FIG. 24.10

5. Detection of Basic Amino Acids

Put a tiny drop of arginine hydrochloride solution on the bottom of an inverted beaker. With a fresh toothpick (that is to be discarded after the test) add a tiny drop of 2% phosphotungstic acid solution and see if a white precipitate forms. Repeat with lysine hydrochloride and, for comparison, with some one of the nonbasic acids.

6. Ninhydrin Spot Test

Mark a piece of filter paper as in Fig. 24.10 and enter the names: alanine, proline (make two applications), methionine, aspartic acid, glutamic acid, arginine. In the box opposite each name make an appropriate spot of any size desired, let the spots dry, spray with ninhydrin-collidine, and let dry. Repeat, using ninhydrin-pyridine spray. The papers can be entered in the notebook, but the initial colors should be recorded; application of label lacquer helps to retard fading.

7. Permanganate Spot Test

Spot a paper as above with alanine, methionine, cystine, tyrosine, and proline (two applications); dry, and spray lightly with an aqueous solution containing 1% potassium permanganate and 2% sodium carbonate. Put a check mark beside any spots that at once appear yellow on a pink background, and without delay bleach the paper by holding it briefly under a watch glass covering a beaker (hood) in which sulfur dioxide is generated by occasional addition of sodium bisulfite and hydrochloric acid. Let the excess dioxide evaporate, spray with ninhydrin–collidine, and let dry.

Permanganate oxidizes the sulfur atom of methionine and cystine and the phenolic group of tyrosine, but the recovery test shows that original acid is still present. The nature of the yellow pigment is not known.[8]

8. Differentiation of Tyrosine from Sulfur Amino Acids

This test is based upon the fact that the phenolic tyrosine couples with diazotized amines, whereas methionine and cystine do not.

Dip a 10-cm. strip of filter paper halfway into a 1% solution of 2,5-dichlorobenzenediazonium chloride[9] and hang it up to dry. Mark one half of the wetted area T and the other M, and put

---

[8] Proline gives a weak positive response in the permanganate test if the spray is left on for $\frac{1}{2}$–1 min. but not if it is bleached at once as specified; proline is adequately identified by the yellow ninhydrin spot test.

[9] Dupont Naphthanil Diazo Scarlet GG.

two spots each of tyrosine and methionine in the appropriate areas. Then dip the strip into 1% aqueous sodium carbonate solution and hang the strip up again; record the initial result (note that both solutions contain hydrochloric acid) and the final appearance (5–10 min.).

9. Protein Hydrolyzate

In a 25 × 150-mm. test tube clamped so that it can be heated over a free flame, place 100 mg. of either hair, silk, or gelatin (cooking gelatin serves well), 3 ml. of constant boiling (20%) hydrochloric acid,[10] and a boiling stone. Insert a cold finger and let its side-tube rest on the rim of the test tube,[11] and reflux for 1 hr. Remove the condenser, introduce an aspirator tube, and boil the solution down to a volume of about 1 ml. Then rinse down the walls with 3 ml. of acetone, add 3 ml. of benzene, and heat the tube in an open steam bath while evacuating at the full force of the water pump to remove the hydrochloric acid and solvents (azeotropic distillation) and leave a film of amino acid hydrochlorides. Add 1 ml. of water, warm briefly, and cool.

1-Hr. reflux; 20-min. workup; overnight chromatogram

Try to identify the major component acids of the mixture (see Table 24.1) by applying such of the tests (5–8) as seem appropriate and by running an overnight chromatogram (Section 2). In some instances it may be possible to identify a group of components of comparable *Rf* values but not to differentiate between the members of the group. Treatment of a small sample with phosphotungstic acid and chromatography of the filtrate may be helpful. Save the residual solution of hydrolyzate and test it for the presence of proline after you have completed the other experiments of Section 11.

10. Unknowns

The above 0.1 *M* test solutions (containing hydrochloric acid) of the following acids serve as satisfactory unknowns:

Cystine	Methionine	Tyrosine
Glycine	Proline	Aspartic acid
Alanine	Lysine	Glutamic acid
Leucine	Arginine	

A 0.1-ml. sample (2 drops delivered by a medicine dropper into a specimen vial) should suffice for identification by a combination of spot tests (5–8) and chromatography, either on the material

---

[10] Mix 2.5 ml. of concd. hydrochloric acid with 2 ml. of water.
[11] The cooling tube close to the boiling liquid breaks up an otherwise troublesome foam.

as supplied or after basification (3). Estimate the weight of sample that you actually used for a successful identification.

11. Separation of Proline, Leucine, and Glycine

Separation of proline from other neutral amino acids is possible because of its extraordinarily high solubility in hydroxylic solvents; its solubility in water (1620 g./l. at 25°) is 18 times that of valine, an acid of nearly the same molecular weight. A partial separation of leucine from glycine is effected with hot butanol, which preferentially extracts the more lipophilic component.

If a mixture of proline and other amino acids is treated with ninhydrin in neutral solution, the weak color of proline yellow is obscured by the strong blue pigments derived from the other components. However, hydrochloric acid solutions of all amino acids except proline (and hydroxyproline) remain colorless when heated with ninhydrin, whereas proline is converted first to proline yellow and then to proline red. Proline red is extracted from

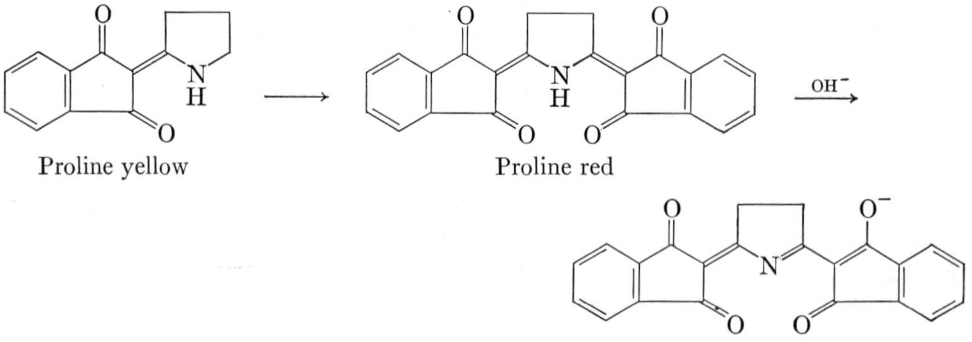

Proline yellow — Proline red — OH^-

Blue anion

water by butanol, and when the butanol solution is shaken with alkali containing a reducing agent, a blue anion passes into the water phase (the function of the reducing agent is to prevent discoloration due to air oxidation).

Pipette into a 20 × 150-mm. test tube 1 ml. of a solution containing 10 mg./ml. each of proline, leucine, and glycine (as dipolar ions), add 3 ml. each of acetone and benzene and a boiling stone, and evaporate to dryness under vacuum on the steam bath. The residue should be a completely dry, white solid. Add 1 ml. of absolute ethanol, heat on the steam bath, and scrape the solid down from the walls with a spatula or stirring rod. Fold a 4.25-cm. filter paper into a 2.5-cm. funnel, moisten it with ethanol and press it down to fit, and rest the funnel in the mouth of a 13 × 100-mm. test tube. Cool the ethanol suspension and transfer it

Procedure

with a capillary dropping tube to the funnel; rinse with 1 ml. of ethanol. Place the funnel containing unextracted residue in a fresh test tube or flask, wash the solid with 2 ml. of ethanol and discard the washings. Put a boiling stone in the tube containing the ethanol extract and evaporate to a solid residue comprising the proline fraction (a); put it aside for testing. Scrape the ethanol-insoluble residue into a 20 × 150-mm. test tube, add 3 ml. of butanol, and boil the mixture briefly. Place a 2.5-cm. funnel fitted with an ethanol-moistened paper into a 25 × 150-mm. test tube, insert a capillary dropping tube into the butanol suspension, boil again to warm the dropping tube, and then transfer the hot solution or suspension in portions onto the filter. Evaporate the filtrate (b) to dryness with suction on the steam bath and let the solid (c) collected on the filter dry.

Now dissolve the proline fraction (a), the butanol extract (b), and the butanol-insoluble residue (c) each in 1 ml. of water and perform the following tests and operations.

(1) Spot the proline fraction (a) on filter paper (2 applications), spray with ninhydrin-collidine, and see if the material is pure proline (yellow spot).

(2) In a 13 × 100-mm. test tube put 1 drop of the proline fraction (a), 1 drop of concd. hydrochloric acid, and 1 drop of 0.3% aqueous ninhydrin solution. Heat for 1–2 min. on the steam bath and see if you can note any color changes. Add 1 ml. of water and 1 ml. of butanol, shake, and let the layers separate; the butanol layer should be pink. Push the tip of a capillary dropping tube through the butanol layer while exerting a slight pressure on the bulb to produce a stream of air sufficient to prevent entrance of butanol, and suck up and remove the aqueous layer. Add 1 ml. of water, shake, and remove the water layer as before. Then add to the butanol solution 1 ml. of an alkaline hydrosulfite solution that is protected from oxidation by a layer of benzene,[12] shake gently, and let the layers separate.

(3) If your proline fraction has responded satisfactorily in tests (1) and (2), pour the remainder into a bottle marked Proline Fraction, for conservation of the expensive chemical.

(4) Run chromatograms on the butanol extract (b) and the butanol-insoluble residue (c) to see if you have effected any separation of leucine and glycine.

(5) Put one drop of the proline–leucine–glycine solution in a test tube, add 1 drop of 0.3% aqueous ninhydrin solution, heat

[12] Cover 100 ml. of 2% aqueous sodium hydroxide with a 2–3 cm. layer of benzene, add 2 g. sodium hydrosulfite, and swirl to effect solution.

the solution for 1–2 min. on the steam bath, and determine whether or not the color of proline yellow is obscured by other pigments.

(6) Put one drop of the proline–leucine–glycine solution in a test tube, add one drop of concd. hydrochloric acid and then 1 drop of 0.3% aqueous ninhydrin solution, and heat the solution for 1–2 min. on the steam bath. Hold the tube against white paper and see if you can detect the color of proline red. Add 0.5 ml. (10 drops) each of water and butanol, shake, and let the layers separate. The upper layer should be about 1 mm. thick (add more butanol if required) and should contain proline red in concentrated form sufficient for recognition.

Protein Hydrolyzate

Clarify the remaining solution (nearly 1 ml.) from the hydrolysis of 100 mg. of hair, silk, or gelatin by shaking it for 1 min. with Norit, and filter through a 2.5-cm. funnel. Put 4 drops (0.2 ml.) of the nearly colorless filtrate into a 10 × 75-mm. test tube, add 4 drops of concd. hydrochloric acid and 4 drops of 0.3% aqueous ninhydrin solution, and heat for 1–2 min. on the steam bath. A red color, best observed by viewing the tube against a light source, is indicative of the presence of proline.[13]

---

[13] The proline red appears to be colloidally dispersed, but if the mixture is filtered, the pigment is retained on the filter paper. If it is extracted from the paper with butanol and the dull-colored solution shaken with alkaline hydrosulfite, a clear blue extract results.

Sodium *p*-Toluenesulfonate

$$\text{CH}_3\text{-C}_6\text{H}_5 + \text{H}_2\text{SO}_4 \longrightarrow \text{CH}_3\text{-C}_6\text{H}_4\text{-SO}_3\text{H} + \text{H}_2\text{O}$$

Phenol is so prone to enter into substitution reactions that it can be sulfonated with dilute sulfuric acid. Naphthalene can be sulfonated with concd. sulfuric acid at 0–60°. Benzene, less reactive than naphthalene, on reaction with fuming sulfuric acid (oleum, 7–30% SO_3) at 40° affords benzenesulfonic acid, and at 200° the product is benzene-*m*-disulfonic acid. Toluene, more reactive than benzene and comparable to naphthalene, is sulfonated by concd. sulfuric acid even at 0°. The proportion of the three isomeric products formed varies with the temperature as follows:

TOLUENESULFONIC ACIDS (% FORMED)

Reaction Temperature	Ortho	Meta	Para
0°	45.2	2.5	52.3
35°	33.3	5.3	61.4
100°	17.4	10.1	72.5

In the present experiment the reaction is conducted at a still higher temperature (about 170°) to further favor formation of the para isomer and to shorten the reaction time. The amount of sulfuric acid is kept at a minimum in order to avoid disulfonation; that some toluene remains unreacted is unimportant, since the hydrocarbon is inexpensive. The chief reaction product, sodium *p*-toluenesulfonate, is isolated as the sodium salt, produced by partial neutralization of the acid mixture and addition of sodium chloride:

$$p\text{-}CH_3C_6H_4SO_3H + NaCl \rightleftharpoons p\text{-}CH_3C_6H_4SO_3Na + HCl$$

Sodium p-toluenesulfonate is infusible, but can be characterized as to purity and identified by conversion to the p-toluidine salt, which has a characteristic melting point:

$$p\text{-}CH_3C_6H_4SO_3^-Na^+ + H_2NC_6H_4CH_3\text{-}p + HCl \longrightarrow$$
$$p\text{-}CH_3C_6H_4SO_3^-H_3\overset{+}{N}C_6H_4CH_3\text{-}p + NaCl$$

EXPERIMENT

1. Sulfonation

Reaction time 1 hr.

In a 200-ml. round bottomed flask provided with a reflux condenser place 32 ml. (0.3 mole) of purified toluene [1] and 19.0 ml. of concd. sulfuric acid, add a boiling stone, and heat the mixture on an asbestos gauze while shaking constantly with a rotary motion. The acid should not be thrown onto the cork. When the upper layer of toluene begins to boil, turn down the flame and note the time. Continue to heat gently and to swirl the mixture thoroughly every two or three minutes so that the two layers are well mixed and able to react. With proper heating there is little activity in the toluene layer and just a slow dropping from the condenser. Shaking produces a mild rush of condensate. Too strong heating only drives the toluene out of the reaction zone and favors disulfonation. Thorough shaking will do more to hasten the reaction and favor a good yield. In one hour the toluene layer should have very nearly disappeared and there should be but little return from the condenser. It is not advisable to continue beyond this point.

The reaction mixture, while still warm, is poured into 100 ml. of water and the flask is rinsed with a little water from a wash bottle. (NOTE: If the mixture is allowed to cool before pouring into water it sets to a stiff paste of crystals of p-toluenesulfonic acid in the form of a monohydrate. This can be dissolved by warming and treated as above.) The acid solution is partly neutralized by adding carefully and in small portions 15 g. of sodium bicarbonate; 40 g. of sodium chloride is then added and the mixture is heated to boiling, with addition of a little more water, if necessary, in order to bring the salt completely into solution. Without filtering, cool the saturated solution thor-

---

[1] Toluene may contain thiophene derivatives that cause a blackening of the reaction mixture. The hydrocarbon supplied should be purified by sulfuric acid treatment (Chapter 48).

 Note for the instructor

oughly in an ice bath and collect the crystalline sodium *p*-toluene-sulfonate that separates. Rinse the crystals out of the beaker with filtered mother liquor, press the cake, and wash it with 20 ml. of saturated sodium chloride solution. (The sulfonate is extremely soluble in the absence of sodium chloride.)

To recrystallize the salt, blow the filter cake out of the funnel into a beaker, wash in the crystals from the paper and funnel with a stream from the wash bottle, and dissolve the product in a total of about 100 ml. of water. Add 40 g. of sodium chloride, heat to boiling, stir, and add just enough more water to bring the solid all into solution. Stir for a minute or two with 1 g. of decolorizing carbon and filter the hot solution by suction. Rinse in any material adhering to the beaker, funnel, and paper, but do this efficiently, so as to avoid introducing any more water than is necessary. In case charcoal is visible in the filtrate refilter through a fresh paper. Transfer the colorless filtrate to a beaker (rinse!) and, since water has been added in the various washings, evaporate the solution by boiling to a volume at which it is saturated (about 170 ml.; pour this amount of water into a beaker of the same size for comparison). Rinse the material which has spattered on the walls, place the beaker in an ice bath and allow crystallization to take place without disturbance. (In case no crystals separate, reduce the volume still further.) Collect and wash the crystals as before.

If dried at room temperature slightly sticky crystals of a hydrate are obtained. The water of crystallization may be eliminated by drying on the steam bath or in an oven at 120°. The yield of pure, anhydrous material is 20–25 g.

2. Characterization

Dissolve 1 g. of the sodium sulfonate in the minimum quantity of boiling water, add 0.5 g. of *p*-toluidine and 1 ml. of concentrated hydrochloric acid, and bring the material into solution by heating and by adding more water if required. (If there are any oily drops of the amine, more HCl should be added.) The solution is cooled at once in an ice bath and the walls of the flask are scratched until the *p*-toluidine salt crystallizes. The product is collected, washed with a very small quantity of water, and a few crystals are saved for seed. The rest is recrystallized from water, with clarification if necessary. If no crystals separate, the solution is inoculated with a trace of seed. The pure salt melts at 197°. A product melting within two or three degrees of this temperature is satisfactory.

QUESTIONS

1. Explain why, when the solution saturated at the boiling point with both sodium chloride and sodium *p*-toluenesulfonate cools, it is the latter rather than the former salt that crystallizes.

2. If you were working with a rare hydrocarbon in place of toluene, how would you recover the unsulfonated material?

3. Potassium *p*-toluenesulfonate is less soluble in water than the sodium salt; how would you prepare it from your sample of sodium salt?

Sulfanilamide from Benzene

This experiment is a six-step synthesis of the first known sulfa drug. Benzene is nitrated with a mixture of nitric and sulfuric acid, the latter acid promoting formation of nitronium ion:

$$HONO_2 + 2H_2SO_4 \rightleftharpoons NO_2^+ + H_3O^+ + 2HSO_4^-$$

The nitrobenzene formed is reduced to aniline by tin and hydrochloric acid. A tin double salt of the formula $(C_6H_5NH_3)_2SnCl_4$ separates partially during the reaction, and at the end it is decomposed by addition of excess alkali, which converts the tin into water-soluble stannite or stannate (Na_2SnO_2 or Na_2SnO_3). The aniline liberated is separated from inorganic salts and insoluble impurities derived from the tin by steam distillation and is then dried, distilled, and acetylated, either with acetic anhydride in aqueous solution or by refluxing the amine with acetic acid. Treatment of the resulting acetanilide with excess chlorosulfonic acid effects substitution of the chlorosulfonyl group and

affords p-acetaminobenzenesulfonyl chloride. The alternative route to this intermediate via sulfanilic acid is unsatisfactory because sulfanilic acid being dipolar is difficult to acetylate. In both processes the amino group must be protected by acetylation to permit formation of the acid chloride group. The next step in the synthesis is ammonolysis of the sulfonyl chloride and the terminal step is removal of the protective acetyl group.

[Use the total product obtained at each step as starting material for the next step and adjust the amounts of reagents accordingly.] You are to choose between alternative procedures and decide whether to purify an intermediate or use it as such to avoid purification losses. Aim both for a high overall yield of pure final product and also for its speedy production. Keep a record of your actual working time. Study the procedures carefully so that your work will be efficient. A combination of consecutive steps that avoids a needless isolation saves time and increases the yield.

EXPERIMENTS

1. Nitrobenzene

Explanation of procedure

The nitration is conducted with a mixture of nitric and sulfuric acids diluted with a small amount of water to inhibit dinitration. The reaction is exothermic at the start, when the concentrations of benzene and nitric acid are maximal, and becomes sluggish toward the end as the concentrations of reactants decrease. Consequently the mixture is cooled during the early stages to prevent the reaction from getting out of hand, and later heat is applied to force the diluted components to react. Since both benzene and nitrobenzene are insoluble in the acid mixture and form an upper layer, thorough agitation must be maintained by swirling throughout the entire reaction period in order to obtain a successful result in the time indicated.

Apparatus

The reaction is carried out in a 200-ml. round bottomed flask fitted with a cork holding a thermometer with the bulb extending to the bottom of the flask. If the cork conceals the stem in the region 25–65°, cut a notch in it to make the scale visible, as in a melting point bath. If no notch is required for visibility make a small groove with a file for equalization of pressure. Prepare an ice-water bath before mixing the reagents.

Procedure

Measure 5 ml. of water into the flask, add 25 ml. of concd. sulfuric acid, and cool. Add 15 ml. of concd. (71%) nitric acid, and again cool. Then add 15.0 g. of benzene, insert the thermometer, note the time, and swirl vigorously to promote interaction of the immiscible layers. [Watch the temperature closely and when it approaches 60° plunge the flask briefly into the ice bath to check a further rise.] Swirl constantly and, by very brief cooling in the ice bath as required, try to maintain the temperature close to 60°, but not above, and not below 55°. Within 7–8 min. the temperature should begin to drop, and after 10 min., if the initial strongly exothermic reaction seems to be over, heat

20 Min. of continuous swirling and careful control of temperature

the flask occasionally on the steam bath, or in a pan of water heated on the steam bath, and maintain a temperature as close as possible to 60° for another 10 min. Then cool in ice to 25°, add 75 ml. of water, cool again, and pour the solution (or a part of it) into a small separatory funnel containing 30 ml. of ether. Shake, draw off and discard the lower aqueous layer, and pour in and extract any further reaction mixture (rinse the flask with a little ether). Wash the ethereal extract once with water and then shake it with 25 ml. of 10% sodium hydroxide solution. In case the extract is yellow, draw it off and save it and extract with two or three further portions of alkali until the pigmented by-product is all removed. Then shake the ethereal solution with saturated salt solution, filter it through anhydrous sodium sulfate, evaporate the ether under an aspirator tube, and evacuate the hot, residual oil at the water pump to remove ether. Pour the crude product through a long-stemmed funnel into a 25-ml. distilling flask and distil the product through an air condenser, after removing a few drops of forerun that can be collected separately in a test tube held over the side arm. Pure nitrobenzene is a straw-colored liquid boiling at 206–207° (uncorr.). Do not distil to dryness, for if m-dinitrobenzene is present in the residue it may decompose explosively if the temperature rises much above 207°. Yield 18.0 g. Nitrobenzene is toxic if gotten on the skin or if the vapor is inhaled.

pan of H₂O on steam bath

← sep. funnel

4/18/61

> *Drain off the lower layer of salt solution before filtering the ether layer*

(aspirator condenser apparatus)

4/25/61 weigh prod.

yellow picric acid

See if you can infer the identity of the yellow pigment extracted from water into ether and extracted from ether by alkali. It is a substance encountered in a previous experiment. It is formed from thiophene-free as well as from thiophene-containing benzene, and is produced as a minor reaction product whether the nitric acid contains oxides of nitrogen (yellow) or is colorless and kept free of oxides of nitrogen by addition of urea. Suggestion: acidify the yellow alkaline extract, introduce a piece of silk, and heat.

Calc. amt. reag.

2. Aniline

The reaction is carried out in a flask suitable for steam distillation of the product: either a 500-ml. long necked flask, which later can be fitted as shown in Fig. 26.1, or a 500-ml. distilling flask, which later requires insertion of a glass tube extending to the bottom. Put 25 g. of granulated tin and 12.0 g. of nitrobenzene in the flask, make an ice bath ready, add 55 ml. of concd. hydrochloric acid, insert a thermometer, and swirl well to promote reaction in the three-phase system. The mixture is let

← Ice bath

← cork + Therm.

factor $\frac{12}{18} = \frac{1}{1.33}$

Reaction time: $\frac{1}{2}$ hr.

warm until the temperature reaches 60° and then is cooled briefly in ice just enough to prevent a rise above 60°, for the reaction might then get out of hand. Continue to swirl, cool as required, and maintain a temperature in the range of 55–60° for 15 min., when the reaction should have moderated. Remove the thermometer (rinse it with water), mount the flask on the steam bath in a spring clip so that it can be disconnected for swirling, insert a cold finger to condense nitrobenzene that steam distils, and heat with occasional swirling until droplets of nitrobenzene are absent and color due to nitrobenzene or intermediates is gone (about

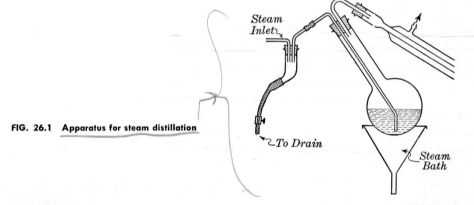

FIG. 26.1 **Apparatus for steam distillation**

Suitable point of interruption

15 min.). During this period dissolve 40 g. of sodium hydroxide in 100 ml. of water and cool to room temperature.

At the end of the reduction cool the acid solution in ice (to prevent volatilization of aniline) during gradual addition of the solution of alkali. Then arrange for steam distillation, either as in Fig. 26.1 or by mounting a distilling flask vertically on the steam bath to deliver into a condenser in the usual way and connecting a steam trap to a tube extending to the bottom of the flask. Distillation without passing in steam (as in earlier experiments) is unsatisfactory in the present case because of bumping. A steam trap is required because steam from the supply line is so wet that the flask soon fills up. By adjustment of the pinch clamp, excess water is drained from the adapter into a beaker. Since aniline is fairly soluble in water (3.6 g./100 g.[18°]) distillation should be continued somewhat beyond the point where the distillate has lost its original turbidity (50–60 ml. more). Estimate the volume of distillate and add 0.2 g. of salt per ml. Pour the mixture into a separatory funnel, rinse the flask with 20 ml. of benzene, shake, and let the layers settle fully. Discard the lower layer and dry the benzene–aniline layer superficially by filtering it through sodium sulfate into a 50-ml. Erlenmeyer flask. The benzene can be removed by distillation from a 50-ml. distilling flask through a water-cooled condenser, but even though the boiling point of aniline (184°) is well above that of benzene a sharp separation cannot be made without some provision for fractionation. This can be done simply by pushing a 1″ piece of metal sponge packing (Chapter 3) into the neck of the flask in the space below the side arm. When the benzene is removed and the temperature starts to rise abruptly, interrupt the process and change to a clean air condenser. When the flask is nearly dry it is permissible to play the flame on the neck of the flask to recover material otherwise held up.

Notes. Pure aniline is a colorless, refractive liquid of characteristic odor. It becomes discolored on exposure to air, particularly rapidly in sunlight. Even a sample that has become very red can be purified by addition of a pinch of zinc dust and distillation. The amine is poisonous; avoid inhaling the vapor, and if the liquid is spilled on the skin wash it off with dilute hydrochloric acid. If bromine water is added dropwise to 2–3 ml. of an aqueous solution of aniline until a faint yellow color persists, *tribromoaniline* (m.p. 116°) precipitates. *o*-Toluidine and *p*-toluidine form dibromo derivatives, m.p. 50° and 73°; *m*-toluidine forms a tribromo compound, m.p. 97°. The *isonitrile* reaction is carried out by adding 2 drops of aniline to 2 ml. of methanol and then adding 10 drops of concentrated potassium hydroxide solution and 5 drops of chloroform. Warm very gently under the hood and smell cautiously.

3. Acetanilide. (a) Refluxing with Acetic Acid

In a 100-ml. flask equipped with an air condenser set for reflux, place 5.0 g. of aniline and 20 ml. of acetic acid; in case the aniline is discolored add a small pinch of zinc dust. Adjust the flame so that the ring of condensate rises to about 15 cm. from the top of the condenser. Reflux for at least 4 hrs. and pour the hot reaction mixture in a thin stream into 200 ml. of cold water. Collect the product and wash it with water. Pure acetanilide is colorless and melts at 114°.

Choice of procedures (a) and (b)

(b) Acetylation in Aqueous Solution

Dissolve 5.0 g. (0.054 mole) of aniline in 135 ml. of water and 4.5 ml. (0.054 mole) of concd. hydrochloric acid, and if the solution is colored filter it by suction through a pad of Norit. Measure out 6.2 ml. (0.065 mole) of acetic anhydride, and also prepare

151

[handwritten marginal calculation:]

1.52
× 5.3
456
760
8.056 g. in 30 ml H₂O

a solution of 5.3 g. (0.065 mole) of anhydrous sodium acetate in 30 ml. of water. Add the acetic anhydride to the solution of aniline hydrochloride with stirring and at once add the sodium acetate solution. Stir, cool in ice, and collect the product. It should be colorless and the m.p. close to 114°. Acetanilide can be crystallized from a large volume of water or from water containing a little alcohol; it may melt when heated with water but all material, solid or liquid, should be brought into solution.

4. Sulfanilamide

The chlorosulfonation is carried out without solvent in a 125-ml. Erlenmeyer flask fitted with a stopper connected by a section of rubber tubing to a glass tube fitted with a cork into the neck of a filtering flask half filled with water. The tube should be about 1 cm. above the surface of the water and must not dip into it. This is a trap for entraining the hydrogen chloride evolved. Since the reaction is most easily controlled when the acetanilide is in the form of a hard cake, place 5.0 g. of acetanilide in the flask, melt it over a free flame, and swirl the melt as it cools to distribute the material as it solidifies over the lower wall of the flask. Cool thoroughly in an ice bath, measure 12.5 ml. of chlorosulfonic acid in a graduate supplied with the reagent and kept away from water, add the reagent all at once, and connect the flask to the gas trap. The flask is now removed from the ice bath and swirled until a part of the solid has dissolved and the evolution of hydrogen chloride is proceeding at a rapid rate. Occasional cooling in ice may be required to prevent a too brisk reaction. In 5–10 min. the reaction subsides and only a few lumps of acetanilide remain undissolved. When this point has been reached, heat the mixture on the steam bath for 10 min. to complete the reaction, cool the flask under the tap, and deliver the oil by drops with a capillary dropper with stirring into 75 ml. of ice water contained in a beaker cooled in an ice bath (hood). Rinse the flask with cold water and stir the precipitated *p*-acetaminobenzenesulfonyl chloride for a few minutes until an even suspension of granular white solid is obtained, and then collect and wash this on a Büchner funnel. After pressing and draining the filter cake, transfer the solid to the rinsed reaction flask, add 15 ml. of concd. aqueous ammonia solution and 15 ml. of water, and heat the mixture over a flame (gauze) with occasional swirling (hood) and maintain it just below the boiling point for 5 min. During this treatment a change can be noted as the sulfonyl chloride undergoes transformation to a more pasty suspension

[margin note:]
Caution: Corrosive chemical, reacts violently with water. Withdraw with pipette and pipetter (Chapter 11.1, Note 3)

[margin note:]
Do not let the mixture stand before addition of ammonia

[handwritten margin note:] Immediate

of the amide. Cool the suspension well in an ice bath, collect the p-acetaminobenzenesulfonamide by suction filtration, press the cake on the funnel, and drain it thoroughly from excess water, which otherwise will unduly dilute the acid used in the next step.

Transfer the still moist amide to the well-drained reaction flask, add 5 ml. of concd. hydrochloric acid and 10 ml. of water, boil the mixture gently until the solid has all dissolved (5–10 min.), note the level of the liquid in the flask, boil the solution gently for 15 min., and maintain the original volume by addition of water as required. Cooling should afford a solution of sulfanilamide hydrochloride and give no precipitate of unhydrolyzed amide. If the solution is not colorless, shake it with a little Norit and filter by suction. Place the solution in a beaker and cautiously add an aqueous solution of 5 g. of sodium bicarbonate with stirring. After the foam has subsided test the suspension with litmus, and if it is still acidic add more bicarbonate until the neutral point is reached. Cool thoroughly in ice and collect the granular, white precipitate of sulfanilamide. The crude product (m.p. 161–163°) on crystallization from alcohol or water affords pure sulfanilamide, m.p. 163–164°, with about 90% recovery.

CHAPTER **27** | Cost Calculation[1]

The problem is to estimate the cost of manufacturing sulfanilamide from acetanilide at a production level of 20,000 lbs. per month by the procedure of your laboratory experiment and in the yield that you obtained. Fill in each item of the following table, A to N, in turn according to the instructions.

A. Fill in the quantities of reagents used in your laboratory preparation and the yield that you obtained. The amount of Norit used can be estimated as 200 mg. per 10 g. of acetanilide. Assume a specific gravity of 1 for reacting acetanilide.

B. The ratio of pounds of monthly production to X grams of product obtained in the laboratory experiment, or $20,000/X$, gives a factor for conversion of grams of a reagent used to pounds required per month. If 4 g. of acetanilide gave 5 g. of sulfanilamide, the monthly requirement is 16,000 lbs. The same factor times 0.12 gives a factor for conversion of the reaction volume from ml. to gals. per month.

C. Unit costs (dollars per lb.) are given for 1955. Costs at the time of the calculation can be obtained from "Oil, Paint, and Drug Reporter."

D and E. The product of the quantity of an item in column B and its unit cost in column C gives the cost per month. The total of column D to this point, less credit for recovered solvents (none in this example), is the net chemical cost, item E.

Batches per Month

Assume that a 500-gal. reactor will be used; this holds about 350 gal. of working volume. To obtain the number of batches

---

[1] By Clarence A. Haverly, Research and Development Division, Merck and Co., Inc.

PRODUCTION OF SULFANILAMIDE: 20,000 LBS./MONTH

(Cost in dollars per lb.)

Chemicals	A Laboratory batch	B Production quantity per month	C Unit cost 1955	C Unit cost 19—	D Cost per month	N Cost per lb.
Acetanilide	g.	lbs.	.29			
Chlorosulfonic acid (sp. gr. 1.79)	ml. g.	lbs.	.0415			
Reaction volume	ml.	gals.				
Ammonium hydroxide (sp. gr. 0.90)	ml. ml. g.	lbs.	.016			
Hydrochloric acid (sp. gr. 1.18)	ml. g.	lbs.	.015			
Norit	g.	lbs.	.25			
Sodium bicarbonate	g.	lbs.	.027			
Product yield	g.	20,000 lbs.				

E. Net chemical cost
F. Labor (_____ man-hours)
G. Supervision, etc.
H. Repairs and supplies
I. Utilities
J. Occupancy
K. Equipment items
L. Allocated expenses

M. Total cost

per month divide the reaction volume shown in column B by 350.

F. Labor is a function of the engineering operations, the number of batches, and the weight of material handled. For this problem estimate labor at 32 man-hours per batch plus 44 man-hours per 1,000 lbs. of product. To calculate the direct labor cost assume the cost of an operator to be $2.00 per hr. (including payroll taxes and employee benefits).

G. In addition to direct labor, a manufacturing operation requires foremen, technical supervisors, control chemists, and clerks, which are a function of the complexity and difficulty of the process and of operating hazards. Assume that these payroll items equal 50% of the direct labor.

H. The cost of repairs depends on the severity of usage (corrosion) and on the replacement cost of the equipment. Operating supplies include filter cloth, gloves, gaskets. For this item H use the figure $2,000 per month.

I. Assume $50 per batch for steam, water, and electricity.

J. Occupancy, which depends largely on the size of the building required, includes not only the depreciation and repairs on the building but a share of costs such as plant protection, heat, and taxes on the land. Assume a cost of $2,000 per month for item *J*.

K. Depreciation, taxes, and insurance costs depend on the installed value of the equipment. Assume an installed value of $125,000 and allow 12% of this cost per year for item *K* ($1250 per month).

L. General manufacturing overhead items including vacation and holiday pay, employment office costs, raw material purchasing, receiving and storage costs, and factory office costs are allocated to a specific process in proportion to the total payroll for that process. Assume a cost of 35% of the total payroll $(F + G)$.

M. Addition of items *E–L* gives the total cost per month.

N. Calculate the cost per lb. of sulfanilamide of chemicals and other items by dividing the figures in column *D* by 20,000. The total cost per lb. is only the manufacturing cost. A company manufacturing the drug for sale would incur expenses for packaging, warehousing, and shipping, and the product would have to carry a share of management, research, and selling expenses. Compare your estimate of cost per pound with the current open market selling price of the sulfa drug.

Diphenylmethane

Condensation of benzyl chloride with benzene under the influence of a catalytic amount of aluminum chloride affords diphenylmethane as the chief product:

$$C_6H_5CH_2Cl + C_6H_6 \xrightarrow{AlCl_3} C_6H_5CH_2C_6H_5 + HCl$$

Since benzyl chloride is considerably more reactive than saturated alkyl halides, the reaction proceeds so readily as to inhibit some of the side reactions usually attending the Friedel-Crafts hydrocarbon synthesis. However, even at 0° some of the material is converted into anthracene, recognizable from its fluorescence:

This reaction and polysubstitution decrease the yield and render isolation of pure hydrocarbon difficult.

EXPERIMENT

In a 200-ml. round bottomed flask fitted with a reflux condenser place 10 g. of benzyl chloride and 50 ml. of benzene. Attach a trap to the top of the condenser to collect the hydrogen chloride produced in the reaction, and cool the contents of the flask thoroughly in an ice bath. Weigh 4 g. of anhydrous aluminum chloride into a stoppered test tube and pour about 1 g. of the material through the top of the condenser into the *well-*

cooled liquid. Shake the mixture and keep it cold. A vigorous reaction should set in within a few minutes, with rapid evolution of hydrogen chloride, which gradually subsides. Then add the remainder of the aluminum chloride in portions through the condenser and continue to shake at ice bath temperature for 5–10 min.; a red, oily substance (aluminum chloride addition product) should have separated by this time. Remove the flask from the cooling bath and allow it to stand at room temperature for one half hour, and then proceed without delay as follows.

Standing for a longer period favors formation of anthracene

Cool the reaction mixture in an ice bath and cautiously introduce about 20 g. of crushed ice, followed by 40 ml. of water, to decompose the aluminum chloride complex. Stir well and then transfer the mixture to a separatory funnel where the water layer can be drawn off from the upper layer of benzene containing diphenylmethane. Wash the benzene solution with dilute hydrochloric acid to remove basic aluminum salts and then with water to remove acid. Dry the benzene solution by warming it with about 2 g. of calcium chloride until it is clear, shake for a minute or two with 0.2 g. of Norit, and filter the solution into an Erlenmeyer flask. Remove the bulk of the benzene by distillation

Use aspirator tube

from the steam bath (let the flask rest below the rings). Distil the remaining oil from a small distilling flask over a free flame using an air condenser. The forerun will contain some benzene and must be kept away from the flame. Pure diphenylmethane boils at 262°, crystallizes to a colorless solid melting at 26–27°, and has a pleasant orange odor. Collect the fraction boiling at 250–275° and see if it can be caused to solidify by cooling in ice and scratching, or by seeding with a crystal of the pure material. If this is not the case redistil the product and collect the fraction boiling at 255–265°. Allow the solid to melt while stirring it with a thermometer. The temperature rises steadily at first and then remains essentially constant for a time until most of the solid has melted; this is the melting point. Material prepared as above usually melts in the range 20–23°; yield 7–10 g.

The high-boiling residue contains anthracene (m.p. 217°), *o*-dibenzylbenzene (m.p. 78°), and *p*-dibenzylbenzene (m.p. 86°); these hydrocarbons all boil in the range 350–380°.

Synthesis and Reduction of Anthraquinone

The Friedel-Crafts reaction of phthalic anhydride with benzene is conducted with excess benzene as solvent and two equiv-

alents of aluminum chloride as catalyst. The reaction proceeds rapidly and the *o*-benzoylbenzoic acid formed separates as a salt in which one mole of aluminum chloride is bound to the acid function and the other to the carbonyl group. On addition of ice and hydrochloric acid the complex is decomposed and basic aluminum salts, $Al(OH)_3$ and $Al(OH)_2Cl$, are converted into the soluble trichloride. On dehydration with sulfuric acid *o*-benzoyl-

benzoic acid is cyclized to anthraquinone. Since the latter is sulfonated only under forcing conditions, a high temperature can be used to shorten the reaction time without loss of product; conditions are so adjusted that anthraquinone separates from the hot solution in crystalline form favoring quick drying.[1]

The next step is reduction of anthraquinone to anthrone, which is isolated in the keto form by either of two alternative pro-

---

[1] Use of polyphosphoric acid for the cyclization is described by H. R. Snyder and F. X. Werber, *J. Am. Chem. Soc.*, **72**, 2967 (1950).

Anthrone
(pale yellow, nonfluorescent,
insoluble in alkali)

Anthranol
(brown-yellow, fluorescent,
deep yellow in alkali)

cedures given. It is suggested that half of the students in an aisle follow procedure (a) and the other half (b) and then compare results. Be sure to observe the alternate procedure in operation.

EXPERIMENTS

1. o-Benzoylbenzoic Acid

The Friedel-Crafts reaction is carried out in a 500-ml. round bottomed flask equipped with a short condenser. A trap for collecting hydrogen chloride liberated is connected to the top of the condenser by a piece of rubber tubing sufficiently long to make it possible to heat the flask on the steam bath or to plunge it into an ice bath. The trap is a suction flask half filled with water and with a delivery tube inserted to within 1 cm. of the surface of the water.

Fifteen grams of phthalic anhydride and 75 ml. of thiophene-free benzene are placed in the flask and this is cooled in an ice bath until the benzene begins to crystallize. This serves to moderate the vigorous reaction which otherwise might be difficult to control. Thirty grams of anhydrous aluminum chloride [2] is added, the condenser and trap are connected, and the flask is shaken well and warmed for a few minutes by the heat of the hand. If the reaction does not start, the flask is warmed very gently by holding it for a few seconds over the steam bath. At the first sign of vigorous boiling, or evolution of hydrogen chloride, the flask is held over the ice bath in readiness to ice it if the reaction becomes too vigorous. This gentle, cautious heating is continued until the reaction is proceeding smoothly enough so that the mixture can be refluxed on the steam bath. This point is reached in about 5 min. Continue the heating on the steam bath, swirl the mixture, and watch it carefully for sudden separation of the addition compound, for the heat of crystallization is so great that it may be necessary to plunge the flask into the ice bath to moderate the process. Once the addition compound has separated as a thick paste, heat the mixture

Short reaction period, high yield

[2] This is best weighed from a freshly opened bottle into a stoppered test tube.

for 10 min. more on the steam bath and then remove the condenser and swirl the flask in an ice bath until cold. Take the flask and ice bath to the hood, weigh out 100 g. of ice, add a few small pieces of ice, swirl and cool as necessary, and wait until the ice has reacted before adding more. After the 100 g. has been added and the reaction of decomposition has subsided, add 20 ml. of concd. hydrochloric acid, 100 ml. of water, swirl vigorously and make sure that the mixture is at room temperature. Then add 50 ml. of water, swirl vigorously and make sure that the mixture is at room temperature. Then add 50 ml. of ether and, with a flattened stirring rod, dislodge solid from the neck and walls of the flask and break up lumps at the bottom. To further promote hydrolysis of the addition compound, extraction of the organic product, and solution of basic aluminum halides, stopper the flask with a cork and shake vigorously for several minutes. When most of the solid has disappeared, pour the mixture through a funnel into a separatory funnel until the funnel is nearly filled and draw off and discard the lower aqueous layer. Pour the rest of the mixture into the funnel, rinse the reaction flask with fresh ether, and again drain off the aqueous layer. To reduce the fluffy, dirty precipitate that appears at the interface, add 10 ml. of concd. hydrochloric acid and 25 ml. of water, shake vigorously for 2–3 min., and drain off the aqueous layer. If some interfacial dirty emulsion still persists, decant the benzene–ether solution from the mouth of the funnel into a paper for gravity filtration and use fresh ether to rinse the funnel. Clean the funnel and return to it the filtered benzene–ether solution. Shake the solution with a further portion of dilute hydrochloric acid, and then isolate the reaction product by either of the following procedures.

(a) Add 50 ml. of 10% sodium hydroxide solution, shake thoroughly, and separate the aqueous layer.[3] Extract with a further 25-ml. portion of alkali and combine the extracts. Wash with 10 ml. of water, and add the aqueous solution to the main extract. Discard the benzene–ether solution. Acidify the combined alkaline extract with concd. hydrochloric acid to pH 1–2, and if the o-benzoylbenzoic acid separates as an oil cool in ice and rub the walls with a stirring rod to induce crystallization of the hydrate; collect the product and wash it well. This material is the monohydrate: $C_6H_5COC_6H_4CO_2H \cdot H_2O$. To convert it into anhy-

Alternative procedures

[3] The nature of a yellow pigment that appears in the first alkaline extract is unknown; the impurity is apparently transient, for the final product dissolves in alkali to give a colorless solution.

Drying time about 1 hr.

drous *o*-benzoylbenzoic acid, put it in a tared 200-ml. round bottomed flask, evacuate the flask at the full force of the suction pump, and heat it in the open rings of a steam bath and cover the flask with a towel. Check the weight after 45 min., 1 hr., and 1.25 hr. Yield 19–21 g., m.p. 126–127°.

Extinguish flames

(b) Filter the benzene–ether solution through sodium sulfate for superficial drying, put it into a 250-ml. distilling flask and distil from the steam bath through a condenser into an ice-cooled receiver until the volume is reduced to about 55 ml. Add ligroin slowly to slight turbidity and let the product crystallize at 25° and then at 5°. Yield of colorless, well-formed crystals, m.p. 127–128°, 18–20 g.

Material not used for making anthraquinone is to be saved for the experiment of Chapter 30.

2. Anthraquinone

Place 5.0 g. of *o*-benzoylbenzoic acid (anhydrous) in a 100-ml. round bottomed flask, add 25 ml. of concd. sulfuric acid, and heat on the steam bath and swirl until the solid is dissolved. Then clamp the flask over a microburner, insert a thermometer,

Reaction time 10 min.

raise the temperature to 150°, and maintain a temperature of 150–155° for 5 min. Let the solution cool to 100°, remove the thermometer after letting it drain, and with a capillary dropping tube, add 5 ml. of water by drops with swirling to keep the initially precipitated material dissolved as long as possible so that it will separate as small but easily filtered crystals. Let the mixture cool, dilute further with water until the flask is full, cool, collect, and wash well with water. Then remove the filtrate and

Apply only gentle suction to avoid breaking filter paper

wash the filter flask, return the funnel but do not apply suction, and test for unreacted starting material as follows. Dilute 10 ml. of concd. ammonia solution with 50 ml. of water, pour the solution onto the filter and loosen the cake so that it is well leached. Then

A final wash with methanol brightens the product and hastens drying

apply suction, wash with water, and acidify a few ml. of the filtrate. If there is no precipitate the yield of anthraquinone should be close to the theory, since it is insoluble in water. Dry the product to constant weight but do not take the melting point (m.p. 286°, corr.).

In the next section adjust the quantities to fit your yield of anthraquinone.

3. Anthrone. (a) Stannous Chloride Reduction

In a 100-ml. round bottomed flask provided with a reflux condenser put 5.0 g. of anthraquinone, 40 ml. of acetic acid, and a solution made by warming a mixture of 13 g. of stannous chloride dihydrate with 13 ml. of concd. hydrochloric acid. Add a boiling stone, note the time, and reflux gently until particles of anthraquinone have completely disappeared; then reflux 20 min. longer and record the total time. Disconnect the flask, heat it on the steam bath and add water (about 5 ml.) by 1-ml. portions until the solution is nearly saturated, and let it stand for crystallization. Collect and dry the product and take the melting point (156° given).

(b) Hydrosulfite Reduction

In a 500-ml. round bottomed flask which is to be heated under reflux put 5.0 g. of anthraquinone, 6 g. of sodium hydroxide, 15 g. of sodium hydrosulfite dihydrate, and 130 ml. of water. Heat over a free flame and swirl for a few minutes to convert the anthraquinone into the deep red vat containing anthrahydroquinone anion. Note that particles of different appearance begin to separate even before the anthraquinone has all dissolved. Reflux for 45 min., cool, filter the product and wash it well, and let it dry. Note the yield and melting point of the crude material and crystallize it from 95% ethanol; the solution may have to be filtered from insoluble impurities. Record the approximate volume of solvent used, and if the recovery in the first crop is not satisfactory, concentrate and secure a second crop.

4. Comparison of Results

Compare your results with those obtained by neighbors using the alternative procedure with respect to yield, quality of product, and working time. Which is the better laboratory procedure? Then consider the cost of the three solvents concerned (Chapter 6), the cost of the two reducing agents (current prices to be posted), and relative ease of recovery of the organic solvents, and decide which method would be preferred as a manufacturing process.

5. Special Experiment: Fluorescent Anthracene

Put 10 g. of zinc dust into a 500-ml. round bottomed flask and activate it by adding 50 ml. of water and 1 ml. of copper sulfate solution (Fehling's solution I) and swirling for a minute or two. Let the zinc settle, decant the bulk of the water, and add 10 g. of sodium hydroxide, 160 ml. of water, 40 ml. of xylene (b.p. 135–140°), and 4.0 g. of anthrone. Attach a condenser and reflux the three-phase mixture vigorously. The initial yellow color of

163

the aqueous phase is due to anthranol anion; the anthrone present is probably largely in the xylene layer. In this, the Martin method of reduction, a water-immiscible solvent is used to dissolve substances like anthrone that are sparingly soluble in water and allow their distribution into the reducing phase at low concentrations. At hourly intervals remove the burner to better observe the color of the aqueous layer. After 3 hrs., when this layer has lost the bright yellow color and is straw-colored, the reaction can be stopped. Cool the mixture thoroughly in ice, collect the anthracene crystals and zinc, invert the flask and let it drain on a piece of filter paper, and save the filtrate. Return the moist solid to the reaction flask and use benzene to rinse material adhering to the funnel, paper, and spatula. Connect the flask to a suction pump, put it inside the rings of the steam bath, cover it with a towel, and evacuate and heat for 15 min. Then disconnect, add a little more benzene to help eliminate water, wash out the glass tube leading to the suction pump with acetone so that fresh droplets of water which appear in it will indicate the progress of drying, and repeat the process for another 15 min. A third repetition should be enough.

Reaction time 3 hrs.

While the solid is drying pour the two-phase filtrate into a separatory funnel and rinse the flask with benzene. Separate the hydrocarbon layer (which is saturated with anthracene), warm it on the steam bath with sodium sulfate until clear, add a little Norit, filter, and rinse with benzene. Scrape as much of the solid as possible out of the reaction flask onto a filter paper and put it into a 125-ml. Erlenmeyer flask, pour the xylene–benzene solution into the reaction flask and heat this with swirling on the steam bath to dissolve residual anthracene, and empty the hot solution into the Erlenmeyer flask. Add benzene for rinsing, warm it and add the solution. Prepare a funnel for gravity filtration and rest it in the mouth of the Erlenmeyer flask, heat this to boiling on a hot plate and let the boiling solvent moisten the paper and warm the funnel, filter into a second flask and rinse with benzene, and let the solution stand for crystallization. Anthracene separates in thin, colorless, highly fluorescent plates, m.p. 216°, corr.; yield 2.8 g.

Caution: Highly flammable solvents

Benzophenone and Benzopinacol

Of several methods for preparation of benzophenone, that used here is decarboxylation of *o*-benzoylbenzoic acid in the presence of copper catalyst derived from copper carbonate. The reaction is conducted by heating the molten acid and catalyst to

$$\text{(o-benzoylbenzoic acid)} \xrightarrow[\text{260-270}^\circ]{\text{Cu catalyst}} \text{(benzophenone)} + CO_2$$

the high temperature required; in the absence of catalyst the acid is cyclized to anthraquinone. When decarboxylation is complete the product is isolated by distillation from the reaction mixture. Benzophenone exists in a labile form, m.p. 26°, and a stable allotropic form, m.p. 48°. Distillation usually gives the labile form, as a liquid which, if let stand undisturbed in the absence of seed, very slowly solidifies to transparent crystals. However, if the liquid is scratched, inoculated with the stable form, or is in an atmosphere carrying seed, it suddenly changes to the stable form and solidifies.

Benzophenone is colorless but, like aliphatic α,β-unsaturated ketones which it resembles, it absorbs ultraviolet light. The light energy absorbed raises the activity sufficiently to permit a photochemical reduction in which isopropyl alcohol serves as hydrogen donor. The products are acetone and benzopinacol, which crystallizes in dramatic fashion on exposure of a solution of benzophenone in isopropyl alcohol to bright sunlight. The experiment should be done only during warm weather when there is good prospect for bright sunshine for several days.

EXPERIMENTS

1. Benzophenone [1]

Place 15 g. of anhydrous o-benzoylbenzoic acid and 0.5 g. of basic copper carbonate in a 50-ml. distilling flask, and heat gently with shaking over a free flame to melt the acid and until the neutralization reaction is over. Then stopper and evacuate the flask and heat it on the steam bath to eliminate the water formed. Then support the flask for heating with a free flame, insert a cork stopper carrying a thermometer with the bulb submerged in the melt, and connect the side arm with a piece of rubber tubing to a glass tube resting in a 10-ml. graduate containing just enough water to seal the tube, so that evolution of carbon dioxide can be followed. More water is dangerous in case of a suck-back.

Reaction time 30 min.

Heat the flask with a small free flame and bring the temperature of the liquid to 265° without delay, and by constant adjustment maintain a temperature as close to this as possible throughout the reaction. Gas should be evolved steadily and in 20–25 min. metallic copper should separate from the clear solution. In another 5 min., with the temperature still at 265°, the bubbling in the trap should cease. When this point is reached the trap is disconnected, the flame is removed, and the thermometer is raised to the usual position for distillation. Use an air condenser, and distil the benzophenone into a weighed 50-ml. Erlenmeyer flask (free flame). The corrected boiling point of benzophenone is 306°; the uncorrected boiling point may be as low as 294°. The condensate is usually colorless or light yellow. Continue the distillation until there is a marked rise in the boiling point (4–5°) or until the distillate becomes dark yellow.[2]

Record the weight of crude benzophenone (11–13 g.) and see if it will solidify on cooling or on being rubbed with a stirring rod. Unless the laboratory air carries sufficient ordinary benzophenone to act as seed, one usually obtains at this point the labile form,

[1] G. Dougherty, *J. Am. Chem. Soc.*, **50**, 571 (1928).
[2] The dark residue in the flask can be loosened and the mass of copper dislodged by adding benzene and heating the flask on the steam bath for one half hour. The dark solution is decanted and if necessary the process is repeated.

which (particularly since it is not quite pure) is very reluctant to solidify. If this is the case fix a barely visible particle of ordinary benzophenone on the end of a stirring rod and rub it into the liquid against the side of the flask. When crystallization sets in note the warming against the palm of the hand. Save a trace of seed. Benzophenone crystallizes well from ligroin, b.p. 60–90° (alcohol leaves too much material in the mother liquor). Without removing the material from the original receiving flask, cover it with ligroin (1.5 ml. per gram) and dissolve by heating on the steam bath. Without using charcoal or filtering, cool the solution in an ice bath until it becomes cloudy and the product oils out. Then remove the flask, allow the liquid to come to rest, and add seed. As crystallization progresses return the flask to the bath and eventually stir the mixture and cool it thoroughly. Collect the crystals on a suction funnel and use 30–40 ml. of fresh, ice-cold solvent to wash any yellow material into the mother liquor. Recrystallize the product if it is not white; very large crystals can be obtained by allowing the solution to cool slowly and without seed; yield, 9.5–11.5 g., m.p. 47–48°.

2. Benzopinacol[3]

In a 100-ml. round bottomed flask dissolve 10 g. of benzophenone in 60–70 ml. of isopropyl alcohol by warming, fill the flask to the neck with more of this alcohol, and add one drop of glacial acetic acid. (If the acid is omitted enough alkali may be derived from the glass to destroy the reaction product by the alkaline cleavage described below.) Stopper the flask with a well-rolled, tightly-fitting cork which is then wired in place. Invert the flask in a 100-ml. beaker and expose it to the best available sunlight. Since benzopinacol is but sparingly soluble in alcohol, its formation can be followed from the separation around the walls of small, colorless crystals (benzophenone forms large, thick prisms). If the sun is shining brightly at the time, the first crystals separate in about 5 hrs. and the reaction is practically complete (95% yield) in four days. In winter the reaction may take as long as two weeks, and any benzophenone which crystallizes must be brought into solution by warming on the steam bath. When the reaction appears to be over, chill the flask if necessary and collect the product. The material should be directly pure, m.p. 188–189°. If the yield is poor, more material can be obtained by further exposure of the mother liquor to sunlight.

[3] *Org. Synth., Coll. Vol.* **2**, 71 (1943).

3. Alkaline Cleavage

Suspend a small test sample of benzopinacol in alcohol, heat to boiling, and make sure that the amount of solvent is insufficient to dissolve the solid. Add one drop of sodium hydroxide solution, heat for a minute or two, and observe the result. The solution contains equal parts of benzhydrol and benzophenone, formed by the following reaction:

$$
\begin{array}{ccc}
\underset{C_6H_5}{\overset{C_6H_5}{>}}\!C\!\!-\!\!C\!\overset{C_6H_5}{\underset{C_6H_5}{<}} & \xrightarrow{\text{RONa}} & \underset{C_6H_5}{\overset{C_6H_5}{>}}\!C\!\overset{H}{\underset{OH}{<}} + O\!=\!C\!\overset{C_6H_5}{\underset{C_6H_5}{<}} \\
\;\;\;\; OH\;\;HO & & \\
\text{Benzopinacol} & & \text{Benzhydrol} \qquad \text{Benzophenone} \\
\text{M.p. } 189° & & \text{M.p. } 68° \qquad\;\; \text{M.p. } 48°
\end{array}
$$

The low-melting cleavage products are much more soluble than the starting material.

Benzophenone can be converted into benzhydrol in nearly quantitative yield by following the procedure outlined above for the preparation of benzopinacol modified by addition, in place of acetic acid, of a very small piece of sodium (0.05 g.). The reaction is complete when, after exposure to sunlight, the greenish-blue color disappears. The solution is diluted with water, acidified, and evaporated. Benzopinacol is produced as before by photochemical reduction, but it is at once cleaved by the sodium alcoholate; the benzophenone formed by cleavage is converted into more benzopinacol, cleaved, and eventually consumed.

4. Pinacolone Rearrangement [4]

This reaction of benzopinacol is characterized by its speed and by the high yield:

$$
\begin{array}{cc}
\underset{C_6H_5}{\overset{C_6H_5}{>}}\!C\!\!-\!\!C\!\overset{C_6H_5}{\underset{C_6H_5}{<}} & \xrightarrow{\text{Cat.}} \;\; \underset{C_6H_5}{\overset{C_6H_5}{>}}\!C\!\!-\!\!COC_6H_5 + H_2O \\
\;\;\;\; OH\;\;HO & \qquad\qquad \text{Benzopinacolone} \\
& \qquad\qquad \text{M.p. } 179\text{–}180°
\end{array}
$$

In a 125-ml. Erlenmeyer flask place 5 g. of benzopinacol, 25 ml. of acetic acid, and two or three very small crystals of iodine (0.05 g.). Heat to the boiling point for a minute or two under a reflux condenser until the crystals are dissolved, and then reflux the red solution for 5 min. On cooling, the pinacolone separates as a stiff paste. Thin this with alcohol, collect the product, and wash it free from iodine with alcohol. The material should be directly pure; yield 95%.

[4] *Org. Synth., Coll. Vol.* **2**, 73 (1943).

Derivatives of 1,2-Diphenylethane[1]

INTRODUCTION

Procedures are given below for rapid preparation of small samples of twelve related compounds starting with benzaldehyde and phenylacetic acid by transformations summarized as follows:

$$C_6H_5CHO \longrightarrow C_6H_5\underset{OH}{CHCOC_6H_5} \longrightarrow C_6H_5COCOC_6H_5 \longrightarrow C_6H_5C(OAc)\!=\!C(OAc)C_6H_5$$

Benzaldehyde   Benzoin   Benzil   *cis*- and *trans*-Diacetates

$$\underset{H}{\overset{H}{C_6H_5C}}\!=\!CC_6H_5 \longrightarrow C_6H_5\underset{Br}{\overset{H}{\dot{C}}}\!-\!\underset{Br}{\overset{H}{\dot{C}}}C_6H_5 \longrightarrow C_6H_5C\!\equiv\!CC_6H_5 \qquad C_6H_5\underset{OH}{\overset{H}{\dot{C}}}\!-\!\underset{OH}{\overset{H}{\dot{C}}}C_6H_5$$

trans-Stilbene   *meso*-Dibromide   Diphenylacetylene   *meso*-Diol

$$+ \; C_6H_5CH_2CO_2H \longrightarrow C_6H_5CH\!=\!\underset{C_6H_5}{\dot{C}}CO_2H \longrightarrow C_6H_5\overset{H}{\dot{C}}\!=\!\overset{H}{\dot{C}}C_6H_5 \longrightarrow C_6H_5\underset{Br}{\overset{H}{\dot{C}}}\!-\!\underset{H}{\overset{Br}{\dot{C}}}C_6H_5$$

α-Phenylcinnamic acid   *cis*-Stilbene   *dl*-Dibromide
cis and *trans*

The quantities of reagents specified in the procedures are such as to provide somewhat more of each intermediate than is required for completion of all of the subsequent steps in the sequences of synthesis. If the experiments are dovetailed, the entire series of preparations can be completed in very short total working time. For example, one can start the preparation of benzoin (record the time of starting and do not rely on memory),

[1] If the work is well organized and proceeds without setbacks the experiments can be completed in about four laboratory periods. The instructor may elect to name a certain number of periods in which the student is to make as many of the compounds as he can; he may also decide to require submission only of the end products in each series.

Note for the instructor

and during the 30-min. reflux period start the preparation of α-phenylcinnamic acid; this requires refluxing for 35 min., and while it is proceeding the benzoin preparation can be stopped when the time is up and the product let crystallize. The α-phenylcinnamic acid mixture can be let stand (and cool) until one is ready to work it up. Also, while a crystallization is proceeding one may want to observe the crystals occasionally but should utilize most of the time for other operations.

Points of interest concerning stereochemistry and reaction mechanisms are discussed in the introductions to the individual procedures. Since several of the compounds have characteristic ultraviolet or infrared absorption spectra, pertinent spectrographic constants are recorded and brief interpretations of the data are presented in sections in small print.

1. *Benzoin*

Self-condensation of benzaldehyde under the specific catalytic influence of potassium cyanide affords benzoin (*dl*-benzoin):

$$C_6H_5CH \overset{CN^-}{\longrightarrow} C_6H_5\overset{\overset{CN}{|}}{\underset{\underset{O^-}{|}}{CH}} \rightleftharpoons C_6H_5\overset{\overset{CN}{|}}{\underset{\underset{OH}{|}}{C}} \overset{\overset{\delta^+}{HCC_6H_5}}{\underset{\delta^-O}{\longrightarrow}} C_6H_5\overset{\overset{CN}{|}}{\underset{\underset{OH}{|}}{C}}-\overset{\overset{H}{|}}{\underset{\underset{O^-}{|}}{CC_6H_5}} \overset{-CN^-}{\longrightarrow}$$

Benzoin
M.p. 135°, mol. wt. 212.24
λ^{EtOH} 247 mμ (E = 14,500), λ^{Chf} 2.88, 5.93, 6.21, 6.28, 6.85μ

Being an α-ketol (compare D-fructose), benzoin reduces Fehling's solution (in alcoholic solution) and forms an osazone (m.p. 225°); the 2,4-dinitrophenylhydrazone forms orange-yellow plates from ethanol, m.p. 239°.

ABSORPTION SPECTROSCOPY

Compounds containing conjugated systems of double bonds, such as CH_2=CH—CH=CH_2, CH_2=CH—CH=O, R(CH=CH)$_n$R, and R(CH=CH)$_n$C(R)=O, have the property of selectively absorbing light of one or more particular wave lengths (λ) in the region defined as ultraviolet, ranging from 210 to 380 mμ (millimicrons). The phenomenon is associated with vibrations of electrons in the unsaturated substance with absorption of light rays of specific oscillation frequency. The wave length of absorption, or the position in the ultraviolet spectrum of a characteristic absorption band, is independent of the concentration of the solution, usually a solution in ethanol. The intensity of absorption, however, is directly proportional to the concentration of the dissolved substance and is expressed as the extinction coefficient E, defined thus:

$$E \text{ (extinction coefficient)} = \frac{A}{l \times c}$$

where

A = Absorbance (= optical density)
l = Length of path through solution in cm.
c = Molar concentration

With a carefully prepared solution of a known amount of substance in a given volume of solvent, both the position and intensity of absorption bands are accurately determinable with the hand-operated Beckman spectrophotometer, or with a Beckman or Cary recording spectrophotometer. The spectrum for benzoin shown in Fig. 31.1 was determined with a solution of 0.062 mg. of material in 10 ml. of 95% ethanol in a 2-cm. cell of a Cary instrument, and the absorbance of the band at 247 mμ as read from the curve is 0.85. Thus:

$$c = 0.062 \times \frac{1}{1000} \times 100 \times \frac{1}{212.24} = 0.0000292 \text{ mole/l.}$$

$$E = \frac{0.85}{2 \times 0.0000292} = 14,500$$

The optical constants are summarized by the expression λ^{EtOH} 247 mμ ($E = 14,500$). If a sample of crude benzoin absorbed at 247 mμ but had $E = 7,250$, it would be recognized as containing only 50% of benzoin. The absorption band at 247 mμ is attributable to the presence of the phenyl ketone grouping,

in which the carbonyl group is conjugated with the unsaturated benzene ring. Aliphatic α,β-unsaturated ketones, RCH=CHC(R)=O, show selective absorption of ultraviolet light of comparable wave length. The 2,4-dinitrophenylhydrazone of benzoin absorbs more intensely and at longer wave length: λ^{EtOH} 386 mμ ($E = 27,500$).

Absorption of infrared light, of wave length from 2–16 μ (microns), is associated not with vibrations of electrons but with longitudinal and transverse stretchings and bendings of specific groups, such as hydroxyl and carbonyl groups. The infrared absorption bands that appear in the region 2–8 μ are largely interpretable as due to specific functional groups such as those named. Not all bands that appear in the region of longer wave length (8–16 μ) are as yet interpretable but the region nevertheless is highly characteristic of the specific compound involved; this part of the infrared spectrum is called the fingerprint region and is often useful for comparison of an unknown with an authentic known sample; if the two intricate spectra are exactly superposable, the compounds can be declared to be identical. The intensity of infrared absorption is not as yet measurable with accuracy and reproducibility comparable with that easily attained in the ultraviolet region, and the intensity factor usually is not reported numeri-

Derivatives of 1,2-Diphenylethane

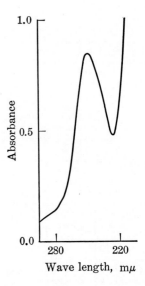

FIG. 31.1 Benzoin

Infrared

171

cally. However, a band due to a particular type of functional group becomes progressively intense, relative to other bands, with the presence of increasing numbers of groups of the same type.

The position of an infrared absorption band can be indicated by citation of the wave length at which absorption is at a maximum; thus the notation λ^{Chf} 6.00 μ means that a solution of the substance in chloroform (Chf, about 20 mg. per ml.) shows an absorption maximum at a wave length of 6.00 μ. An alternative method is to cite the frequency of oscillation (ν) of the infrared light selectively absorbed, measured in wave numbers (cm.$^{-1}$). The wave number is merely the reciprocal of the wave length in centimeters:

$$\lambda \text{ (in } \mu) = \frac{1 \times 10^4}{\nu \text{ (in cm.}^{-1})}$$

For example, if $\lambda = 5.737$, the corresponding wave number is 1743 cm.$^{-1}$

The infrared spectrum of benzoin as determined in chloroform solution with a Baird double beam spectrophotometer is shown in Fig. 31.2.

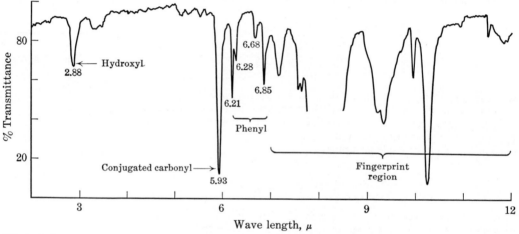

FIG. 31.2 Benzoin

The identifiable bands are as follows: a, 2.88 μ, hydroxyl group; b, 5.93 μ, conjugated carbonyl group; c, 6.21 μ, 6.28, 6.68, and 6.85 μ, phenyl group in conjugation with the carbonyl group. The part of the spectrum of wave length beyond 7 μ is the fingerprint region.

Procedure

Place 1.5 g. of potassium cyanide (poison, do not spill!) in a 100 ml. round bottomed flask, dissolve it in 15 ml. of water, add 30 ml. of 95% ethanol and 15 ml. of pure benzaldehyde,[2] intro-

[2] Commercial benzaldehyde inhibited against autoxidation with 0.1% hydroquinone is usually satisfactory. If the material available is yellow or contains benzoic acid it should be shaken with equal volumes of 5% sodium carbonate solution until carbon dioxide is no longer evolved and the upper layer dried over calcium chloride and distilled (b.p. 178–180°), with avoidance of exposure of the hot liquid to air.

duce a boiling stone, attach a 35-cm. air condenser by means of a No. 2 Neoprene adapter, and reflux the solution gently on the steam bath for 30 min. Remove the flask, and if no crystals appear within a few minutes, withdraw a drop on a stirring rod and rub it against the neck of the flask to induce crystallization. When crystallization is complete, collect the product and wash it free of yellow mother liquor with a 1:1 mixture of 95% ethanol and water (wash the cyanide-containing mother liquor down the sink with plenty of water). Usually this first-crop material is colorless and of satisfactory melting point (134–135°); yield 10–12 g.[3]

2. Benzil and a Derivative

Benzil	o-Phenylenediamine	Quinoxaline derivative
M.p. 96°, mol. wt. 210.22	M.p. 103°. mol. wt.	M.p. 126°, mol. wt. 282.33
λ^{EtOH} 260 mμ (22,000)	108.14	λ^{EtOH} 245 mμ (41,900)
λ^{Chf} 5.93, 6.22, 6.85 μ		

Benzoin can be oxidized to the α-diketone benzil very efficiently by nitric acid in acetic acid solution or by copper sulfate in pyridine. On oxidation with sodium dichromate in acetic acid the yield is lower because some of the material is converted into benzaldehyde by cleavage of the bond that is between two oxidized carbon atoms and further activated by both phenyl groups (a). Similarly, hydrobenzoin (b) on oxidation with dichromate or permanganate yields chiefly benzaldehyde and only a trace of benzil.

(a) $C_6H_5C—CHC_6H_5 \xrightarrow{2[OH]} C_6H_5COH + \left[HOCHC_6H_5 \right] \xrightarrow{-H_2O} O{=}CHC_6H_5$
       $\underset{O\ \ \ OH}{\|\ \ \ \ |}$ $\underset{O}{\|}$ $\underset{OH}{|}$

(b) $C_6H_5CH—CHC_6H_5 \xrightarrow{Oxid.} 2C_6H_5CHO$
       $\underset{OH\ \ \ OH}{|\ \ \ \ \ |}$

[3] Concentration of the mother liquor to a volume of 20 ml. gives a second crop (1.8 g., m.p. 133–134.5°); best total yield 13.7 g. (87%). Recrystallization can be accomplished with either methanol (11 ml./g.) or 95% ethanol (7 ml./g.) with 90% recovery in the first crop.

A reaction that characterizes benzil as an α-diketone is condensation with o-phenylenediamine to the quinoxaline derivative formulated; the aromatic heterocyclic ring formed in the condensation is fused to a benzene ring to give a bicyclic system analogous to naphthalene.

Benzil contains two carbonyl groups, each of which is conjugated with an unsaturated phenyl group. It is yellow, whereas benzoin, which contains only one phenyl-conjugated carbonyl group, is colorless. Also, benzil shows ultraviolet absorption at longer wave length (λ^{EtOH} 260 mμ) and higher intensity ($E = 22{,}000$) than benzoin. The infrared spectrum is similar to that of benzoin except that the band attributable to a hydroxyl group is missing.

Ultraviolet absorption

Oxidation Procedure

Heat a mixture of 4 g. of benzoin, 20 ml. of acetic acid, and 10 ml. of concd. nitric acid in a 125-ml. Erlenmeyer flask on the steam bath for 2 hrs. Then cool under the tap, add 75 ml. of water, swirl for a minute or two to coagulate the precipitated product, and collect and wash the faintly yellow solid on a Hirsch funnel; press the solid well on the filter to squeeze out the water. The crude product (dry weight 3.7–3.9 g.; m.p. 90–92°) need not be dried but can be crystallized at once from methanol; record the crystalline form, color, and m.p. of the purified material.

Test for the Presence of Unoxidized Benzoin

Dissolve about 0.5 mg. of crude or purified benzil in 0.5 ml. of 95% ethanol or methanol and add one drop of 10% sodium hydroxide. If benzoin is present the solution soon acquires a purplish color owing to a complex of benzil with a product of autoxidation of benzoin. If no color develops in 2–3 min., an indication that the sample is free from benzoin, add a small amount of benzoin, observe the color that develops, and note that if the test tube is stoppered and shaken vigorously, end-to-end, the color momentarily disappears; when the solution is then let stand, the color reappears.

Benzil Quinoxaline

Commercial o-phenylenediamine is usually badly discolored (air oxidation) and gives a poor result unless purified as follows. Place 200 mg. of material in the bottom of a 20 $\times$ 150-mm. test tube, evacuate the tube at the maximum suction of the water pump, clamp it in a horizontal position, and heat the bottom part of the tube with a free flame to distil or sublime colorless o-phenylenediamine away from the dark residue into the upper half of the tube. Let the tube cool in position until the melt has solidified, and scrape out the white solid.

Weigh 0.2 g. of benzil (theory = 210 mg.) and 0.1 g. of pure *o*-phenylenediamine (theory = 108 mg.) into a 20 × 150-mm. test tube and heat in the rings of a steam bath for 10 min., by which time the initially molten mixture should have changed to a light tan solid. Dissolve the solid in hot methanol (about 5 ml.) and let the solution stand undisturbed. If crystallization does not occur fairly soon, reheat the solution and dilute it with a little water to the point of saturation. The crystals should be filtered as soon as formed, for brown oxidation products accumulate on standing. The quinoxaline forms colorless needles, m.p. 125–126°; yield 185 mg.

3. meso-*Hydrobenzoin*

Benzil	*meso*-Hydrobenzoin	*dl*-Hydrobenzoin
Mol. wt. 210.22	M.p. 137°, λ^{Chf} 2.82, 2.96 μ	M.p. 120°
	Mol. wt. 214.25	

Addition of two atoms of hydrogen to benzoin or of four atoms of hydrogen to benzil gives a mixture of stereoisomeric diols of which the predominant isomer is the nonresolvable *meso*-hydrobenzoin. Reduction is accomplished rapidly with sodium borohydride ($Na^+BH_4^-$) in ethanol. The high cost of the reagent is offset by its low molecular weight and the fact that one mole of hydride reduces four moles of a ketone:

$$4R_2C{=}O + Na^+BH_4^- \rightarrow (R_2CHO)_4BNa$$
$$(R_2CHO)_4BNa + 2H_2O \rightarrow 4R_2CHOH + NaBO_2$$

The procedure below specifies use of benzil rather than benzoin because the progress of the reduction can then be measured by the discharge of the yellow color. The amount of reagent required for reduction of 500 mg. of benzil is calculated as follows:

$$500 \text{ mg.} \left| \frac{37.85}{210.22} \right| \frac{2}{4} = 45 \text{ mg. NaBH}_4$$

Procedure

In a 50-ml. Erlenmeyer flask, dissolve 0.5 g. of benzil in 5 ml. of 95% ethanol and cool the solution under the tap to produce a fine suspension. Then add 0.1 g. of sodium borohydride (large excess). The benzil dissolves, the mixture warms up, the yellow color disappears in 2–3 min. After a total of 10 min., add 5 ml. of water, heat to the boiling point, filter in case the solution is not clear, dilute to the point of saturation with more water (10 ml.), and set the solution aside to crystallize. *meso*-Hydrobenzoin separates in lustrous thin plates, m.p. 136–137°; yield 0.35 g.

4. Reductive Acetylation of Benzil

$$C_6H_5-\overset{\overset{O}{\|}}{C}-\overset{\overset{O}{\|}}{C}-C_6H_5 \xrightarrow{\text{2H (1,4-addition)}} \left[C_6H_5-\overset{\overset{OH}{|}}{C}=\overset{\overset{OH}{|}}{C}-C_6H_5 \right] \xrightarrow{\text{Ac}_2\text{O, H}^+}$$

I (*trans*)	II (*cis*)
M.p. 155°	M.p. 119°
λ^{EtOH} 271 mμ ($E = 23{,}400$)	λ^{EtOH} 265 mμ ($E = 12{,}800$)

Mol. wt. 296.31, λ^{Chf} 5.70, 7.9–8.0 μ

In one of the first demonstrations of the phenomenon of 1,4-addition, Johannes Thiele (1899) established that reduction of benzil with zinc dust in acetic anhydride–sulfuric acid involves 1,4-addition of hydrogen to the α-diketone grouping and acetylation of the resulting enediol before it can undergo ketonization to benzoin. The process of reductive acetylation affords a mixture of the geometrical isomers I and II. Thiele and subsequent investigators isolated the more soluble, lower-melting *cis*-stilbene-α,β-diol diacetate II in only impure form, m.p. 110°. Separation by chromatography is not feasible, because the two isomers have the same degree of adsorbability on alumina. However, it is possible by the procedure of fractional crystallization described below to isolate both isomers in pure condition. In the method prescribed for preparation of the isomer mixture, hydrochloric acid is substituted for sulfuric acid because the latter acid gives rise to colored impurities and becomes reduced to sulfur and to hydrogen sulfide.[4]

The configurations of this pair of geometrical isomers remained unestablished for over 50 years, but the tentative inference that the higher-melting isomer has the more symmetrical *trans* configuration I eventually was found to be correct. Evidence of infrared spectroscopy is of no avail; Fig. 31.3 shows that the spectra are nearly iden-

[4] If acetyl chloride (2 ml.) is substituted for the hydrochloric acid–acetic anhydride mixture in the procedure below, the *cis*-isomer is the sole product.

tical in the interpretable region $(2-8\ \mu)$ characterizing the acetoxyl groups, but differ in the fingerprint region $(8-12\ \mu)$. However, the isomers differ markedly in ultraviolet absorption and, in analogy to *trans*- and *cis*-stilbene (Section 5) the conclusion is justified that the higher-melting isomer, since it has an absorption band at longer wave length and higher intensity than its isomer, does indeed have the configuration I.

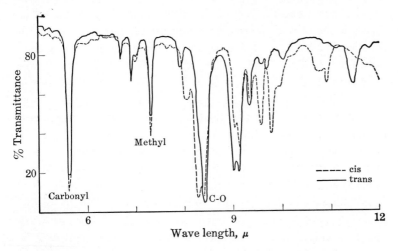

FIG. 31.3 Stilbene-α, β-diol diacetates (in CCl_4)

Procedure

Place one test tube $(20 \times 150$-mm.$)$ containing 7 ml. of acetic anhydride and another $(13 \times 100$-mm.$)$ containing 1 ml. of concd. hydrochloric acid in an ice bath and, when thoroughly chilled, transfer the acid to the anhydride dropwise in not less than one minute by means of a capillary dropping tube. Wipe the test tube dry, pour the chilled solution into a 50-ml. Erlenmeyer flask containing 1 g. of pure benzil and 1 g. of zinc dust, and swirl for 2–3 min. in an ice bath. Remove the flask and hold it in the palm of the hand; if it begins to warm up, cool further in ice. When there is no further exothermic effect, let the mixture stand for 5 min. and then add 25 ml. of water. Swirl, break up any lumps of product, and allow a few minutes for hydrolysis of excess acetic anhydride. Then collect the mixture of product and zinc dust, wash with water, and press and suck the cake well until there is no further drip. Digest the solid (drying is not necessary) with 70 ml. of ether to dissolve the organic material, add about 4 g. of anhydrous sodium sulfate and swirl briefly, filter the solution into a 125-ml. Erlenmeyer flask, concentrate the filtrate (steam bath, boiling stone, vapor aspirator) to a volume of approximately 15 ml.,[5] and let the flask stand, corked and undisturbed.

Reaction time 10 min.

[5] Measure 15 ml. of a solvent into a second flask of the same size and compare the levels in the two flasks.

The *trans*-diacetate I soon begins to separate in prismatic needles, and after 20–25 min. crystallization appears to have stopped. Removal and evaporation of the mother liquor can be done efficiently as follows. Warm a 25-ml. Erlenmeyer flask on the steam bath under an aspirator and, with use of a capillary dropping tube, suck up a portion of the ethereal solution covering the crystals and transfer it, by drops, to the warm evaporation flask; if the ether is caused to evaporate at the same rate as the solution is added, the solvent can be eliminated rapidly without need for a boiling stone. When all the solution has been transferred, wash the crystals with a little fresh ether and transfer the washings as above. The crystals of *trans*-diacetate I can then be scraped out of the larger flask and the weight and m.p. determined (e.g., 294 mg., 154–156°).

Dissolve the white solid left in the evaporation flask in 10 ml. of methanol, let the solution stand undisturbed for about 10 min., and drop in one tiny crystal of the *trans*-diacetate I. This should give rise, in 20–30 min., to a second crop of I (e.g., 58 mg., m.p. 153–156°). Then concentrate the mother liquor and washings to a volume of 7–8 ml., let cool to room temperature as before, and again seed with a crystal of *trans*-diacetate I; this usually affords a third crop of I (e.g., 62 mg., m.p. 153–155°).

At this point the mother liquor should be rich enough in the more soluble *cis*-diacetate II for its isolation. Concentrate the methanol mother liquor and washings from the third crop of I to a volume of 4–5 ml., stopper the flask and let the solution stand undisturbed overnight. The *cis*-diacetate II sometimes separates spontaneously in large rectangular prisms of great beauty. If the solution remains supersaturated, addition of a seed crystal of II causes prompt separation of II in a paste of small crystals (e.g., 215 mg., m.p. 118–119°; then: 70 mg., m.p. 116–117°).

5. trans-*Stilbene*

trans-Stilbene   cis-Stilbene

M.p. 125°   Mol. wt. 180.24   M.p. 6°
λ^{EtOH} 301 mμ ($E = 28,500$) λ^{EtOH} 280 mμ ($E = 13,500$)
226 mμ ($E = 17,700$)   223 mμ ($E = 23,000$)
Heat of hydrog. -20.1 kg. cal.   Heat of hydrog. -25.8 kg. cal.

One method of preparing *trans*-stilbene is by reduction of benzoin with zinc amalgam in ethanol–hydrochloric acid, presumably through the intermediate formulated:

$$C_6H_5COCHC_6H_5 \xrightarrow{\text{Zn-Hg, HCl}} \left[C_6H_5CH_2CHC_6H_5\right] \xrightarrow{\text{-H}_2\text{O}} C_6H_5CH{=}CHC_6H_5$$
$$\quad\quad |\quad\quad\quad\quad\quad\quad\quad\quad\quad\quad | $$
$$\quad OH \quad\quad\quad\quad\quad\quad\quad\quad OH$$

The procedure given below is quicker and affords hydrocarbon of high purity. It involves three steps: replacement of the hy-

$$C_6H_5COCHC_6H_5 \xrightarrow{\text{SOCl}_2} C_6H_5C{-}CHC_6H_5 \xrightarrow{\text{NaBH}_4}$$
$$\quad\quad |\quad\quad\quad\quad\quad\quad\quad\quad || \quad |$$
$$\quad OH \quad\quad\quad\quad\quad\quad O \quad Cl$$

Benzoin   Desyl chloride
Mol. wt. 212.23   M.p. 68°

$$\left[C_6H_5CH\ CHC_6H_5\right] \xrightarrow{\text{Zn-HOAc}} C_6H_5CH{=}CHC_6H_5$$
$$\quad\quad |\quad\quad |$$
$$\quad OH \ Cl$$

Mixture of *dl*- and *d'l'*-isomers   *trans*-Stilbene

droxyl group of benzoin by chlorine (desyl chloride), reduction of the keto group with sodium borohydride to give what appears to be a mixture of the two diastereoisomeric chlorohydrins, and elimination of the elements of hypochlorous acid with zinc and acetic acid. The last step is analogous to the debromination of an olefin dibromide.

    trans-Stilbene is higher melting and has a lower energy content than the *cis*-isomer. The ultraviolet absorption spectra shown in Figs. 31.4 and 31.5 were taken at different drum speeds and hence the wavelength scales do not correspond; slowing the speed has the effect of spreading the spectral tracing over a greater distance with resulting better definition of the details of the bands. The more intense band in the spectrum of *trans*-stilbene has two peaks, but the band as a whole is described for brevity by the averages of the two sets of constants: λ^{EtOH} 301 mμ (28,500). *cis*-Stilbene differs markedly from the isomer: the longer wave-length band is shifted to 276 mμ and has only half the intensity, and the shorter wave-length band is of greater, rather than lower, intensity than the first band. The bands at 301 and 276 mμ appear to characterize the complete conjugated system made up of the two phenyl groups and the ethylenic double bond, and this band is of longer wave length and greater intensity with the *trans*- than with the *cis*-isomer. The diminished light absorption of *cis*-stilbene is attributed to interference between the two ortho hydrogen atoms of the phenyl groups, which prevents coplanarity of these rings and hence diminishes resonance.

    The infrared absorption spectrum of *trans*-stilbene (Fig. 31.6) is characterized by a pattern of four bands attributable to the phenyl groups; exactly the same pattern is seen in the spectrum of benzoin (Fig. 31.2).

Absorption spectra

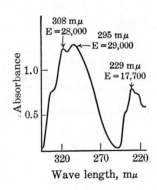

FIG. 31.4 *trans*-Stilbene

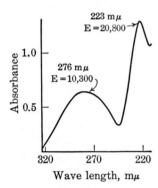

FIG. 31.5 *cis*-Stilbene

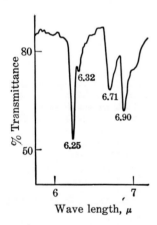

FIG. 31.6 *trans*-Stilbene

Procedure

Place 4 g. of benzoin (crushed to a powder) in a 100-ml. round bottomed flask, cover it with 4 ml. of thionyl chloride,[6] warm gently on the steam bath (hood) until the solid has all dissolved, and more strongly for 5 min. To remove excess reagent (b.p. 77°), evacuate at the water pump for a few minutes, add 10 ml. of petroleum ether (b.p. 30–60°), boil it off, and evacuate again. Desyl chloride is thus obtained as a viscous, pale yellow oil (it will solidify if let stand). Dissolve this in 40 ml. of 95% ethanol, cool under the tap, and add 360 mg. of sodium borohydride (an excess is harmful). Stir, break up lumps of reagent, and after 10 min. add to the solution of chlorohydrins 2 g. of zinc dust and 4 ml. of acetic acid and reflux for 1 hr. Then cool under the tap; when white crystals separate, add 50 ml. of ether and decant the solution from the bulk of the zinc into a separatory funnel. Wash the solution twice with an equal volume of water containing 1–2 ml. of concd. hydrochloric acid (to dissolve basic zinc salts), then, in turn, with 5% sodium carbonate solution and saturated sodium chloride solution. Filter through a cone of anhydrous sodium sulfate (4 g.), evaporate the filtrate to dryness, dissolve the residue in the minimum amount of hot 95% ethanol (30–40 ml.), and let the product crystallize. *trans*-Stilbene separates in diamond-shaped iridescent plates, m.p. 124–125°; yield 1.8–2.2 g.

Special experiment. Chromatograph the mother liquor material on acid-washed alumina and observe fluorescent bands of by-products that appear on ultraviolet illumination under a light shield.

6. meso-*Stilbene Dibromide*

C₆H₅—C—H ‖ H—C—C₆H₅	+	(pyridinium NHBr₃⁻)	$\xrightarrow{\text{(trans-addition)}}$

$$\text{C}_6\text{H}_5\text{—C—H} \quad + \quad \text{pyridinium} \xrightarrow{\text{(trans-addition)}} \begin{array}{c} \text{C}_6\text{H}_5 \\ | \\ \text{H—C—Br} \\ | \\ \text{H—C—Br} \\ | \\ \text{C}_6\text{H}_5 \end{array}$$

trans-Stilbene
Mol. wt. 180.24

Pyridinium bromide
perbromide
Mol. wt. 319.87

meso-Dibromide
M.p. 238°
Mol. wt. 340.08

trans-Stilbene reacts with bromine predominantly by the usual process of *trans* addition and affords the optically inactive, non-

---

[6] The reagent can be dispensed from a burette or measured by pipette; in the latter case the liquid should be drawn into the pipette with a pipetter or by gentle suction at the water pump, and not by mouth.

resolvable *meso*-dibromide; the much lower-melting *dl*-isomer (Section 9) is a very minor product of the reaction.

Procedure

In a 125-ml. Erlenmeyer flask dissolve 2 g. of *trans*-stilbene in 40 ml. of acetic acid by heating on the steam bath, and then add 4 g. of pyridinium bromide perbromide. Mix by swirling, if necessary rinse crystals of reagent down the walls of the flask with a little acetic acid, and continue the heating for 1–2 min. longer. The dibromide separates almost at once in small plates. Cool the mixture under the tap, collect the product, and wash it with methanol; yield of colorless crystals, m.p. 236–237°, 3.2 g. Use 0.5 g. of this material for the preparation of diphenylacetylene and save the rest for a later experiment (Chapter 32).

Total time required
10 min.

7. Diphenylacetylene (Tolan)

$$
\begin{array}{ccc}
\underset{\substack{\text{$meso$-Stilbene dibromide}\\ \text{Mol. wt. 340.08}}}{\begin{array}{c} C_6H_5 \\ | \\ H-C-Br \\ | \\ H-C-Br \\ | \\ C_6H_5 \end{array}} & \xrightarrow[\substack{\text{HOCH}_2\text{CH}_2\text{OCH}_2\text{CH}_2\text{OCH}_2\text{CH}_2\text{OH}\\ \text{b.p. 290}°}]{\substack{\text{2KOH}\\ \text{(Mol. wt. 56.10; the pellets are 85% pure)}}} & \underset{\substack{\text{Diphenylacetylene}\\ \text{M.p. 61°, mol. wt. 178.22}}}{\begin{array}{c} C_6H_5 \\ | \\ C \\ \| \| \\ C \\ | \\ C_6H_5 \end{array}}
\end{array}
$$

One method for preparation of diphenylacetylene consists in oxidation of benzil dihydrazone with mercuric oxide; the intermediate diazide loses nitrogen under the conditions of its formation and affords the hydrocarbon:

$$
\underset{\substack{\\ \text{N}\quad\text{N}\\ | \quad | \\ \text{NH}_2\ \text{NH}_2}}{C_6H_5C - CC_6H_5} \xrightarrow[C_6H_6]{\text{HgO}} \left[\underset{\substack{\\ +\text{N}\quad\text{N}+\\ \| \quad \| \\ -\text{N}\quad\text{N}-}}{C_6H_5C-CC_6H_5} \right] \xrightarrow{-2\text{N}_2} C_6H_5C{\equiv}CC_6H_5
$$

The method described below involves dehydrohalogenation of *meso*-stilbene dibromide. An earlier procedure called for refluxing the dibromide with 43% alcoholic potassium hydroxide in an oil bath at 140° for 24 hours. In the following procedure the reaction time is cut down to a few minutes by use of the high-boiling triethyleneglycol as solvent to permit operation at a higher reaction temperature.

The ultraviolet absorption spectrum of diphenylacetylene (Fig. 31.7) is characterized by considerable fine structure (multiplicity of bands). The infrared spectrum (Fig. 31.8) shows four bands characteristic of the phenyl groups, but the relative intensities of the bands at 6.7 and 6.9 are the reverse of those of *trans*-stilbene (Fig. 31.6).

Absorption spectra

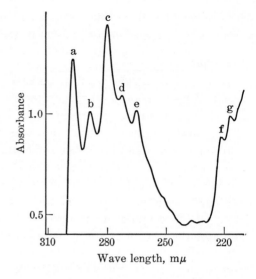

FIG. 31.7 Diphenylacetylene

Wave lengths (mμ) and extinction coefficients of ultraviolet absorption bands:

a. 297 (29,400) e. 269 (23,450)
b. 288 (23,250) f. 221 (20,300)
c. 279 (33,000) g. 216 (20,600)
d. 272 (25,200)

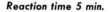

Reaction time 5 min.

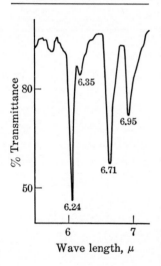

FIG. 31.8 Diphenylacetylene

Procedure

In a 20 × 150-mm. test tube place 0.5 g. of *meso*-stilbene dibromide, 3 pellets of potassium hydroxide (250 mg.), and 2 ml. of triethylene glycol. Insert a thermometer into a 10 × 75-mm. test tube containing enough triethylene glycol to cover the bulb, and slip this assembly into the larger tube. Clamp the tube in a vertical position about two inches above a microburner, and heat the mixture with a tiny flame to a temperature of 160°, when potassium bromide begins to separate. By intermittent heating, keep the mixture at 160–170° for 5 min. more, then cool to room temperature, remove the thermometer and small tube, and add 10 ml. of water. The diphenylacetylene that separates as a nearly colorless, granular solid is collected by suction filtration. The crude product need not be dried but can be crystallized directly from 95% ethanol. Let the solution stand undisturbed in order to observe the formation of beautiful, very large spars of colorless crystals. After a first crop has been collected, the mother liquor on concentration affords a second crop of pure product; total yield, 0.23 g.; m.p. 60–61°.

8. α-Phenylcinnamic Acid (cis and trans)

$$C_6H_5CHO \ + \ \overset{\overset{\displaystyle CO_2H}{|}}{CH_2C_6H_5} \xrightarrow{OH^-} \left[C_6H_5CH\underset{\underset{\displaystyle OH}{|}}{\overset{\overset{\displaystyle COO^-}{|}}{C}}HC_6H_5 \right] \xrightarrow[-H_2O]{H^+}$$

Benzaldehyde Phenylacetic acid
B.p. 179°   M.p. 77°,
Mol. wt. 106.12   B.p. 265°
Sp. gr. 1.046   Mol. wt. 136.14

cis

M.p. 174°, pK$_a$[7]6.1
λ^{EtOH} 280 mμ (19,500),
223 mμ (32,100)

trans

M.p. 138°, pK$_a$[7]4.8
λ^{EtOH} 289 mμ (22,500),
222 mμ (14,500)

Mol. wt. 224.35

The reaction of benzaldehyde with phenylacetic acid to produce a mixture of the α-carboxylic acid derivatives of *cis-* and
*trans-*stilbene, a form of aldol condensation known as the Perkin
reaction, is effected by heating a mixture of the components with
acetic anhydride and triethylamine (b.p. 89.5°, sp. gr. 0.729).
In the course of the reaction the phenylacetic acid is probably
present both as anion and as the mixed anhydride resulting from
equilibration with acetic anhydride. A reflux period of 5 hrs.
specified in an early procedure has been shortened by a factor
of 10 by restriction of the amount of the volatile acetic anhydride,
use of an excess of the less expensive, high-boiling aldehyde component, and use of a condenser that permits some evaporation
and consequent elevation of the reflux temperature.

*trans-*Stilbene is a by-product of the condensation, but experiment has shown that neither the *trans-* nor *cis-*acid undergoes
decarboxylation under the conditions of the experiment. Probably the hydrocarbon arises from the intermediate aldol anion
(written in brackets) by expulsion of carbon dioxide and hydroxide ion.

At the end of the reaction the α-phenylcinnamic acids are
present in part as the neutral mixed anhydrides, but these can be
hydrolyzed by addition of excess hydrochloric acid. The organic
material is taken up in ether and the acids extracted with alkali.
Neutralization with acetic acid (pK$_a$ 4.76) then causes precipitation of only the less acidic *cis-*acid (see pK$_a$ values under the
formulas); the *trans-*acid separates on addition of hydrochloric
acid.

Whereas *cis-*stilbene is less stable and lower melting than *trans-*
stilbene, the reverse is true of the α-carboxylic acids, and in this
preparation the more stable, higher-melting *cis-*acid is the predominant product. Evidently the steric interference between

[7] In 60% ethanol.

the carboxyl and phenyl groups in the *trans*-acid is greater than that between the two phenyl groups in the *cis*-acid. Steric hindrance is also evident from the fact that the *trans*-acid is not subject to Fischer esterification whereas the *cis*-acid is.

As indicated by the notations under the formulas of the *cis*- and *trans*-acids, these substances have two-banded ultraviolet absorption spectra, like *cis*- and *trans*-stilbene. In the wave length and intensity of absorption, and even in the relative intensity of the two bands, the carboxylic acids correspond closely to the parent hydrocarbons.

Absorption spectra

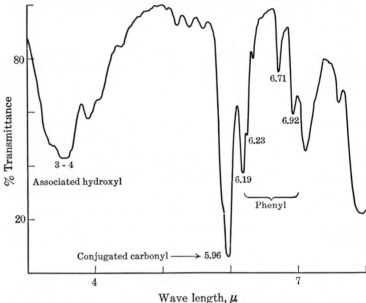

FIG. 31.9 *cis-α-Phenylcinnamic acid*

The infrared spectrum of the *cis*-acid (Fig. 31.9) shows, in addition to the usual bands associated with the phenyl group, two bands characteristic of the carboxyl function. One, a broad and irregular band extending from about 3 to 4 μ, is attributed to the associated hydroxyl group of the acid, and the other, at 5.96 μ, is due to the conjugated carbonyl group.

Procedure

Reflux time: 35 min.

Measure into a 25 × 150-mm. test tube 2.5 g. of phenylacetic acid, 3 ml. of benzaldehyde, 2 ml. of triethylamine, and 2 ml. of acetic anhydride. Insert a boiling stone, mount a cold-finger condenser as in Fig. 14.1, and reflux the mixture for 35 min. Cool the yellow melt, add 4 ml. of concd. hydrochloric acid, and swirl, when the mixture sets to a stiff paste. Add ether, warm to dissolve the bulk of the solid, and transfer to a separatory funnel with use of more ether. Wash the ethereal solution twice with water and then extract it with a mixture of 25 ml. of water and 5 ml. of 10% sodium hydroxide solution.[8] Repeat the extraction

[8] If stronger alkali is used the sodium salt may separate.

twice more and discard the dark-colored ethereal solution.[9]
Acidify the combined, colorless alkaline extract to pH 6 by adding
5 ml. of acetic acid, collect the *cis*-acid that precipitates, and save
the filtrate and washings. The yield of *cis*-acid, m.p. 163–166°,
is 2.9 g. Crystallize 0.3 g. of material by dissolving it in 8 ml. of
ether, adding 8 ml. of petroleum ether (b.p. 30–60°), heating
briefly to the boiling point, and letting the solution stand: silken
needles, m.p. 173–174°.

Addition of 5 ml. of concd. hydrochloric acid to the aqueous
filtrate from precipitation of the *cis*-acid produces a cloudy emulsion that on standing for about one half hour coagulates to crystals of the *trans*-acid: 0.3 g., m.p. 136–137°.[10]

9. cis-*Stilbene* and dl-*Stilbene Dibromide*

$$C_6H_5CCO_2H \quad \xrightarrow[\text{Quinoline}]{\text{Cu-Cr}} \quad C_6H_5-C-H \longrightarrow$$
$$\underset{\|}{C_6H_5CH} \qquad\qquad\qquad \underset{\|}{C_6H_5-C-H}$$

$$\begin{array}{c} C_6H_5 \\ | \\ H-C-Br \\ | \\ Br-C-H \\ | \\ C_6H_5 \end{array}$$

Mol. wt. 224.45   Mol. wt. 180.24   *dl*-Dibromide
M.p. 114°
Mol. wt. 340.08

Decarboxylation of *cis*-α-phenylcinnamic acid is effected by
refluxing the acid in quinoline in the presence of a trace of copper
chromite catalyst; both the basic properties and boiling point
(237°) of quinoline make it a particularly favorable solvent. *cis*-
Stilbene, a liquid at room temperature, can be characterized by
trans addition of bromine to give the crystalline *dl*-dibromide.
A little *meso*-dibromide derived from *trans*-stilbene in the crude
hydrocarbon starting material is easily separated by virtue of its
sparing solubility.

Although free rotation is possible around the single bond connecting
the asymmetric carbon atoms of the stilbene dibromides and hydro-
benzoins, evidence from dipole-moment measurements indicates that
the molecules tend to exist predominantly in the specific shape or
conformation in which the two phenyl groups repel each other and
occupy positions as far apart as possible. The optimal conformations

Stereochemical conformations

[9] For isolation of stilbene, wash this ethereal solution with saturated sodium
bisulfite solution for removal of benzaldehyde, dry, evaporate, and crystallize the
residue from a little methanol. Large, slightly yellow spars, m.p. 122–124°, separate (90 mg.).
[10] The *trans*-acid can be recrystallized by dissolving 0.3 g. in 5 ml. of ether, filtering
if necessary from a trace of sodium chloride, adding 10 ml. of petroleum ether
(b.p. 30–60°), and evaporating to a volume of 5 ml.; the acid separates as a hard
crust of prisms, m.p. 138–139°.

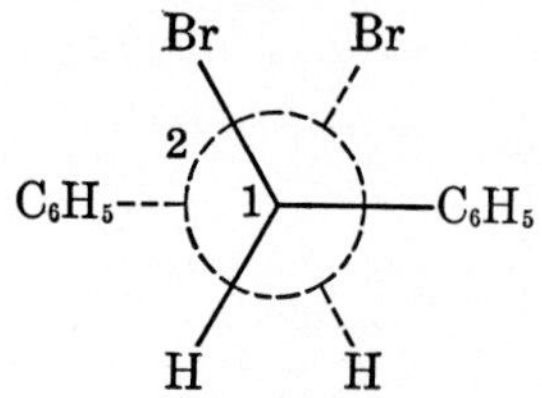

d- (or *l*)-Dibromide

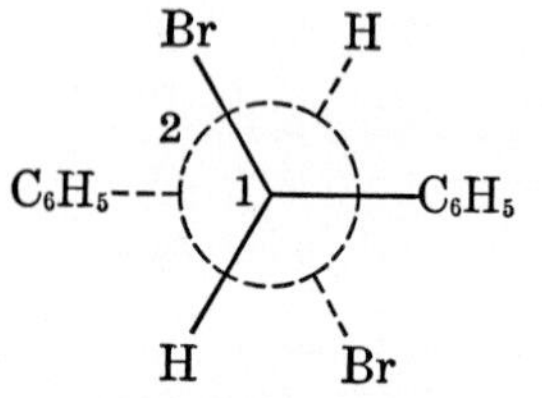

meso-Dibromide

FIG. 31.10 **Favored conformations**

**Reaction time in first
step 10 min.**

---

of the *d-* or *l*-dibromide and the *meso*-dibromide are represented in Fig. 31.10 by projection formulas, in which the molecules are viewed along the axis of the bond connecting the two asymmetric carbon atoms. The carbon atom nearest to the eye is numbered 1 and its other three valence bonds are represented by full lines; the carbon atom to the rear (2) is represented by a dotted circle and its valences by dotted lines. In the *meso*-dibromide the two repelling phenyl groups are on opposite sides of the molecule, and so are the two large bromine atoms, and hence the structure is much more symmetrical than that of the *d-* (or *l*-) dibromide. X-ray diffraction measurements of the dibromides in the solid state confirm the conformations indicated in Fig. 31.10, the Br-Br distances found are: *meso*-dibromide, 4.50Å; *dl*-dibromide, 3.85Å. The difference in symmetry of the two optically inactive isomers accounts for the marked contrast in properties:

	M.p.	*Solubility in ether* (*18°*)
dl-Dibromide	114°	1 part in 3.7 parts
meso-Dibromide	237°	1 part in 1025 parts

Procedure

Since a trace of moisture causes troublesome spattering, a drying operation is performed prior to decarboxylation. Stuff 2.5 g. of crude, "dry" *cis-α*-phenylcinnamic acid and 0.2 g. of copper chromite catalyst [11] into a 20 × 150-mm. test tube, add 3 ml. of quinoline [12] (b.p. 237°) and let it wash down the solids. Make connection with a rubber stopper to the suction pump, turn the pump wide open, make sure that you have a good vacuum (pressure gauge), and heat the tube strongly on the steam bath with most of the rings removed. Heat and evacuate for 5–10 min. to remove all traces of moisture. Then wipe the outside walls dry, insert a thermometer, clamp the tube over a microburner (screw pinchcock), raise the temperature to 240° and note the time. Then maintain a temperature close to 240° for 10 minutes. Cool the yellow solution containing suspended catalyst to 25°, add 30 ml. of ether, and filter the solution by gravity (use more ether for rinsing). Transfer the solution to a separatory funnel and remove the quinoline by extraction twice with water containing 3–4 ml. of concd. hydrochloric acid. Then shake the ethereal solution well with water containing a little sodium hydroxide solution, draw off the alkaline liquor and acidify it. A substantial precipitate will show that decarboxylation was incomplete, and the starting material can be recovered. If there is only a trace of precipitate, shake the ethereal solution with

[11] The preparations described in *J. Am. Chem. Soc.*, **54**, 1138 (1932) and *ibid.*, **72**, 2626 (1950) are both satisfactory.
[12] Material that has darkened in storage should be redistilled over a little zinc dust.

saturated sodium chloride solution for preliminary drying, filter the ethereal solution through sodium sulfate, and evaporate the ether. The residual brownish oil (1.3–1.8 g.) is crude *cis*-stilbene containing a little *trans*-isomer formed by rearrangement during heating.

Dissolve the crude *cis*-stilbene (e.g., 1.5 g.) in 10 ml. of acetic acid and, in subdued light, add double the weight of pyridinium bromide perbromide (e.g., 3.0 g.). Warm on the steam bath until the reagent is dissolved, and then cool under the tap and scratch to effect separation of a small crop of plates of the *meso*-dibromide (10–20 mg.). Filter the solution by suction, dilute extensively with water, and extract with ether. Wash the solution twice with water and then with 5% sodium bicarbonate solution until neutral; shake with saturated sodium chloride solution, filter through sodium sulfate, and evaporate to a volume of about 10 ml. If a little more of the sparingly soluble *meso*-dibromide separates, remove it by gravity filtration and then evaporate the remainder of the solvent. The residual *dl*-dibromide is obtained as a dark oil that readily solidifies when rubbed with a rod. Dissolve it in a small amount of methanol and let the solution stand to crystallize. The *dl*-dibromide separates as colorless prismatic plates, m.p. 113–114°; yield 0.6 g.

Second step requires about one half hour

CHAPTER 32 *dl*-Hydrobenzoin

dl-Hydrobenzoin (VII) is one of a small number of *dl*-compounds that can be resolved into the optically active components by crystallization. Most methods of preparation give difficultly separable mixtures of *dl*- and *meso*-diols in which the more solu-

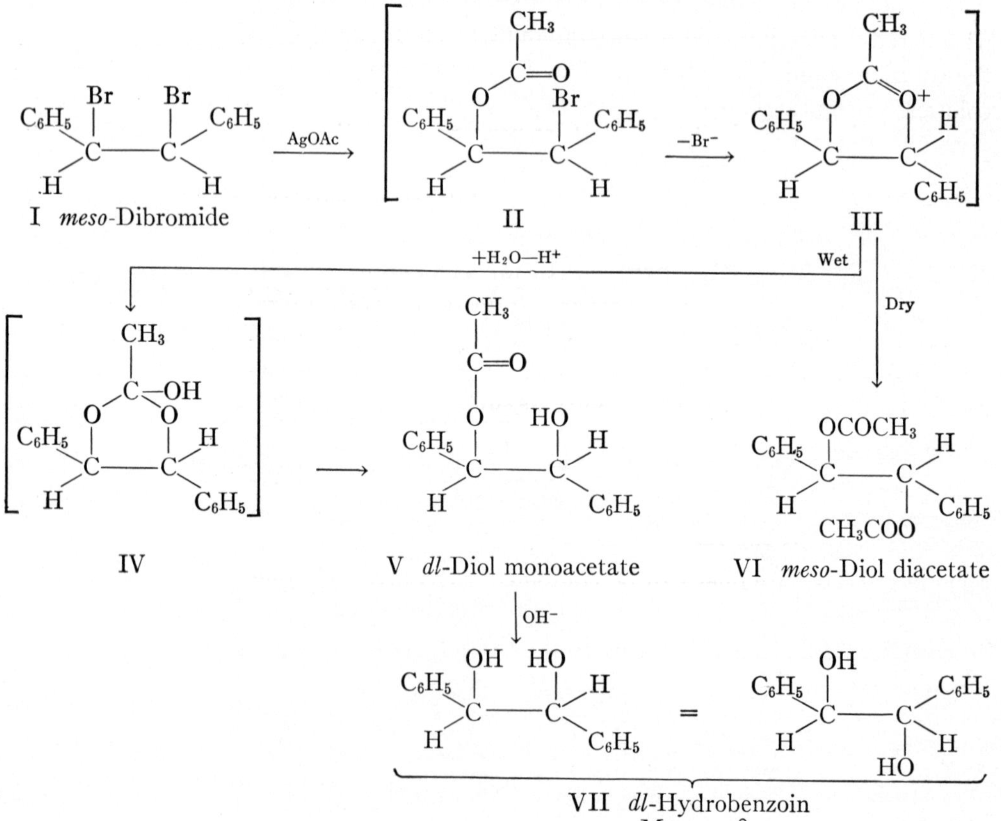
I meso-Dibromide
AgOAc
II
−Br⁻
III
Wet
Dry
+H₂O—H⁺
IV
V dl-Diol monoacetate
VI meso-Diol diacetate
OH⁻

VII *dl*-Hydrobenzoin
M.p. 120°

ble *dl*-diol is the minor component. However, silver acetate reacts with *meso*-stilbene dibromide in acetic acid containing 4% of water to give a mixture which contains considerable *dl*-diol monoacetate (V) and none of the isomeric *meso*-diol monoacetate.[1] Although the mixture contains both diacetates and both diols, the sole monoacetate present can be separated from these substances by chromatography.

Procedure

Place 2 g. of *meso*-stilbene dibromide (Chapter 31.6), 2 g. of silver acetate, 25 ml. of acetic acid, and 1 ml. of water in a 50-ml. Erlenmeyer flask, and heat the mixture on the steam bath for 10 min. with frequent swirling. The initially uniform white suspension changes to a curdy, dense precipitate of silver bromide, a transient pink color disappears, and the solution clears and becomes colorless. Cool to room temperature, filter by suction, and wash the silver bromide with a little alcohol or acetone. Pour the filtrate into a separatory funnel, add water (60 ml.) to produce a milky suspension, and extract with ether (40 ml.). Wash the ethereal extract twice with water and once with 10% sodium hydroxide (25 ml.), dry, filter, and evaporate the ether (aspirator tube).

$\frac{1}{2}$ *Hr. of work prior to chromatography*

Dissolve the residual oil in 3–4 ml. of benzene, pour the solution onto a column of 25 g. of alumina, and rinse the flask with a little more benzene. Chromatograph in 25-ml. fractions with the following sequence of solvents: 50 ml. of petroleum ether, 50 ml. of 1:1 petroleum ether–benzene, 50 ml. of benzene, 50 ml. of 1:1 benzene–ether, 50 ml. of ether. If early fractions afford oily products (diacetates) and are then followed by negative fractions, the oils can be discarded and the flasks cleaned and reused. The *dl*-diol monoacetate (m.p. 87°) should appear in intermediate fractions as an oil that slowly solidifies on standing (e.g., overnight). If you obtain a consecutive set of solid fractions, scrape out a little of the first and the last and take the melting points. If the two end fractions correspond, then these and the intermediate ones can be combined. Dissolve each one in a little ether, transfer with a capillary dropper to a 50-ml. Erlenmeyer flask heated on the steam bath (aspirator tube), and determine the weight of product (0.6 g.). Dissolve the monoacetate in 10 ml. of 95% ethanol, add 5 ml. of 10% sodium hydroxide, and heat for 10 min. on the steam bath. Dilute with

[1] If anhydrous acetic acid is used the chief product is *meso*-hydrobenzoin diacetate (VI). According to the mechanism postulated in the formulation, Walden inversions occur in the reactions II → III and III → VI.

30 ml. of water, cool and scratch to cause separation of *dl*-hydrobenzoin. Since the diol often separates from the aqueous medium as a low-melting hydrate, it is best collected by ether extraction. The dried and filtered ethereal solution is evaporated to a volume of about 10 ml., 15 ml. of petroleum ether is added, and the solution is evaporated slowly until crystals begin to separate. M.p. 120°; yield 0.35 g.

Formation of separate hemihedral prisms of the optically active *d*- and *l*-forms requires slow recrystallization from ether, best of several pooled preparations.[2]

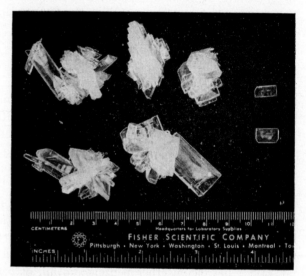

FIG. 32.1
d- and *l*-Hydrobenzoin. Upper crystal to the far right, αD — 97.0° Chf; crystal below it, αD + 97.6° Chf).

[2] If crystals of opposite hemihedrism are not at first identifiable, individual crystals will be found to give solutions that are strongly dextro- or levorotatory. Crystals obtained by evaporation of *d*- and *l*-solutions can then be introduced as seed to a concentrated ethereal solution of *dl*-diol, one on each side of the flask. If the flask is plugged with absorbent cotton and let stand in a spark-free refrigerator, two masses of crystals develop in which opposite hemihedrism is discernible (Fig.32.1).

Directions are given below for diazotizing sulfanilic acid and for coupling the diazonium salt with a phenol and with an amine. Because sulfanilic acid in the dipolar ion form is sparingly soluble in water, it is converted into the soluble sodium salt, a solution of which is treated with sodium nitrite and then acidified. The amino group is diazotized as it is liberated and the diazonium salt separates as the dipolar ion:

$$2H_3\overset{+}{N}C_6H_4SO_3^- + Na_2CO_3 \longrightarrow 2H_2NC_6H_4SO_3Na + CO_2 + H_2O$$

$$H_2NC_6H_4SO_3Na + 2HCl + NaNO_2 \longrightarrow \overset{+}{N}{\equiv}NC_6H_4\overset{-}{SO_3} + 2NaCl + 2H_2O$$

One dye, Orange II, is made by coupling diazotized sulfanilic acid with β-naphthol in alkaline solution; the other, Methyl Orange, is prepared by coupling the same diazonium salt with

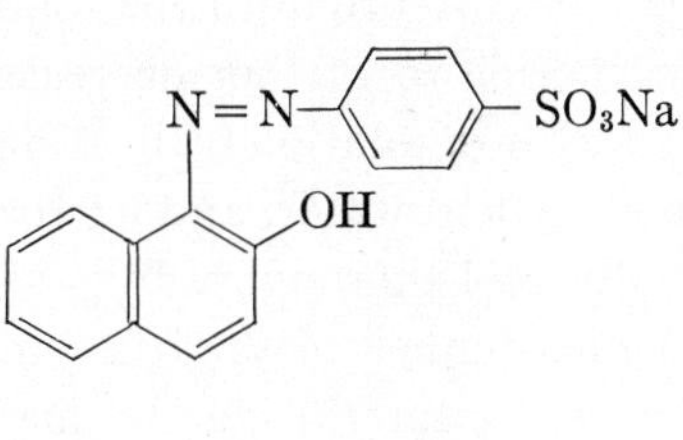

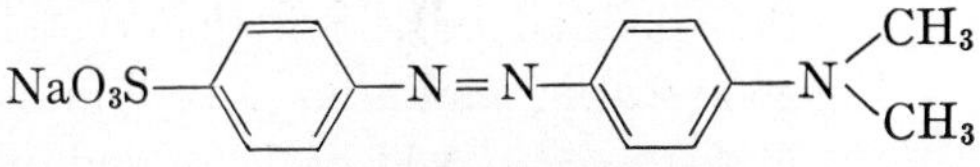

(Alkali-stable form)

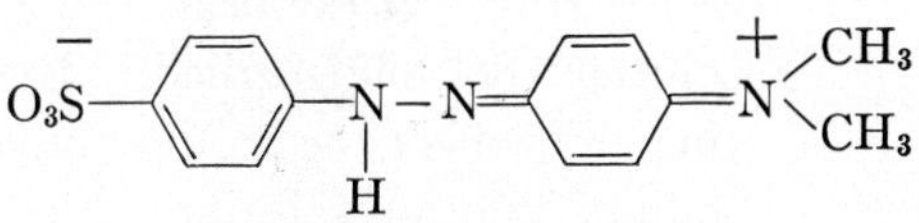

(Acid-stable form)
Methyl orange

Orange II

N,N-dimethylaniline in a weakly acidic solution (aqueous acetic acid). Methyl Orange is an indicator; it changes color at pH 3.2–4.4 owing to transition from one chromophore (azo group) to another (quinonoid system).

You are to prepare one of the two dyes and then exchange

samples with a neighbor and do the tests on both dyes. Both substances dye wool, silk, and skin, and you must work carefully to avoid getting them on the hands. Hands can be cleaned by soaking them in warm, slightly acidic (H_2SO_4) permanganate solution until heavily stained with manganese dioxide and then removing the stain in a bath of warm, dilute bisulfite solution.

EXPERIMENTS

1. Diazotization

In a 125-ml. Erlenmeyer flask dissolve 4.8 g. of sulfanilic acid crystals (monohydrate) in 50 ml. of 2.5% sodium carbonate solution (or use 1.33 g. of anhydrous sodium carbonate and 50 ml. of water) by boiling. Cool the solution under the tap, add 1.9 g. of sodium nitrite and stir until it is dissolved. Pour the solution into a beaker or flask containing about 25 g. of ice and 5 ml. of concentrated hydrochloric acid. In a minute or two a powdery white precipitate of the diazonium salt should separate and the material is then ready for use. The product is not collected but is used as the suspension. It is more stable than most diazonium salts, and it will keep for a few hours.

2. Orange II (1-p-Sulfobenzeneazo-2-naphthol Sodium Salt)

In a 400-ml. beaker dissolve 3.6 g. of β-naphthol in 20 ml. of cold 10% sodium hydroxide solution and pour into this solution, with stirring, the suspension of diazotized sulfanilic acid (rinse). Coupling occurs very rapidly and the dye, being a sodium salt, separates easily from the solution on account of the presence of a considerable excess of sodium ion (from the soda, the nitrite, and the alkali added). Stir the crystalline paste thoroughly to effect good mixing and after 5–10 min. heat the mixture until the solid is dissolved. Add 10 g. of sodium chloride to further decrease the solubility of the product, bring this all into solution by heating and stirring, set the beaker in a pan of ice and water, and let the solution cool undisturbed.[1] Eventually cool thoroughly by stirring and collect the product on a Büchner funnel. Use saturated sodium chloride solution rather than water for rinsing the material out of the beaker and for washing the filter cake free from the dark-colored mother liquor. The filtration is somewhat slow.[2]

Choice of 2 or 3

---

[1] This gives a more easily filterable product. If time permits, it is still better to allow the solution to cool at room temperature.

[2] If the filtration must be interrupted, close the rubber suction tubing (while the pump is still running) with a screw pinch clamp placed close to the filter flask and then disconnect the tubing from the pump. Fill the funnel and set the unit aside; suction will be maintained and filtration will continue.

The product dries only slowly and it contains about 20% of sodium chloride. The crude yield is thus not significant and the material need not be dried before being purified. This azo dye is too soluble to be crystallized from water; it can be obtained in a fairly satisfactory form by adding saturated sodium chloride solution to a hot, filtered solution in water and cooling, but the best crystals are obtained from aqueous ethanol. Transfer the filter cake to a beaker, wash the material from the paper and funnel with water, and bring the substance into solution at the boiling point. Avoid a large excess of water, but use enough to prevent separation of solid during filtration (volume: about 50 ml.). Filter by suction through a Büchner funnel that has been preheated on the steam bath. Pour the filtrate into an Erlenmeyer flask (wash), estimate the volume, and if this is greater than 60 ml., evaporate by boiling. Cool to 80°, add 100–125 ml. of alcohol, and allow crystallization to proceed. Cool well before collecting. Rinse the beaker with mother liquor and wash finally with a little alcohol. The yield of pure, crystalline material is 6–8 g. Orange II separates from aqueous alcohol with two molecules of water of crystallization and allowance for this should be made in calculation of the yield. When the water of hydration is eliminated by drying at 120° the material becomes fiery red.

Extinguish flames

3. Methyl Orange (p-Sulfobenzeneazo-4-dimethylaniline Sodium Salt)

In a test tube mix well 3.2 ml. of dimethylaniline and 2.5 ml. of glacial acetic acid. To the suspension of diazotized sulfanilic acid contained in a 400-ml. beaker add with stirring the solution of dimethylaniline acetate (rinse). Stir and mix thoroughly and within a few minutes the red, acid-stable form of the dye should separate. A stiff paste should result in 5–10 min. and 35 ml. of 10% sodium hydroxide solution is then added to produce the orange sodium salt. Stir well and heat the mixture to the boiling point, when a large part of the dye should dissolve. Place the beaker in a pan of ice and water and allow the solution to cool undisturbed.[1] Then cool thoroughly, collect the product on a Büchner funnel, using saturated sodium chloride solution rather than water to rinse the flask and to wash the dark mother liquor out of the filter cake.

The crude product need not be dried but can be crystallized at once from water after making preliminary solubility tests to determine the proper conditions. The yield is 5–6 g.

193

1. Solubility and Color

Compare the solubility in water of Orange II and Methyl Orange and account for the difference in terms of structure. Treat the first solution with alkali and note the change in shade due to salt formation; to the other solution alternately add acid and alkali.

2. Reduction

Characteristic of an azo compound is the ease with which the molecule is cleaved at the double bond by reducing agents to give two amines. Since amines are colorless, the reaction is easily followed by the color change. The reaction is of use in preparation of hydroxyamino and similar compounds, in analysis of azo dyes by titration with a reducing agent, and in identification of azo compounds from an examination of the cleavage products.

(a) *Acid Reduction.* Dissolve about 0.5 g. of stannous chloride in 1 ml. of concd. hydrochloric acid, add a small quantity of the azo compound (0.1 g.), and heat. A colorless solution should result and no precipitate should form on adding water. The aminophenol or the diamine derivative is present as the soluble hydrochloride; the other product of cleavage, sulfanilic acid, is sufficiently soluble to remain in solution.

(b) *Neutral Reduction.* Suspend a small spatulaful of the azo dye in 1 ml. of water, add a small quantity of sodium hydrosulfite, and heat the mixture until no further change occurs. Test the precipitate formed in the reduction of Orange II and see if it dissolves in alkali, as would be expected. If after the reduction of Methyl Orange a clear solution is obtained, cool the solution and see if a solid can be caused to crystallize. If not, repeat the test with a somewhat greater amount of material.

The reduction with sodium hydrosulfite proceeds as follows:

$$RN{=}NR' + 2Na_2S_2O_4 + 4H_2O \longrightarrow RNH_2 + H_2NR' + 4NaHSO_3$$

If in the test it is desired to prove that the substance which separates is an amine, the material should be collected before testing the solubility in hydrochloric acid, since addition of acid to the reduction mixture causes decomposition of the hydrosulfite with separation of sulfur.

3. Addition of Bisulfite

That a given colored compound yields an amine on reduction is not sufficient evidence that it is an azo compound; it might

be a nitro compound. A further characteristic test is the reaction
with sodium bisulfite, which probably proceeds as follows:

$$RN{=}NR' + NaHSO_3 \longrightarrow \underset{\underset{H \quad SO_3Na}{|\qquad|}}{RN{-}NR'}$$

The N=N group resembles the C=O group in this addition
reaction. The addition product is either colorless or else faintly
colored in comparison to the original azo compound. Nitro compounds do not react with sodium bisulfite.

Add two drops of 10% sodium hydroxide solution to 1 ml. of
saturated sodium bisulfite solution, heat the mixture, add a few
drops of an aqueous solution of the azo compound, heat again,
and if no change is apparent at once allow the mixture to stand
under observation for several minutes.

CHAPTER 34 | p-Chlorotoluene

p-Toluidine is dissolved in the required amount of hydrochloric acid, two more equivalents of acid are added, and the mixture cooled in ice to produce a paste of the crystalline hydrochloride. When this is treated at 0–5° with one equivalent of sodium nitrite, nitrous acid is liberated and reacts to produce the diazonium salt, p-CH$_3$C$_6$H$_4$N$_2$$^+Cl^-$. The hydrochloric acid beyond the two equivalents required to form the amine hydrochloride and react with sodium nitrite is to maintain acidity sufficient to prevent formation of the diazoamino compound and rearrangement of the diazonium salt.

Cuprous chloride is made by reduction of copper sulfate with sodium sulfite (which is produced as required from the cheaper sodium bisulfite). The white solid is left covered with the reducing solution for protection against air oxidation until it is to be used and then dissolved in hydrochloric acid. On addition of the diazonium salt solution a complex forms and rapidly decomposes to give p-chlorotoluene and nitrogen. The mixture is badly discolored, but steam distillation leaves most of the impurities and all salts behind and gives material substantially pure except for the presence of a trace of yellow pigment which can be eliminated by distillation of the dried oil.

EXPERIMENTS

1. Cuprous Chloride Solution

In a 500-ml. distilling flask (to be used later for steam distillation) dissolve 30 g. of copper sulfate crystals (CuSO$_4 \cdot$5H$_2$O) in 100 ml. of water by boiling and then add 10 g. of sodium chloride, which may give a small precipitate of basic copper chloride. Prepare a solution of sodium sulfite from 7 g. of sodium bisulfite, 4.5 g. of sodium hydroxide, and 50 ml. of water and add this, not too rapidly, to the hot copper sulfate solution (rinse flask and neck). Shake well and put the flask in a pan of cold water in a slanting position favorable for decantation and let the mixture stand to cool and settle while doing the diazotization. When you are ready to use the cuprous chloride, decant the supernatant liquid, wash the white solid once with water by decantation, and dissolve the solid in 45 ml. of concd. hydrochloric acid to form the double compound. The solution is susceptible to air oxidation and should not stand for an appreciable time before being used.

p-Chlorotoluene

Stop here

2. Diazotization

Put 11.0 g. of p-toluidine and 15 ml. of water in a 125-ml. Erlenmeyer flask, measure 25 ml. of concd. hydrochloric acid and add 10 ml. of it. Heat over a free flame and swirl to dissolve the amine and hence insure that it is all converted into the hydrochloride. Add the rest of the acid and cool thoroughly in an ice bath and let the flask stand in the bath while preparing a solution of 7 g. of sodium nitrite in 20 ml. of water. To maintain a temperature of 0–5° during diazotization add a few pieces of ice to the amine hydrochloride suspension and add more later as the first ones melt. Pour in the nitrite solution in portions during 5 min. with swirling in the ice bath. The solid should dissolve to a clear solution of the diazonium salt. After 3–4 min. test for excess nitrous acid: dip a stirring rod in the solution, touch off the drop on the wall of the flask, put the rod in a small test tube, and add a few drops of water. Then insert a strip of starch-iodide paper; an instantaneous deep blue color due to a starch-iodine complex indicates the presence of nitrous acid. (The sample tested is diluted with water because strong hydrochloric acid alone produces the same color after a slight induction.) Leave the solution in the ice bath.

3. Sandmeyer Reaction

Complete the preparation of cuprous chloride solution, cool it in the ice bath, pour in the solution of diazonium chloride through a long-stemmed funnel and rinse the flask. Swirl occasionally at room temperature for 10 min. and observe initial separation of a complex of the two components and its decomposition with liberation of nitrogen and separation of an oil. Arrange for steam distillation from the steam bath by inserting a tube connected to a steam trap and connecting a condenser, but do not turn on the steam until bubbling has practically ceased and an oily layer has separated. Then turn on the steam bath but wait until the liquid is hot before admitting steam (otherwise steam condenses and increases the volume).

While the mixture is warming, calculate the amount of water required for steam distillation of all the product in case the yield is 100%. The p-chlorotoluene–water azeotrope distils at 95.0° (see Chapter 8). Then steam distil, and decide for yourself whether a trace of oil that continues to appear after the main batch is over is product or impurity. Note that p-chlorotoluene, (sp. gr. 1.07) is heavier than water but lighter than the solution of inorganic salts in which it was formed. Extract the distillate with a little ether, wash the solution with 10% sodium hydroxide solution to remove any p-cresol present, then wash with salt solution, filter the solution through anhydrous sodium sulfate into a tared flask, evaporate the ether, and determine the yield and percentage yield of crude product (about 9 g.).

Caution! Aspirator

The crude material usually contains a yellow impurity that has not been identified. It is not an azo compound, since the color is not discharged by hydrosulfite. It is not removed by shaking the oil with concd. sulfuric acid, and it is not separable by chromatography on alumina. It can, however, be removed by distillation from a 25-ml. flask through a short air condenser. Since the amount is so small that losses will be large, aim in this distillation for a middle fraction of high purity regardless of yield. Pure p-chlorotoluene is a colorless liquid, b.p. 162°, corr., m.p. 7°. The uncorrected boiling point will be a little lower, about 159°. Distil slowly and collect a forerun until pure material seems to be coming over, and stop. Then distil with a clean condenser and receiver and try to collect material boiling over a 1° range, and stop before yellow material spatters over. The criterion of success is whether or not your sample will crystallize when cooled and scratched and show the correct melting point.

5-Amino-1,4-phthalazdione (III), commonly known as luminol because oxidation of the substance is attended with a striking emission of light, is made by reduction of the nitro derivative (II) formed on thermal dehydration of the salt of 3-nitrophthalic acid (I) with hydrazine. An earlier procedure for effecting the

I	II	III
M.p. 222°	M.p. 316°, dec.	M.p. 332°
Mol. wt. 211.13	Mol. wt. 207.14	Mol. wt. 177.16

first step called for addition of hydrazine sulfate to an alkaline solution of the acid, evaporation to dryness, and baking the resulting mixture of the hydrazine salt and sodium sulfate in an oven at 165°, and required a total of 4.5 hrs. for completion. The working time can be drastically reduced by adding high-boiling (b.p. 290°) triethylene glycol to an aqueous solution of the hydrazine salt, distilling the excess water, and raising the temperature to a point where dehydration to II is complete in a few minutes. Nitrophthalazdione (II) is insoluble in dilute acid but soluble in alkali, by virtue of enolization, and it is conveniently reduced to luminol (III) by sodium hydrosulfite in alkaline solution. In dilute, weakly acidic or neutral solution luminol exists largely as the dipolar ion IV and exhibits beautiful blue fluorescence. An alkaline solution contains the doubly enolized anion V and displays particularly marked chemilu-

IV   V

minescence when oxidized with a combination of hydrogen peroxide and potassium ferricyanide.[1]

Procedure

The two-step synthesis of a chemiluminescent substance can be completed in 25 min.

First put a flask containing 15 ml. of water on the steam bath to get hot. Then heat a mixture of 1 g. of 3-nitrophthalic acid and 2 ml. of an 8% aqueous solution of hydrazine [2] in a 20 × 150-mm. test tube over a free flame until the solid is dissolved, add 3 ml. of triethylene glycol, and clamp the tube in a vertical position about two inches above a Bunsen burner. Insert a thermometer and an aspirator connected to a suction pump (Fig. 23.3), and boil the solution vigorously to distil the excess water (110–130°). Let the temperature rise rapidly until (3–4 min.) it reaches 215°. Remove the burner, note the time, and by intermittent gentle heating, maintain a temperature of 215–220° for 2 min. Remove the tube, cool to about 100° (crystals of the product often appear), add the 15 ml. of hot water, cool under the tap, and collect the light yellow granular nitro compound (I, dry weight, 0.7 g.).[3]

The nitro compound need not be dried and can be transferred at once, for reduction, to the uncleaned test tube in which it was prepared. Add 5 ml. of 10% sodium hydroxide solution, stir with a rod, and to the resulting deep brown-red solution add 3 g. of sodium hydrosulfite dihydrate (mol. wt. 210.15). Wash the solid down the walls with a little water. Heat to the boiling point, stir, and keep the mixture hot for 5 min., during which time some of the reduction product may separate. Then add 2 ml. of acetic acid, cool under the tap and stir, and collect the resulting precipitate of light yellow luminol (III). The filtrate on standing overnight usually deposits a further crop of luminol (0.1–0.2 g.).

[1] Theoretical interpretations of the phenomenon are summarized by A. Étienne, *Hétérocycles Hexatomique avec deux atomes d'azote. Group de la Pyridazine*, pp. 1134–1136, Masson et Cie., Paris, 1953. Several methods of demonstrating the chemiluminescence of luminol are described by E. H. Huntress, L. N. Stanley, and A. S. Parker, *J. Chem. Ed.* **11**, 142 (1934).
[2] Dilute 31.2 g. of the commercial 64% hydrazine solution to a volume of 250 ml.
[3] The reason for adding hot water and then cooling rather than adding cold water is that the solid is then obtained in more easily filterable form.

Dissolve the first crop of moist luminol (dry weight, 0.2–0.3 g.) **Luminol** in 10 ml. of 10% sodium hydroxide solution and 90 ml. of water; this is stock solution A. Prepare a second solution (B) by mixing 20 ml. of 3% aqueous potassium ferricyanide, 20 ml. of 3% hydrogen peroxide, and 160 ml. of water. Now dilute 25 ml. of solution A with 175 ml. of water and, in a relatively dark corner or cupboard, pour this solution and solution B simultaneously into a funnel resting in the neck of a large Erlenmeyer flask. Swirl the flask and, to increase the brilliance, gradually add further small quantities of alkali.

CHAPTER 36 | Benzoic Acid and Phenylglyoxylic Acid

The initial product of oxidation of mandelic acid is phenyl-glyoxylic acid:

$$\underset{\underset{OH}{\displaystyle |}}{\overset{\overset{H}{\displaystyle |}}{C_6H_5-C-COOH}} + [O] \longrightarrow C_6H_5-\underset{\displaystyle O}{\overset{\displaystyle ||}{C}}-COOH + H_2O$$

If oxidation is done with permanganate in acid solution the α-keto acid suffers decarboxylation to benzaldehyde, which is then oxidized further to benzoic acid. A part of the permanganate is

$$C_6H_5CO\!\!\mid\!\!COO\!\!\mid\!\!H \longrightarrow C_6H_5CHO + CO_2$$

converted to insoluble manganese dioxide even in a solution containing considerable sulfuric acid. Instead of filtering the solution from the voluminous precipitate and concentrating the filtrate, the manganese dioxide can be reduced to soluble manganous sulfate by addition of sodium bisulfite.

Phenylglyoxylic acid is more stable in an alkaline medium and is formed in good yield by oxidation of mandelic acid with an equivalent amount of permanganate in alkaline solution at a low temperature. The acid is highly soluble in water but can be isolated easily as the phenylhydrazone.

EXPERIMENTS

1. Acid Oxidation: Benzoic Acid

Pour 10 ml. of concd. sulfuric acid into 100 ml. of water in a 250-ml. Erlenmeyer flask, dissolve 3.8 g. of mandelic acid in the hot solution, cool to room temperature, and add in small portions and with good stirring 7.5 g. of potassium permanganate crystals.

Note the odor of the oil which separates in the early stages of the reaction. After the permanganate has been added, wash the walls of the beaker and heat the mixture with stirring for 10 min. on the steam bath. Some benzoic acid may be noted at this point, mixed with manganese dioxide. Make a spot test for permanganate, the color of which may be obscured by the brown dioxide: touch a drop of liquid to a filter paper and hold this to the light. The liquid rim around the brown spot will reveal any color in the solution. If there is no unchanged permanganate, transfer the flask to the hood and stir in 10 g. of sodium bisulfite ($NaHSO_3$) in small portions. A small additional quantity of the reducing agent may be added if the precipitate of benzoic acid is still brown, but a few hard particles of manganese dioxide in the white product will be removed later in crystallization. Cool well in an ice bath, collect the material, and wash it with water. The crude product (about 2.2 g.) need not be dried but can be crystallized at once from about 100 ml. of water; yield, 1.9 g.

Pure benzoic acid melts at 121.5°; the solubility in water at 0° is about 0.2 g. per 100 ml. Place a little of the material in a 100-ml. beaker and on the top of this rest a 100-ml. round bottomed flask filled with cold water. Heat the beaker gently with a small flame for some time and note the character of the sublimate.

2. Benzamide

Place 0.2 g. of benzoic acid in a test tube (150 mm.) and cover it with enough thionyl chloride to wet the solid and form a thin paste. Heat gently on the steam bath under the hood, when sulfur dioxide and hydrogen chloride are evolved. Evacuate and heat for 5 minutes on the steam bath to volatilize the excess thionyl chloride (b.p. 77°), then cool the tube and add a little water. Note the oily appearance and the characteristic odor of benzoyl chloride. Pour off the water, add 1 ml. of concd. ammonia solution, and shake. The white solid formed is benzamide, $C_6H_5CONH_2$. It melts at 128°, crystallizes well from alcohol, and is easily hydrolyzed by a boiling, aqueous alkali solution.

3. Alkaline Oxidation: Phenylglyoxylic Acid

Dissolve 1 g. of mandelic acid in a mixture of 3 ml. of 10% sodium hydroxide solution and 15 ml. of water and add 150 g. of crushed ice. Measure 73 ml. of 1% potassium permanganate solution, add a few milliliters of it to the iced solution and wait a

Acetylsalicylic Acid (Aspirin)

This experiment demonstrates the action of four acetylation catalysts: two bases, sodium acetate and pyridine; a Lewis acid, boron fluoride; and a mineral acid, sulfuric.

EXPERIMENT

Place 1 g. of salicylic acid in each of four 13 × 100-mm. test tubes and add to each tube 2 ml. of acetic anhydride. To the first tube add 0.2 g. of anhydrous sodium acetate, note the time, stir with a thermometer, and record the time required for a 4° rise in temperature and the estimated proportion of solid that has dissolved. Replace the thermometer and continue to stir occasionally while starting the next acetylation. Clean the thermometer, put it in the second tube, add 5 micro drops of pyridine, observe as before, and compare with the first results. To the third and fourth tubes add 5 micro drops each of boron fluoride etherate and concd. sulfuric acid.[1] What is the order of activity of the four catalysts?

Put all the tubes in a beaker of hot water for 5 min. to dissolve solid and complete the reactions, and then pour each solution into 50 ml. of water in a 125-ml. Erlenmeyer flask and rinse with water. Swirl to aid hydrolysis of excess acetic anhydride and then cool thoroughly in ice, scratch, and collect the crystalline solid; yield 4 g.

Acetylsalicylic acid melts with decomposition at temperatures reported from 128 to 137°. It can be crystallized by dissolving it in ether, adding an equal volume of petroleum ether, and letting the solution stand undisturbed in an ice bath.

Test the solubility of your sample in benzene and in hot water and note the peculiar character of the aqueous solution when it

[1] Commercial reagent if dark should be redistilled (b.p. 126°, water-white).

Note for the instructor

is cooled and when it is then rubbed against the tube with a stirring rod. Note also that the substance dissolves in cold sodium bicarbonate solution and is precipitated by addition of an acid. Compare a tablet of commercial aspirin with your sample. Test the solubility in water and in benzene and observe if it dissolves completely. Compare its behavior when heated in a melting point capillary with the behavior of your sample. If an impurity is found present this probably is some substance used as binder for the tablets. Is it organic or inorganic? What harmless, edible type of substance do you suppose it is, judging from the various properties?

In the first experiment Orange II is reduced in aqueous solution with sodium hydrosulfite to water-soluble sodium sulfanilate and 1-amino-2-naphthol, which precipitates. This intermediate is purified as the hydrochloride and oxidized to β-naphthoquinone:

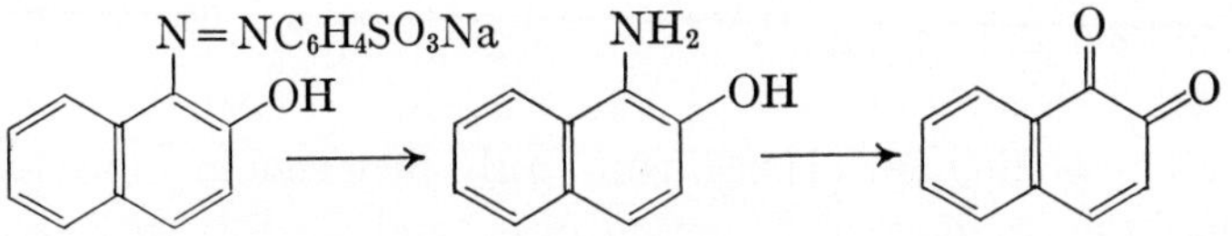

The next three experiments are a sequence of steps for the synthesis of the antihemorrhagic Vitamin K_1 (or an analogue) starting with a coal-tar hydrocarbon. β-Methylnaphthalene is oxidized with chromic acid to 2-methyl-1,4-naphthoquinone, the

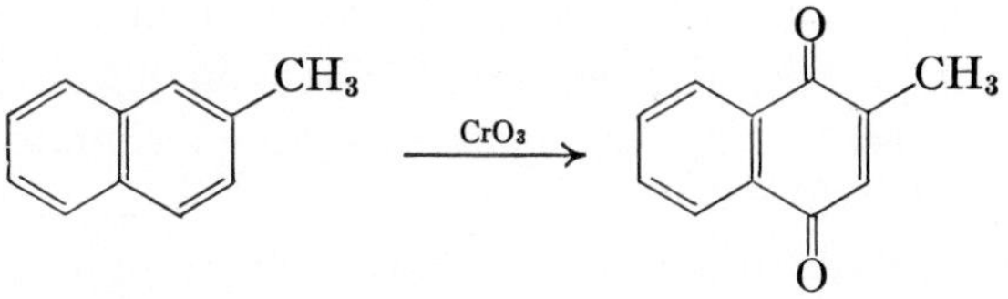

yellow quinone is purified and reduced to its hydroquinone by shaking an ethereal solution of the substance with aqueous hydrosulfite solution, the colorless hydroquinone is condensed with phytol, and the substituted hydroquinone oxidized to vitamin K_1.

An additional or alternative experiment is conversion of 2-methyl-1,4-naphthoquinone through the oxide into the 3-hydroxy compound phthiocol, which has been isolated from human

$$\text{1,4-dihydroxy-2-methylnaphthalene} \xrightarrow{C_{20}H_{39}OH} \text{(2-phytyl product)} + \text{By-Product (} H_2 \text{)}$$

$$\xrightarrow{Ag_2O}$$

Vitamin K$_1$

tubercle bacilli after saponification, probably as a product of cleavage of vitamin K$_1$ (see p. 212).

EXPERIMENTS

1. β-Naphthoquinone

In a 125-ml. Erlenmeyer flask dissolve 3.9 g. of Orange II in 50 ml. of water and warm the solution to 40–50°. Add 4.5 g. of sodium hydrosulfite dihydrate and swirl until the red color is discharged and a cream-colored or pink precipitate of 1-amino-2-naphthol separates. To coagulate the product heat the mixture nearly to boiling until it begins to froth, then cool in an ice bath, collect the product on a suction filter, and wash it with water. Prepare a solution of 1 ml. of concd. hydrochloric acid, 20 ml. of water, and an estimated 50 mg. of stannous chloride (antioxidant), and transfer the precipitate of aminonaphthol to this solution and wash in material adhering to the funnel. Swirl, warm gently, and when all but a little fluffy material has dissolved filter the solution by suction through a thin layer of Norit. Transfer the solution to a clean flask, add 4 ml. of concd. hydrochloric acid, heat over a free flame until the precipitated aminonaphthol hydrochloride has been brought into solution, and then cool thoroughly in an ice bath. Collect the crystalline, colorless hydrochloride and wash it with a mixture of 1 ml. of concd. hydrochloric acid and 4 ml. of water. Leave the air-sensitive crystalline product in the funnel while preparing a solution for its oxidation. Dissolve 5.5 g. of ferric chloride crystals (FeCl$_3 \cdot 6H_2O$) in 2 ml. of concd. hydrochloric acid and 10 ml. of water by heating, cool to room temperature, and filter by suction. Wash the crystalline aminonaphthol hydrochloride into a beaker, stir, add more water, and warm to about 35° until the salt is all dissolved. Filter the solution quickly by suction from a trace of residue and stir in the ferric chloride solution. β-

Naphthoquinone separates at once as a voluminous precipitate and is collected on a suction filter and washed thoroughly to remove all traces of acid. The yield from pure, salt-free Orange II is 75%.

β-Naphthoquinone, highly sensitive and reactive, does not have a well-defined melting point but decomposes at about 145–147°. Suspend a sample in hot water and add concd. hydrochloric acid. Dissolve a small sample in cold methanol and add a drop of aniline; the red product is 4-anilino-1,2-naphthoquinone.

2. 2-Methyl-1,4-naphthoquinone

In the hood, clamp a separatory funnel in place to deliver into a 600-ml. beaker which can be cooled in an ice bath when required. The oxidizing solution to be placed in the funnel is prepared by dissolving 50 g. of chromic anhydride (CrO_3) in 35 ml. of water and diluting the dark red solution with 35 ml. of acetic acid.[1] In the beaker prepare a mixture of 14.2 g. of β-methylnaphthalene and 150 ml. of acetic acid, and without cooling run in small portions of the oxidizing solution, and stir with a thermometer until the temperature rises to 60°. At this point ice cooling will be required to prevent a further rise. By alternate addition of reagent and cooling the temperature is maintained close to 60° throughout the addition, which can be completed in about 10 min. When the temperature begins to drop spontaneously the solution is heated gently on the steam bath (85–90°) for one hour to complete the oxidation.

Reaction time 1¼ hrs.

Dilute the dark green solution with water nearly to the top of the beaker, stir well for a few minutes to coagulate the yellow quinone, collect the product on a Büchner funnel, and wash it thoroughly with water to remove chromic acetate. The crude material can be crystallized from methanol (40 ml.) while still moist (without filtering), and gives 6.5–7.3 g. of satisfactory 2-methyl-1,4-naphthoquinone, m.p. 105–106°. The substance must be kept away from light, which converts it into a pale yellow, sparingly soluble polymer.

3. 2-Methyl-1,4-naphthohydroquinone

In an Erlenmeyer flask dissolve 2 g. of the quinone in 35 ml. of ether by warming, pour the solution into a separatory funnel,

---

[1] The anhydride is hygroscopic; weigh it quickly and do not leave the bottle unstoppered. The substance dissolves very slowly in acetic acid–water mixtures, and solutions are prepared by adding the acetic acid only after the substance has been completely dissolved in water.

and shake with a fresh solution of 4 g. of sodium hydrosulfite in 30 ml. of water. After passing through a brown phase (quinhydrone) the solution should become colorless or pale yellow in a few minutes; if not, add more hydrosulfite solution. After removing the aqueous layer, shake the ethereal solution with 25 ml. of saturated sodium chloride solution and 1–2 ml. of saturated hydrosulfite solution to remove the bulk of water, and filter the ethereal layer by gravity through a paper moistened with ether and about one third filled with sodium sulfate. Evaporate the filtrate on the steam bath until nearly all the solvent has been removed, cool, and add petroleum ether. The hydroquinone separating as a white or grayish powder is collected, washed with petroleum ether, and dried; yield 1.9 g. (the substance has no sharp m.p.).

Aspirator tube

4. Vitamin K₁ (2-Methyl-3-phytol-1,4-naphthoquinone)

Phytol, being an allylic alcohol, is reactive enough to condense with 2-methyl-1,4-naphthohydroquinone under mild conditions of acid catalysis as specified below. Overheating must be avoided or the alcohol is dehydrated to phytadiene. The reaction mixture is diluted with water and extracted with ether and unchanged starting material removed by extraction with aqueous alkali containing hydrosulfite to keep the hydroquinones from being oxidized by air. The hydroquinone of K₁ has a methyl group adjacent to one hydroxyl group and the long phytol side chain adjacent to the other; it is a cryptophenol (hidden phenolic properties), insoluble in aqueous alkali. It is separated from the nonhydroxylic by-product by crystallization from petroleum ether and oxidized to K₁ quinone.

Explanation

Place 1.5 g. of phytol [2] and 10 ml. of dioxane in a 50-ml. Erlenmeyer flask and warm to 50° in a water bath kept hot on the steam bath. Prepare a solution of 1.5 g. of 2-methyl-1,4-naphthohydroquinone and 1.5 ml. of boron fluoride etherate in 10 ml. of dioxane, and add this in portions with a capillary dropper in the course of 15 min. with constant swirling and while maintaining a temperature of 50°. Continue in the same way for 20 min. longer. Cool to 25°, wash the solution into a separatory funnel with 40 ml. of ether, and wash the orange-colored ethereal solution with two 40-ml. portions of water to remove boron fluoride and dioxane. To extract unchanged hydroquinone, add a freshly

Procedure

[2] Suppliers: Matheson, Coleman and Bell Co., American Chlorophyll Division, Strong, Cobb and Co., National Chlorophyll and Chemical Co. Geraniol can be used as a substitute; the product is similar in chemical and physical properties to the natural vitamin and has pronounced antihemorrhagic activity.

Note for the instructor

prepared solution of 2 g. of sodium hydrosulfite in 40 ml. of 2% aqueous sodium hydroxide and 10 ml. of saturated sodium chloride solution (which helps break the resulting emulsion). Shake vigorously for a few minutes, when any red color should disappear and the alkaline layer should acquire a bright yellow vat color. After releasing the pressure through the stopcock, keep the funnel stoppered until the layers separate, as a precaution against oxidation. Draw off the yellow liquor and repeat the extraction a second and a third time, or until the alkaline layer remains practically colorless. Separate the faintly colored ethereal solution, dry it over sodium sulfate, filter into a tared flask, and evaporate the filtrate on the steam bath, eventually with evacuation at the water pump. The total oil, which becomes waxy on cooling, amounts to 1.7–1.9 g.

Add 10 ml. of petroleum ether (b.p. 20–40°) and boil and manipulate with a spatula until the brown mass has changed to a paste of white solid. Wash the paste into small centrifuge tubes with 10–20 ml. of fresh petroleum ether, make up the volume of paired tubes to the same point, cool well in ice, and centrifuge. Decant the brown supernatant liquor into the original tared flask, fill the tubes with fresh solvent, and stir the white sludge to an even suspension. Then cool, centrifuge, and decant as before. Evaporation of the liquor and washings gives 1.1–1.3 g. of residual oil. Dissolve the portions of washed sludge of vitamin K_1 hydroquinone in a total of 10–15 ml. of absolute ether, and add a little Norit for clarification if the solution is pink or dark. Add 1 g. of silver oxide and 1 g. of sodium sulfate. Shake for 20 min., filter into a tared flask, and evaporate the clear yellow solution on the steam bath, removing traces of solvent at the water pump. Undue exposure to light should be avoided when the material is in the quinone form. The residue is a light yellow, rather mobile oil consisting of pure vitamin K_1; yield 0.6–0.9 g.

To observe a characteristic color reaction, transfer a small bit of vitamin on the end of a stirring rod to a test tube, stir with 1 ml. of alcohol, and add 1 ml. of 10% alcoholic potassium hydroxide solution; the end pigment responsible for the red color is phthiocol. A sample for preservation is transferred with a capillary dropper to a small specimen vial wrapped in metal foil or black paper to exclude light.

5. Phthiocol (2-Methyl-3-hydroxy-1,4-naphthoquinone)

Dissolve 1 g. of 2-methyl-1,4-naphthoquinone in 10 ml. of alcohol by heating, and let the solution stand while the second reagent is prepared by dissolving 0.2 g. of anhydrous sodium carbonate in 5 ml. of water and adding (cold) 1 ml. of 30% hydrogen peroxide solution. Cool the quinone solution under the

2-Methyl-1,4-naptho-quinone $\xrightarrow{\text{HOONa}}$ Oxide $\xrightarrow{\text{H}_2\text{SO}_4}$ Phthiocol

tap until crystallization begins, add the peroxide solution all at once, and cool the mixture. The yellow color of the quinone should be discharged immediately. Add about 100 ml. of water, cool in ice, and collect the colorless, crystalline oxide; yield 0.97 g., m.p. 93.5–94.5° (pure: 95.5–96.5°).

To 1 g. of the dry oxide in a 25-ml. Erlenmeyer flask add 5 ml. of concd. sulfuric acid; stir if necessary to produce a homogeneous deep red solution, and after 10 min. cool this in ice and slowly add 20 ml. of water. The precipitated phthiocol can be collected, washed, and crystallized by dissolving in methanol (25 ml.), adding a few drops of hydrochloric acid to give a pure yellow color, treating with Norit, concentrating the filtered solution, and diluting to the saturation point. Alternatively, the yellow suspension is washed into a separatory funnel and the product extracted with a mixture of 25 ml. each of benzene and ether. The organic layer is dried over sodium sulfate and evaporated to a volume of about 10 ml. for crystallization. The total yield of pure phthiocol, m.p. 172–173°, is 0.84–.88 g.

Vacuum Distillation

CHAPTER 39

Many substances cannot be distilled satisfactorily in the ordinary way either because they boil at such high temperatures that decomposition occurs or because of sensitivity to oxidation. In such cases purification can be accomplished by distillation at diminished pressure. A few of many forms of apparatus are described in the following pages. Round bottomed Pyrex ware and thick-walled suction flasks are not liable to collapse, but even so the beginner should wear goggles in carrying out a vacuum distillation.

1. Distillation Assemblies

One simple arrangement for distillation in vacuum is illustrated in Fig. 39.1. It is constructed of two distilling flasks, one of which serves as the receiver. The side arm of the first flask must extend well beyond the tube of the other flask that makes connection to the suction pump. The receiving flask is cooled with running water as described below. Liquids bump badly when boiled at reduced pressure and most boiling stones lose their activity in an evacuated system; it is therefore essential to make special provision for controlling the bumping. This is done by allowing a fine stream of air bubbles to be sucked into the boiling liquid through a glass tube drawn to a fine capillary and provided at the top with a section of suction tubing which can be closed with a screw pinchcock, which serves to regulate the flow of air. The pinchcock is closed at the beginning of the operation and carefully opened after the system has been evacuated until there is a steady stream of bubbles. Some further adjustment usually is required during the heating to secure even boiling. The capillary should extend to the very bottom of the flask and it should

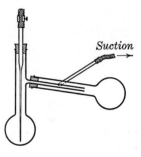

FIG. 39.1 Arrangement of flasks for distillation at reduced pressure

Prevention of bumping

be slender and flexible so that it will whip back and forth in the boiling liquid. Another method of preventing bumping is to introduce sufficient glass wool into the flask to fill a part of the space above the liquid.

To remove a fraction it is necessary to break the vacuum and change the receiving flask. If the suction is released at the end of the system next to the pump, liquid may be drawn up into the evacuated capillary and even into the rubber tubing. Consequently, after allowing the hot liquid to cool somewhat, the pressure is released as much as possible at the other end by gradually opening the pinchcock; the connection to the pump is then broken, also gradually. After a clean flask has been put in place and the pinchcock closed, the system is evacuated and the air flow is regulated before heating is recommenced.

Pressure gauge

The pressure gauge of Fig. 6.7 can be used to test for leaks; the pointer should not move when the suction tubing leading to the assembly is kinked with the fingers.

The apparatus described has faults that are corrected in the assembly shown in Fig. 39.2. Provision is made for a ther-

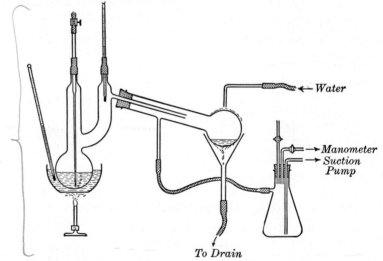

FIG. 39.2 Vacuum distillation assembly

Water

Manometer
Suction
Pump

To Drain

Claisen flask

mometer, essential in most distillations, by use of a Claisen flask with two necks. This form of flask has the advantage of minimizing the chance of liquid being carried over into the distillate by frothing or spattering. The flask shown has constricted necks into which the tube drawn out to a capillary and the thermometer are inserted and held in place by sections of suction tubing. The rubber tubing is first coated on the inside with a thin film of glycerol and slipped over the constricted neck, and the tube of the thermometer is then inserted. The purpose of this construction is to prevent contact of the hot vapor with rubber. The stopper making connection to the receiving flask is not a source of contamination for little hot vapor ordinarily reaches it. A rubber stopper is employed except for distillations above 160°, where rubber softens. A cork stopper is satisfactory if carefully prepared. The cork should be selected carefully for quality and fit, it should be cleanly cut, and the system should be evacuated and tested before use. A slight porosity sometimes may be corrected by lightly charring the surfaces which are to come in contact with glass or by painting the cork with a thin coating of collodion after the system has been evacuated.

The drawing calls for use of a heating bath rather than a free flame to promote even boiling and make possible accurate determination of the boiling point. The bath is filled with a suitable oil, flaky graphite, or a fusible metal and heated to a temperature about 20° higher than that at which the substance in the flask distils, and the bath temperature is kept constant throughout the distillation. The surface of the liquid in the flask should be below that of the heating medium, for this condition lessens the tendency to bump. Heating of the flask is begun only after the system has been evacuated; otherwise the liquid might boil too suddenly on reduction of the pressure.

The condensing flask is conveniently cooled by means of a stream of water so directed that the bulb is completely bathed. The overflow is caught in a funnel.

Additional features of design are shown in Fig. 39.3. The

Heating baths

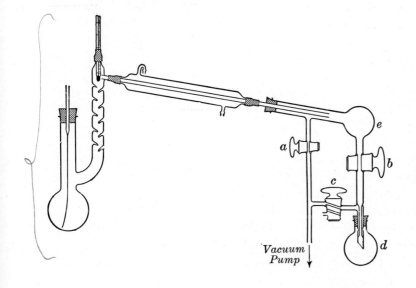

FIG. 39.3 Apparatus for fractional distillation in vacuo

Vacuum Pump

215

distillation neck of the Claisen flask is longer than before and has a series of indentures made from four directions so that the points nearly meet in the center, and it thus serves as a fractionating column. The side-arm outlet extends for a short distance into the neck, to prevent condensate contaminated by contact with the rubber connection at the top from running down into the side arm. Indeed, this neck can be finished like an ordinary flask and the thermometer inserted through a stopper. It is a convenience to have the neck of the flask carrying the capillary open rather than constricted for both filling and cleaning the flask. Another feature is that the flask is provided with a particularly long side arm to serve as the inner tube of a condenser. A cooling jacket is slipped over it and held in place by sections of rubber tubing. The capillary tube in the distilling flask is not supplied with a pinchcock, as in the previous cases, for the capillary is made of bore so fine that none is needed.

Hair-fine capillary

The glass tube is first drawn out in a flame to a fairly slender capillary and this is drawn out again in a smaller flame to a very fine thread. This is tested by blowing into the tube with the capillary tip submerged in a little ether. If a fine stream of bubbles can be produced the capillary should prove satisfactory. This is the best form of capillary.

Fraction cutter

The flask shown in Fig. 39.3 is fitted with an adapter for taking successive fractions without interrupting the distillation or breaking the vacuum. Stopcock b has a particularly wide bore to allow free passage of condensate into the receiver d, and the two-way stopcock c if turned through an angle of 180° makes connection to the outside atmosphere. At the beginning of the distillation the stopcocks are adjusted to the positions shown and the distillate collects in d. When this fraction is to be removed b is closed and c is turned in such a way as to open d to the atmosphere. With the suction released d can be removed and replaced by a fresh flask. Stopcock a is then closed, c is turned to the original position (that shown) and air now present in the closed system below a and b is pumped out. When a good vacuum has been attained a and b are again opened. The original condition is restored and the liquid which has collected in the reservoir e runs down into the second receiver. Successive fractions are collected in the same way and there is only one limitation to the smooth course of the fractionation: while the lower part of the system is being evacuated with a and b closed, air is being sucked into the flask through the capillary and the pressure in the upper part of the system thus rises. Although the vacuum is later reestablished it is impossible to conduct the entire distillation at an entirely constant pressure.

Fractionation at strictly constant pressure can be accomplished with the adapter shown in Fig. 39.4. The end of the condenser tube is fitted into a stopper lubricated with glycerol at *a*, the suction line is connected at *b*, and flasks for receiving fractions are attached to the arms *c*, *d*, and *e*. By turning the adapter through the proper angle a small forerun can be caught in the bulb of the adapter (*f*) and then three successive fractions can be run into receivers at *c*, *d*, and *e*. With low-boiling liquids this method has the disadvantage that the three receiving flasks are all open to the same vapor space and there may be some interchange of vapors between the three fractions.

The flask shown in Fig. 39.5 is useful for distillation of a very small amount of material. Toward the end of a distillation the liquid draining from the walls is confined to a small area by the conical bulb and little material is lost as undistilled residue.

2. Suction Pumps

A water pump in good order gives suction nearly corresponding to the vapor pressure of water at the temperature of flow. If a manometer is not available and the distillation assembly is free from leaks, an approximate estimate of the pressure can be made by measuring the water temperature and reading the pressure from the accompanying table. An oil pump in perfect condition

Vacuum Distillation

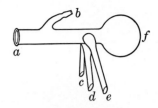

FIG. 39.4 Adapter for collecting fractions at constant pressure

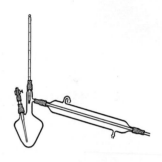

FIG. 39.5 Pointed flask for the distillation of small quantities

TABLE 39.1

VAPOR PRESSURE OF WATER

(mm. Mercury)

t	p	t	p	t	p	t	p
0°	4.58	20°	17.41	24°	22.18	28°	28.10
5°	6.53	21°	18.50	25°	23.54	29°	29.78
10°	9.18	22°	19.66	26°	24.99	30°	31.55
15°	12.73	23°	20.88	27°	26.50	35°	41.85

can give pressures as low as 0.1 mm.; one with average wear will go down to 2–3 mm. if not abused.

3. Relationship between Boiling Point and Pressure

It is not possible to calculate the boiling point of a substance at some reduced pressure from a knowledge of the boiling temperature at 760 mm., for the relationship between boiling point and pressure varies from compound to compound and is unpredictable. It is true, however, that boiling point curves for organic substances have much the same general disposition, as illustrated by the two lower curves in Fig. 39.6. These are similar and do not differ greatly from the curve for water. For substances boiling in the region 150–250° at 760 mm., the boiling point at 20 mm. is 100–120° lower than at 760 mm. Benzaldehyde, which is very sensitive to air oxidation at the normal boiling point of 178°,

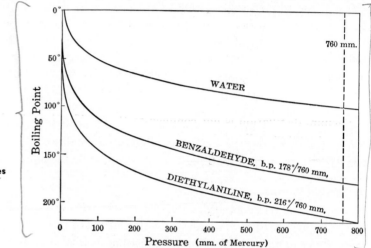

FIG. 39.6 Boiling point curves

distils at 76° at 20 mm. pressure, and the concentration of oxygen in the rarefied atmosphere is just 20/760, or 3%, of that in an ordinary distillation.

The curves all show a sharp upward inclination in the region of very low pressure. The lowering of the boiling point attending a reduction in pressure is much more pronounced at low than at high pressures. A drop in the atmospheric pressure of 10 mm. lowers the normal boiling point of an ordinary liquid by less than a degree, but a reduction of pressure from 20 mm. to 10 mm. causes a drop of about 15° in the boiling point. The effect at pressures below 1 mm. is still more striking, and with development of practical forms of the highly efficient mercury vapor pump, distillation at a pressure of a few thousandths or ten thousandths of a millimeter has become a standard operation in many research laboratories. High vacuum distillation, that is at a pressure below 1 mm., affords a useful means of purifying extremely sensitive or very slightly volatile substances. The following table indicates the order of magnitude of the reduction in boiling point attainable by operating in different ways and illustrates the importance of keeping suction pumps in good repair.

DISTILLATION OF A (HYPOTHETICAL) SUBSTANCE AT VARIOUS PRESSURES

Method		Pressure (mm.)	B.p.
Ordinary distillation		760	250°
Water pump	summer	25	144°
	winter	15	134°
Oil pump	poor condition	10	124°
	good condition	3	99°
	excellent condition	1	89°
Mercury vapor pump...............		0.01	30°

4. Distillation of Solids

Vacuum distillation is not confined to the purification of substances liquid at ordinary temperatures but often can be used to advantage for solid substances. The operation is conducted for a different purpose and by a different technique. A solid is seldom distilled with the object of effecting a separation of constituents of different degrees of volatility but rather to cleanse the solid. It is often possible in one vacuum distillation to remove foreign coloring matter and tar without appreciable loss of product, whereas several wasteful crystallizations might be required to attain the same purity. It is often good practice to distil a crude product and then to crystallize it. Time is saved in the latter operation because the hot solution usually requires neither filtration nor clarification. The solid must be dry and a test should be made to determine if it will distil without decomposition at the pressure of the pump available. That a compound lacks the required stability at high temperatures may sometimes be foretold from the structure, but a high melting point should not be taken as an indication that distillation will fail. Substances melting as high as 300° have been distilled with success at the pressure of an ordinary oil pump.

It is not necessary to observe the boiling point in distillations of this kind because the purity and identity of the distillate can be checked by melting point determinations. The omission of the customary thermometer simplifies the technique. A simple and useful assembly is shown in Fig. 39.7. A rather stout capillary tube carrying an adjustable vent at the top is fitted into the neck of the two-bulb flask by means of a rubber stopper and the suction pump is connected through a trap at the other bulb. It is not necessary to insert in the mouth a rubber stopper of

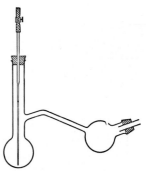

FIG. 39.7 Two-bulb flask for the distillation of solids

219

just the right size; a somewhat larger stopper may be put on backwards as shown and held in place by the suction. The same scheme can be used for the other stopper. Water cooling is unnecessary. If some cooling of the receiving bulb is required it is best to use an air blast. Since the connection between the distilling and the receiving flask is of glass any material that solidifies and tends to plug the side arm can be melted with a free flame. A heating bath should not be used; it is best to heat the flask with a rather large flame. Hold the burner in the hand and play the flame in a rotary motion around the side walls of the flask. This allows less bumping than when the flask is heated from the bottom. If there is much frothing at the start direct the flame upon the upper walls and the neck of the flask. If the liquid froths over into the receiving bulb, the flask is tilted to such a position that this bulb can drain through the connecting tube back into the distillation bulb when suitably warmed.

At the end of the distillation the vacuum is broken by careful opening of the pinchcock and the contents of the receiving bulb melted and poured out. This method of emptying the bulb is sometimes inadvisable because the hot, molten material may be susceptible to air oxidation. In such a case the material is allowed to solidify and cool completely before the vacuum is broken. The solid is then chipped out with a clean knife or with a strong nickel spatula and the last traces recovered with the solvent to be used in the crystallization. The bad tar usually remaining in the distillation bulb is best removed by adding small quantities of concentrated nitric and sulfuric acids, mixing the layers well, and heating the mixture while the flask is supported by a clamp under the hood. After cooling and pouring the acid mixture down the drain, loose char is removed with water and a brush and the process is repeated.

Dyes and Dyeing CHAPTER **40**

In carrying out the following experiments keep in mind that considerable damage to the laboratory or the clothing may result from careless work. It is entirely possible to avoid staining the working space or the person. Stirring rods are nearly as convenient as fingers for manipulating dyed cloth until it is thoroughly washed and are more easily cleaned.

Most cotton cloth available contains inorganic material as filler or sizing and this may have a mordanting action which will obscure the true behavior of cellulose material toward some of the dyes. The cotton supplied for the experiment should be freed of sizing by boiling it with soda solution.[1]

Unless otherwise specified the small quantities of dyes and reagents called for may be estimated, and it is better to use too little material rather than too much.[2]

Dry small samples of dyed material and mount them in your notebook.

EXPERIMENTS

1. Picric Acid (direct to wool and silk)[3]

Dissolve 0.5 g. of the acid in a little hot water to which a few drops of sulfuric acid have been added. Heat pieces of wool, silk, and cotton in this bath for one minute, then remove them with a stirring rod, rinse well, wring, and dry. Describe the results.

[1] Boil for 2 hours with 2 % sodium carbonate solution, repeat with fresh solution and wash thoroughly.
[2] The dyes required are best supplied in individual waxed envelopes.
[3] Picric acid stains on the skin can be removed by applying a coating of collodion and, after 10 minutes, peeling this off with a knife blade.

2. Congo Red, a Benzidine Dye

Dissolve 0.1 g. of Congo Red in 400 ml. of water, add about 1 ml. each of 10% solutions of sodium carbonate and sodium sulfate, heat to a temperature just below the boiling point, and introduce pieces of cotton, wool, and silk. At the end of 10 min. remove the fabrics and wash in warm water as long as the dye is removed. Place pieces of the dyed material in very dilute hydrochloric acid solution and observe the result. Rinse and wash with soap.

3. Orange II

The dye bath is prepared from 0.5 g. of Orange II, 5 ml. of sodium sulfate solution, 300 ml. of water, and 5 drops of concd. sulfuric acid. Dye wool, silk, and cotton for 5 min. at a temperature near the boiling point.

Replace the dyed wool in the bath, make the solution alkaline with sodium carbonate, and add sodium hydrosulfite ($Na_2S_2O_4$) until the color of the bath is discharged. Account for the result.

4. Eosin (direct to silk or wool)

Dissolve 0.1 g. of sodium eosin in 200 ml. of water and dye a piece of silk by heating it with the solution for about 10 min.

5. Triphenylmethane Dyes

Mordant pieces of cotton cloth by allowing them to stand in a hot solution of 0.5 g. of tannic acid in 500 ml. of water for 5 min. The mordant must now be fixed to the cloth, otherwise it would wash out. For this purpose, transfer the cloth to a hot bath made from 0.2 g. of tartar emetic (potassium antimonyl tartrate) in 200 ml. of water. After 5 min., wring the cloth. A dye bath is prepared by dissolving 0.1 g. of one of the following dyes in 200 ml. of water (boiling). Dye the mordanted cloth in this bath for 5–10 min. at a temperature just below the boiling point.

Dyes: Malachite Green, Crystal Violet, Methyl Violet.

Try further dyeings with unmordanted cotton and with untreated wool or silk.

NOTE: The stains on glass produced by triphenylmethane dyes can be removed with concd. hydrochloric acid, which forms a di- or trihydrochloride more soluble than the original monosalt.

6. A Developed Dye: Primuline

Dye three pieces of cotton cloth in a solution of 0.2 g. of primuline and 5 ml. of sodium carbonate solution in 500 ml. of water,
at a temperature just below the boiling point for 15 min. Wash
the cloth twice in about 500 ml. of water. Prepare a diazotizing
bath by dissolving 0.2 g. of sodium nitrite in 500 ml. of water
containing a little ice and, just before using the bath, add 5 ml.
of concd. hydrochloric acid. Allow the cloth dyed with primuline
to stay in this diazotizing bath for about 5 min. Now prepare
three baths for the coupling reaction. Dissolve 0.1 g. of β-naphthol in 2 ml. of 5% sodium hydroxide solution and dilute with
100 ml. of water; prepare similar baths from phenol, resorcinol,
Naphthol-AS, or other phenolic substances.

Transfer the cloth from the diazotizing bath to a beaker containing about 500 ml. of water and stir. Put one piece of cloth
in each of the developing baths and allow them to stay for 5 min.

7. Para Red, an Ingrain Color

Prepare a solution of *p*-nitrobenzenediazonium chloride as
follows: dissolve 1.4 g. of *p*-nitroaniline in a mixture of 30 ml.
of water and 6 ml. of 10% hydrochloric acid, by heating. Cool
the solution in ice (the hydrochloride of the amine may crystallize), add all at once a solution of 0.7 g. of sodium nitrite in a
little water and filter the solution by suction. The material to
be dyed (cotton cloth, filter paper) is first soaked in a solution
prepared by suspending 0.5 g. of β-naphthol in 100 ml. of water,
stirring well and adding alkali, a drop at a time, until the material
all dissolves. This solution may also be painted onto the cloth.
The cloth is then dried and dipped into the solution of the diazotized amine, after diluting the latter with about 300 ml. of
water.

Better results can be obtained by substituting Naphthol-AS
for β-naphthol; in this case it is necessary to warm with alkali
and to break the lumps with a flattened stirring rod in order to
bring the material into solution.

8. Vat Dyes

Use 0.2 g. of a solid dye; if a dye is available in the form of a
paste use as much as will adhere to about 1 cm. of the end of a
stirring rod. Boil the dye with 100–200 ml. of water, 5 ml. of
10% sodium hydroxide solution, and about 1 g. of sodium hydrosulfite until it is reduced. Introduce a piece of cotton cloth and

boil the solution gently for 10 min. Rinse the cloth well in water and allow it to dry.

> Dyes: Indigo, Indanthrene Brilliant Violet, Indanthrene Yellow.

FORMATION OF DYES

1. Phenolphthalein

Mix 0.1 g. of phthalic anhydride and 0.1 g. of phenol in a test tube, add 2 drops of concd. sulfuric acid, and heat gently over a small flame with constant agitation for about 2 min. The melt will become dark red but should not blacken. When cool, treat with 5 ml. of water and then add very gradually, with shaking, a dilute solution of sodium hydroxide until a permanent pink color is obtained. Then test the suitability of the material as an indicator by adding first a trace of acid and then a trace of alkali.

2. Fluorescein

Heat gently for 2 min. a mixture of 0.1 g. each of phthalic anhydride and resorcinol to which 3–4 drops of concd. sulfuric acid have been added. Allow to cool, add 5 ml. of water, make alkaline with sodium hydroxide. Add a drop of this solution to a test tube full of water.

3. Crystal Violet, a Triphenylmethane Dye

Michler's ketone (p,p'-tetramethyldiaminobenzophenone) has the structure: $(CH_3)_2N \cdot C_6H_4 \cdot CO \cdot C_6H_4 \cdot N(CH_3)_2$. In the presence of phosphorus oxychloride, aniline adds to this compound in such a way that the para carbon of aniline becomes joined to the carbon of the carbonyl group, while the para hydrogen becomes attached to the oxygen. In the presence of an acid, here derived from the phosphorus oxychloride, a dye is formed.

Place 0.1 g. of Michler's ketone, 5 drops of dimethylaniline, and 2 drops of phosphorus oxychloride in a test tube, and heat the tube in boiling water for one half hour. Add 10 ml. of water and stir.

Add several drops of this solution to 20 ml. of water and treat with a little ammonia. Let stand until the color has disappeared and then add hydrochloric acid.

Write the formula for crystal violet and account for the color changes noted.

If the original solution is allowed to stand overnight, crystals of crystal violet should separate.

Qualitative Organic Analysis | CHAPTER 41

Since previous experiments have been devoted to identification of unknown aliphatic compounds (aldehydes and ketones, amines, sugars, amino acids), the present experiment is limited to aromatic compounds. Hydrocarbons, as well as hydrocarbon derivatives containing no functional group other than halogen and alkoxyl, are excluded because no simple tests for these inert substances are available. The unknowns are all individual compounds rather than mixtures, but they may contain more than one functional group.

After examination of physical properties and qualitative analysis for elements other than carbon, hydrogen, and oxygen, the unknown is placed into one of six groups on the basis of its solubility in water, ether, dilute acid, dilute base, and concd. sulfuric acid.[1] This information provides a clue to the possible functional group or groups present; application of standard class tests then limits the solubility classification still further. Complete identification should always be attempted, although in some cases it may not be practicable.

Tests for substances of given types have been described in appropriate chapters, which should be consulted for details. The order given in the following procedure need not be followed rigidly. If the unknown has a color or odor characteristic of a given group, pertinent specific tests can be carried out immediately.

PROCEDURE

1. Physical State

Note the color. Common colored aromatic compounds include α-diketones (yellow), quinones (mostly yellow to red), nitro and

_____
_____ *Color* _____
_____

[1] D. Davidson, *J. Chem. Ed.*, **19**, 221 (1942), has described a classification based upon acidic and basic properties.

nitroso compounds (yellow), azo compounds (yellow to red). A color due to a trace of impurity is usually dull and should not be considered in diagnosis. Note the odor. Some phenols have characteristic, pungent odors. Some liquid and solid amines are recognizable by smell. Esters are often pleasantly fragrant. Benzoquinone induces sneezing.

Note the crystalline form (needles, plates, prisms) and distinguish between a microcrystalline and an amorphous solid. Make an ignition test by heating a small sample carefully on a knife blade or on a small loop at the end of a copper wire; first hold the sample at the side of a microburner flame to see if it melts normally and then heat it in the flame. If a large ashy residue is left after ignition, the unknown is probably a metal salt. If normal melting is observed determine the *melting point;* in case this is not sharp you may care to purify by crystallization to constant melting point.

For determination of the *boiling point* of a liquid unknown it is advisable to use a 25-ml. flask and condenser (Fig. 2.1) rather than a test tube, for then you can observe the boiling range and, if you find the distillate lighter colored than the sample, purify the whole sample by distillation. Calibration of a capillary dropper for delivery of the unknown liquid will establish its *specific gravity.*

Whether the unknown is a liquid or solid, Rast determination of the molecular weight (Chapter 4.6), carried out at some stage of the investigation, may provide useful information.

2. Elementary Analysis. Sodium Fusion [2]

This method for detection of nitrogen, sulfur, and halogen in organic compounds depends upon the fact that fusion of substances containing these elements with sodium [3] yields NaCN, Na_2S, and NaX (X = Cl, Br, I). These products can, in turn, be readily identified. The method has the advantage that the most usual elements other than C, H, and O present in organic compounds can all be detected following a single fusion, although the presence of sulfur sometimes interferes with the test for nitrogen. Unfortunately even in the absence of sulfur the test for nitrogen is sometimes unsatisfactory (nitro compounds in

[2] S. H. Tucker, *J. Chem. Ed.*, **22**, 212 (1945).
[3] Metallic potassium, which is more reactive, is also used; F. Feigl, *Spot Tests,* Elsevier (1954). A method of fusion with potassium carbonate and magnesium is described by R. H. Baker and C. Barkenbus, *Ind. Eng. Chem., Anal. Ed.*, **9**, 135 (1937).

particular). In an alternative method,[4] the sample is pyrolyzed with calcium oxide and zinc, which liberates ammonia, detected by litmus paper; a rather elaborate combustion assembly is required.

Procedure. Place a 3-mm. cube of sodium (30 mg., no more; note size of dummy 3-mm. cube of rubber attached to sodium bottle) in a 10 × 75-mm. Pyrex test tube and support the tube in a vertical position (either clamp it in a spring clothes clip or push it through a square of asbestos paper, and let the clip or asbestos rest on the open jaws of a clamp). Make a microburner with small flame ready to move under the tube, place an estimated 20 mg. of solid on a spatula or knife blade, put the burner in place and heat until the sodium first melts and then vapor begins to rise in the tube, then remove the burner and at once drop the sample onto hot sodium. If the substance is a liquid add 2 micro drops of it. If there was a flash or small explosion the fusion is complete; if not, heat briefly to produce a flash or a charring. Then let the tube cool to room temperature (air blast), be sure it is cold, add a micro drop of methanol and let it react (heat effect), and repeat until 10 micro drops have been added. With a stirring rod break up the char to uncover sodium. When you are sure that all sodium has reacted, empty the tube into a 13 × 100-mm. test tube, hold the small tube pointing away from you or a neighbor, and pipette into it 1 ml. of water. Boil and stir the mixture and pour the water into the larger tube; repeat with 1 ml. more water. Then transfer the solution with a capillary dropper to a 2.5-cm. funnel with paper, resting in a second 13 × 100-mm. test tube. Portions of the alkaline filtrate are used for the tests below.

Nitrogen. The test is done by boiling the alkaline solution with ferrous sulfate and then acidifying. Sodium cyanide reacts with ferrous sulfate to produce ferrocyanide, which combines with ferric salts, inevitably formed by air oxidation in the alkaline solution, to give Prussian Blue, $NaFe^{III}Fe^{II}(CN)_6$. Ferrous and ferric hydroxides precipitate along with the blue pigment but dissolve on acidification.

Place 50 mg. of powdered ferrous sulfate (this is a large excess) in a 13 × 100-mm. test tube, add 0.5 ml. of the alkaline solution from the fusion, heat the mixture gently with shaking to the boiling point, and then without cooling acidify with dilute sulfuric acid (hydrochloric acid is unsatisfactory). A deep blue pre-

[4] E. L. Bennett, C. W. Gould, E. H. Swift, and C. Niemann, *Anal. Chem.*, **19**, 1035 (1947).

Caution! Manipulate sodium with a knife and forceps; never touch it with the fingers. Wipe it free of kerosene with a dry towel or filter paper; return scraps to the bottle or destroy scraps with methyl or ethyl alcohol, never with water.

Safety glasses!

Do not use CHCl₃ or CCl₄ as samples in sodium fusion

Run each test on a known and an unknown

cipitate indicates the presence of nitrogen. If the coloration is dubious, filter through a 2.5-cm. funnel and see if the paper shows blue pigment.

Sulfur. (a) A drop of the alkaline fusion solution placed on a silver coin (cleaned with acetone) will give a brown stain if sulfur is present. (b) Dilute one drop of the alkaline solution with 1 ml. of water and add a drop of sodium nitroprusside; a purple coloration indicates the presence of sulfur. (c) Prepare a fresh solution of sodium plumbite by adding 10% sodium hydroxide solution to 0.2 ml. of 0.1 M lead acetate solution until the precipitate just dissolves, and add 0.5 ml. of the alkaline test solution. A black precipitate or a colloidal brown suspension indicates the presence of sulfur.

Halogen. Acidify 0.5 ml. of alkaline solution from the fusion with dilute nitric acid (indicator paper) and, if nitrogen or sulfur has been found present, boil the solution (hood) to expel HCN or H_2S. On addition of a few drops of silver nitrate solution, halide ion is precipitated as silver halide. Filter on a 2.5-cm. funnel, wash with water, and then with 1 ml. of concd. ammonia solution. If the precipitate is white and readily soluble in ammonia it is AgCl; if it is pale yellow and difficultly soluble it is AgBr; if yellow and insoluble it is AgI. Fluorine is not detected in this test since silver fluoride is soluble in water.

Beilstein test (Chapter 9). This test is so sensitive that minute impurities can lead to a positive reaction. Fluorine is not detected since copper fluoride is nonvolatile.

Differentiation of the halogens

3. Solubility Tests

The solubility of a substance in various solvents is the basis of a method of qualitative analysis developed by Kamm [5] and used here in simplified form. The principle is that a substance is most soluble in that solvent to which it is most closely related in structure; whereas lower members of a homologous series are easily classified, higher members become more like the hydrocarbons from which they are derived. Compounds are divided on the basis of water-solubility into two main groups, which are then subdivided on the basis of solubility in other solvents. All solubility measurements are done at room temperature with 1 micro drop of a liquid, or 5 mg. of solid (finely crushed), and 0.2 ml. of solvent. The mixture should be rubbed with a rounded stirring rod and shaken vigorously. Carry out the tests in the

[5] O. Kamm, *Qualitative Organic Analysis*, 2nd Ed., Wiley (1922).

order shown in the charts and from the results tentatively assign the unknown to one of the groups, I–VI.

If an unknown seems to be more soluble in dilute acid or base than in water, the observation can be confirmed by neutralization of the solution; the original material will precipitate if it is less soluble in a neutral medium.

If both acidic and basic groups are present, the substance may be amphoteric, that is, soluble in both acid and base. Aromatic aminocarboxylic acids are amphoteric, like aliphatic ones, but do not exist as inner salts. They are soluble in both dilute hydrochloric acid and sodium hydroxide, but not in bicarbonate solution. Aminosulfonic acids exist as inner salts; they are soluble in alkali but not in acid.

The solubility tests are not infallible and many borderline cases are known.

4. Specific Class Tests

After the unknown is assigned to one of the groups on the basis of solubility tests, for example group V, the possible type should be further narrowed by application of class tests. Thus members of this group contain a carbonyl group and may be quinones, ketones, aldehydes, esters, or anhydrides. Properties characteristic of these types have usually been discussed in previous chapters, which should be consulted for details. If not, the notes contain suggested tests.

5. Complete Identification

Once the unknown is recognized as a carboxylic acid, for example, the physical properties should be compared with those of representative carboxylic acids.[6] Usually several possibilities present themselves and the choice can be narrowed further by preparation of derivatives. Pick derivatives that distinguish most clearly between the possibilities.

NOTES (Groups I, II, see p. 230)

1. Test the solution with Hydrion paper. If the compound is not *easily* soluble in cold water, treat it as water-insoluble but test with indicator paper.

---

[6] Useful tables giving the physical constants of the more common compounds and of suitable derivatives for characterization can be found in the following books: F. Wild, *Characterization of Organic Compounds*, Cambridge (1947); N. D. Cheronis and J. B. Entrikin, *Semimicro Qualitative Organic Analysis*, Crowell (1947); R. L. Shriner and R. C. Fuson, *The Systematic Identification of Organic Compounds*, Wiley (1948).

Groups I and II

GROUP I SOLUBLE IN ETHER	GROUP II INSOLUBLE IN ETHER [Note 2]	
	A	B
	Acid to litmus, fusible	Neutral
Some Phenols (See IV B, below.) Some Hydroxy Acids	Sulfonic Acids Polycarboxylic Acids Amine Salts (weakly acidic)	Metal Salts (infusible) Ammonium Salts (fusible)

2. The addition of hydrochloric acid to a water solution of the unknown may give a precipitate of a carboxylic acid (solid); sodium hydroxide may precipitate an amine (oil or solid), particularly if the solution is concentrated or if solid sodium chloride is added, or it may cause the liberation of ammonia (odor). In either case the material (from a larger sample of the unknown) should be collected (either by filtration or by extraction with ether) and the carboxylic acid or the amine then can be studied further as in IV A or III. The salt of a sulfonic acid is not affected by adding hydrochloric acid. If such a salt is suspected, it should be analyzed for sulfur. A sulfonic acid or its salt often can be identified from the melting point of the p-toluidine salt (preparation: Chapter 25.2).

INSOLUBLE IN COLD WATER

Groups III and IV

GROUP III SOLUBLE IN 5% HCl [Note 1]	GROUP IV SOLUBLE IN DIL. NaOH [Note 2]	
	A	B
	Soluble in 5% NaHCO₃	Insoluble in NaHCO₃
Amines (3 classes) (See Chapter 20.)	Carboxylic Acids [Note 3] Certain Phenols [Note 4] Amino Sulfonic Acids	Phenols [Note 5]

NOTES

1. Some amines dissolve only when the mixture is heated; if solution then occurs, neutralize with alkali and see if the amine precipitates. If a part of the solid appears to dissolve, decant and neutralize the supernatant liquor.

2. Use 2–3 drops of 10% sodium hydroxide solution and 0.5 ml. of water. If the substance dissolves partially add more water; the sodium salts of some phenols are less soluble in alkali than in water. If the unknown is colored, be careful to distinguish between the *dissolving* and the *reacting* of the sample. Some

quinones (colored) *react* with alkali and give highly colored solutions. On the other hand, some phenols (colorless) *dissolve and then* become oxidized to give colored solutions. Some compounds (e.g. benzamide) are hydrolyzed with such ease that careful observation is required to distinguish them from acidic substances.

3. Carboxylic acids can be identified by conversion to an ester, recognizable by being insoluble in dilute alkali. A methyl ester can be made by refluxing a mixture of 0.2 g. of acid, 2–3 ml. of methanol, and 2–3 drops of concd. sulfuric acid under a cold finger for 1 hr.

The *p*-nitrobenzyl esters, all of which are crystalline solids of sharp melting point, are prepared as follows. Dissolve 0.2 g. of acid in water or aqueous alcohol and neutralize carefully with 10% sodium hydroxide solution and adjust to pH 6–7 with dilute acid. Add a solution of 0.2 g. of *p*-nitrobenzyl bromide (lachrymatory) in 2 ml. of methanol and reflux under a cold finger for 1 hr. If the ester has partially separated, add enough methanol to dissolve it for crystallization. If no ester separates add water.

Amide and anilide derivatives are prepared by conversion to the acid chloride and treatment of this with ammonia or aniline (see preparation of benzamide, Chapter 36.2).

4. Nitrophenols (yellow), aldehydo phenols, and polyhalo phenols are sufficiently strongly acidic to react with sodium bicarbonate.

5. Some phenols give characteristic colors on addition of a drop of ferric chloride solution to a dilute aqueous or alcoholic solution of the material. The test is negative with nitrophenols and with *m*- and *p*-phenolcarboxylic acids.

Polyhydroxy phenols having *o*- or *p*-hydroxyl groups undergo air oxidation in alkaline solution with development of color.

A reaction useful for both phenols and amines is that with bromine water (Chapter 26.2).

Urethans, useful derivatives of phenols, are made by reaction with α-naphthylisocyanate under basic catalysis:

$$C_{10}H_7N{=}C{=}O + ArOH \longrightarrow C_{10}H_7NHCO_2R$$

The phenol (0.2 g.), the isocyanate (0.2 g.), and 1 drop of pyridine or triethylamine are heated in a test tube over a small flame. The mixture generally becomes red within a few minutes and is then cooled and the solid crystallized from ligroin.

The 3,5-dinitrobenzoates are also useful, high-melting derivatives. Four procedures for the preparation of acetates are given in Chapter 37.

	SOLUBLE IN COLD, CONCD. H_2SO_4 Notes 1, 2				
	GROUP V CARBONYL COMPOUNDS			GROUP VI NEUTRAL NITROGEN COMPOUNDS	
A	B	C	A	B
Colored compounds	React with phenylhydrazine	Hydrolyzed by hot NaOH Note 4	Reducible, Note 5 colored	Hydrolyzable, Note 6 usually colorless solids
Quinones Note 3 Diketones (See tests for benzil, Chapter 31.2.)	Aldehydes Ketones (See Chapter 14.)	Esters Anhydrides	Polynitro Compounds (yellow) Azo Compounds (orange or red)	Amides (RCONH₂) Acetyl Amines (RNHCOCH₃)

Groups V and VI

NOTES

1. This general property of oxygen- and nitrogen-containing compounds depends upon formation of oxonium or ammonium salts. The test distinguishes phenol ethers (not included here), which dissolve, from hydrocarbons, which do not dissolve.

2. Test for the presence of nitrogen.

3. Quinones (colored) can be recognized by their easy reduction to hydroquinones (usually colorless). Suspend a small sample in a little water, add a small pinch of sodium hydrosulfite ($Na_2S_2O_4$), and heat. A green quinhydrone is sometimes observed as an intermediary product. The hydroquinone may separate or it may remain dissolved in the hot solution. If an anthraquinone is suspected (high melting point, slight solubility, slow reduction), add sodium hydroxide solution along with the hydrosulfite and keep the solution alkaline; a characteristic red vat will then develop if the quinone belongs to the anthracene series.

4. Reflux 0.2 g. of the sample under a cold finger, with 5 ml. of 5% sodium hydroxide solution for 10–20 minutes. If a clear solution is obtained, cool and acidify the solution. If the acid fails to separate, use a more concentrated solution.

5. On reduction in the presence of hydrochloric acid these compounds form water-soluble amine hydrochlorides. Dissolve 0.5 g. of stannous chloride in 1 ml. of concd. hydrochloric acid, add 0.1 g. of the unknown, and warm. The material should dissolve with disappearance of the color and give a clear solution when diluted with water. See Chapter 33.

6. Most amides can be hydrolyzed by short boiling with 10%

sodium hydroxide solution; the acid dissolves with evolution of
ammonia.   An acetyl amine can be hydrolyzed by either acid or
alkali.   Using the cold finger, reflux for 15–20 min. a mixture of
0.2 g. of the sample and 5 ml. of either 10% sodium hydroxide
or 20% hydrochloric acid (equal parts of the concd. acid and
water).   If hydrolysis occurs, determine if the product is an
amine.

CHAPTER 42 | Martius Yellow

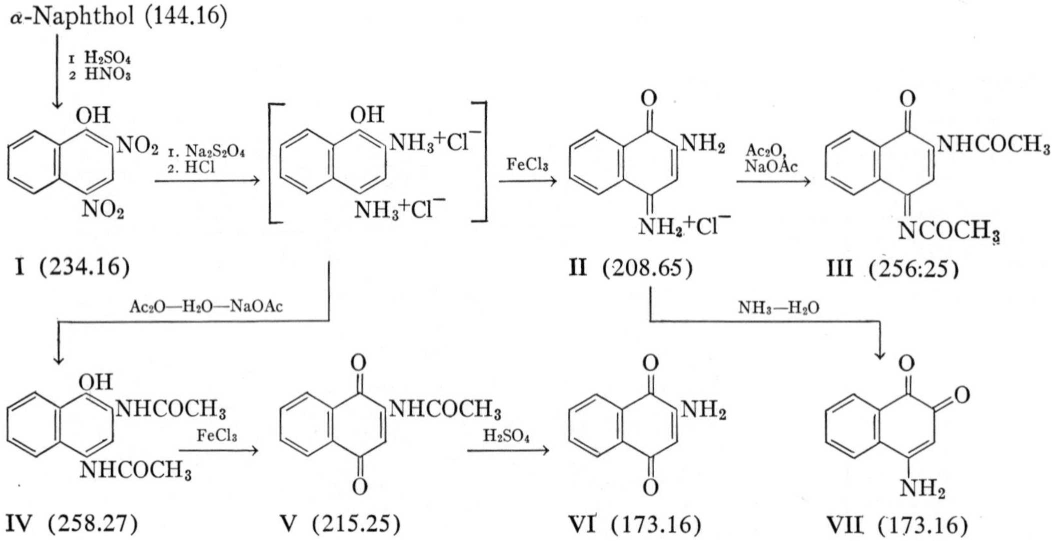

α-Naphthol (144.16)

1 H₂SO₄
2 HNO₃

I (234.16) II (208.65) III (256:25)

Ac₂O—H₂O—NaOAc   NH₃—H₂O

IV (258.27) V (215.25) VI (173.16) VII (173.16)

Martius Yellow, a mothproofing dye for wool (1 g. dyes 200 g.) discovered in 1868 by Karl Alexander von Martius, is the ammonium salt of 2,4-dinitro-1-naphthol (I), the first of seven compounds that can be prepared in two laboratory periods. It is obtained by sulfonation of α-naphthol and treatment of the resulting mono- or disulfonic acid with nitric acid in aqueous solution. It is purified by precipitation of the ammonium salt, a small part of which is converted by acidification and crystallization into a sample of pure 2,4-dinitro-1-naphthol that is saved. The rest is suspended in water and reduced with sodium hydrosulfite [1] to the diaminonaphthol which, because it is very sensitive

---

[1] The reduction is formulated as follows:

$C_{10}H_5(NO_2)_2ONH_4 + 6Na_2S_2O_4 + 8H_2O \rightarrow$

$C_{10}H_5(NH_2)_2OH + 11NaHSO_3 + Na(NH_4)SO_3$

to air oxidation as the free base, is at once dissolved in dilute hydrochloric acid. The solution of diaminonaphthol dihydrochloride is clarified and divided into equal parts. One part on oxidation with ferric chloride affords the fiery red 2-amino-1,4-naphthoquinonimine hydrochloride (II), which on acetylation yields the yellow diacetate III and on hydrolysis the orange 4-amino-1,2-naphthoquinone (VII). The other half of the solution of 2,4-diamino-1-naphthol dihydrochloride is treated with acetic anhydride and then sodium acetate; the reaction in aqueous solution effects selective acetylation of the amino groups and affords 2,4-diacetylamino-1-naphthol (IV). Oxidation of IV is attended with cleavage of the acetylamino group at the 4-position and the product is 2-acetylamino-1,4-naphthoquinone (V). This yellow substance is hydrolyzed by sulfuric acid to the red 2-amino-1,4-naphthoquinone (VI), the last member of the series. The reaction periods are brief and the yields high.[2]

I. 2,4-Dinitro-1-naphthol

Place 5 g. of pure α-naphthol[3] in a 125-ml. Erlenmeyer flask, add 10 ml. of concd. sulfuric acid, and heat the mixture with swirling on the steam bath for 5 min., when the solid should have dissolved and an initial red color should be discharged. Cool in an ice bath, add 25 ml. of water, and cool the solution rapidly to 15°. Measure 6 ml. of concd. nitric acid into a test tube and transfer it with a capillary dropping tube in small portions (0.5 ml.) to the chilled aqueous solution while keeping the temperature in the range 15–20° by swirling the flask vigorously in the ice bath. When the addition is complete and the exothermic reaction has subsided (1–2 min.), warm the mixture gently to 50° (1 min.), when the nitration product should separate as a stiff

---

[2] In the Martius Yellow prize competition held annually in the author's course the rules are at present as follows: (1) No practice or advance preparation is allowable except collection of reagents not available at the contestant's bench (ammonium chloride, sodium hydrosulfite, ferric chloride solution, acetic anhydride). (2) The time scored is the actual working time, including that required for bottling the samples and cleaning the apparatus and bench; labels can be prepared out of the working period. (3) Time is not charged during an interim period (overnight) when solutions are let stand to crystallize or solids are let dry, on condition that during this period no adjustments are made and no cleaning or other work is done. (4) Melting point and color test characterizations are omitted. (5) Successful completion of the contest requires preparation of authentic and macroscopically crystalline samples of all seven compounds. (6) Judgment of the winners among the successful contestants is based upon quality and quantity of samples, technique and neatness, and working time (superior performance: 3–4 hrs.).

[3] If the α-naphthol is dark it can be purified by distillation at atmospheric pressure. The colorless distillate is most easily pulverized before it has completely cooled and hardened.

yellow paste. Apply the full heat of the steam bath for 1 min. more, fill the flask with water, stir to an even paste, collect the product I, wash it well with water, and then wash it into a 600-ml. beaker with water (100 ml.). Add 150 ml. of hot water and 5 ml. of concd. ammonia solution (sp. gr. 0.90) and heat to the boiling point and stir to dissolve the solid. Filter the hot solution by suction from a little dirt, add 10 g. of ammonium chloride to the filtrate to salt out the ammonium salt (Martius Yellow), cool in an ice bath, collect the orange salt, and wash it with water containing 1–2% of ammonium chloride. The salt does not have to be dried (dry weight 7.7 g., 88.5 %).

Set aside an estimated 0.3 g. of the moist ammonium salt. This sample is to be dissolved in hot water, the solution acidified (HCl), and the free 2,4-dinitro-1-naphthol (I) crystallized from methanol or ethanol (Norit); it forms yellow needles, m.p. 138°.

Reduction to 2,4-Diamino-1-naphthol

Wash the rest of the ammonium salt into a beaker with a total of about 200 ml. of water, add 40 g. of sodium hydrosulfite, stir until the original orange color has disappeared and a crystalline tan precipitate has formed (5–10 min.), and cool in ice. Make ready a solution of 1–2 g. of sodium hydrosulfite in 100 ml. of water for use in washing and a 400-ml. beaker containing 6 ml. of concentrated hydrochloric acid and 25 ml. of water. In collecting the precipitate by suction filtration use the hydrosulfite solution for rinsing and washing, avoid even briefly sucking air through the cake after the reducing agent has been drained away, and wash the solid at once into the beaker containing dilute hydrochloric acid and stir to convert all the diamine to the dihydrochloride.

The acid solution, often containing suspended sulfur and filter paper, is clarified by filtration by suction through a moist bed of Norit made by shaking 2 g. of the decolorizing carbon with 25 ml. of water in a stoppered flask to produce a slurry and pouring this on the paper of an 85-mm. Büchner funnel. Pour the water out of the filter flask and then filter the solution of dihydrochloride. Divide the pink or colorless filtrate into two approximately equal parts and at once add the reagents for conversion of one part to II and the other to IV.

II. 2-Amino-1,4-naphthoquinonimine Hydrochloride

To one half of the diamine dihydrochloride solution add 25 ml.

of 1.3 M ferric chloride solution,[4] then cool in ice and if necessary initiate crystallization by scratching. Rub the liquid film at a single spot slightly above the surface of the liquid. If unsuccessful, add more hydrochloric acid. Collect the red product and wash it with dilute hydrochloric acid. Dry weight 2.4–2.7 g.

Divide the moist product into three equal parts and spread out one part to dry for conversion to III. The other parts can be used while still moist for conversion to VII and for recrystallization. Dissolve the latter by gentle warming in a little water containing 2–3 drops of hydrochloric acid, shake for a minute or two with Norit, filter, and add concentrated hydrochloric acid to decrease the solubility.

III. 2-Amino-1,4-naphthoquinonimine Diacetate

A mixture of 0.5 g. of the dry quinonimine hydrochloride II, 0.5 g. of sodium acetate (anhydrous), and 3 ml. of acetic anhydride is stirred in a test tube and warmed gently over the steam bath. With thorough stirring the red salt should soon change into yellow crystals of the diacetate. The solution may appear red, but as soon as particles of red solid have disappeared the mixture can be poured into a little water. Stir until the excess acetic anhydride has either dissolved or become hydrolyzed, collect and wash the product (dry weight 0.5 g.), and (drying is unnecessary) crystallize it from ethanol or methanol; yellow needles, m.p. 189°.

This requires dry II

IV. 2,4-Diacetylamino-1-naphthol

To one half of the diaminonaphthol dihydrochloride solution add 3 ml. of acetic anhydride, stir vigorously, and add a solution of 3 g. of sodium acetate (anhydrous) and about 100 mg. of sodium hydrosulfite in 20–30 ml. of water. The diacetate may precipitate as a white powder or it may separate as an oil that solidifies when chilled in ice and rubbed with a rod. Collect the product and, to remove dirt and to hydrolyze any triacetate present, dissolve it in 5 ml. of 10% sodium hydroxide and 50 ml. of water by stirring at room temperature. If the solution is colored, a pinch of sodium hydrosulfite may bleach it. Filter by suction and acidify by gradual addition of well-diluted hydrochloric acid (2 ml. of concd. acid). The diacetate tends to remain in supersaturated solution and hence, either to initiate crystallization or to insure maximum separation, it is advisable to stir well,

[4] Dissolve 90 g. of FeCl$_3$·6H$_2$O (270.32) in 100 ml. of water and 100 ml. of concd. hydrochloric acid by warming, cool and filter (248 ml. of solution).

rub the walls with a rod, and cool in ice. Then collect the product, wash it with water, and divide it into thirds (dry weight 2.1–2.6 g.).

Two thirds of the material can be converted without drying into V and the other third used for preparation of a crystalline sample. Dissolve the material (moist or dry) in the requisite amount of hot acetic acid, add a solution of a small crystal of stannous chloride in a few drops of dilute hydrochloric acid to inhibit oxidation, and dilute gradually with 5–6 volumes of water at the boiling point. Crystallization may be slow, and cooling and scratching may be necessary. The pure diacetate forms colorless prisms, m.p. 224°, dec.

V. 2-Acetylamino-1,4-naphthoquinone

Dissolve 1.5 g. of diacetylaminonaphthol IV (two thirds of the moist reaction product) in 10 ml. of acetic acid (hot), dilute with 20 ml. of hot water, and add 10 ml. of 1.3 M ferric chloride solution. The product separates promptly in flat, yellow needles that are collected after cooling and washed with a little alcohol; yield 1.2 g. Dry half of the material for conversion to VI and crystallize the rest from 95% ethanol; m.p. 204°.

VI. 2-Amino-1,4-naphthoquinone

To 0.5 g. of 2-acetylamino-1,4-naphthoquinone (V) in a 25-ml. Erlenmeyer flask add 2 ml. of concd. sulfuric acid and heat the mixture on the steam bath with swirling to promote rapid solution (1–2 min.). After 5 min. cool the deep red solution, dilute extensively with water, and collect the precipitated product; wash it with water and crystallize the moist sample (dry weight 0.37 g.) from alcohol or alcohol–water; red needles, m.p. 206°.

VII. 4-Amino-1,2-naphthoquinone

Dissolve 1 g. of aminonaphthoquinonimine hydrochloride (II) in 25 ml. of water, add 2 ml. of concd. ammonia solution (sp. gr. 0.90), and boil the mixture for 5 min. The free quinonimine initially precipitated is hydrolyzed to a mixture of the aminoquinone VII and the isomer VI. Cool, collect the precipitate, and suspend it in about 50 ml. of water and add 25 ml. of 10% sodium hydroxide. Stir well, filter by suction from a small residue of 2-amino-1,4-naphthoquinone (VI), and acidify the filtrate with acetic acid. The orange precipitate of VII is collected, washed, and crystallized while still wet from 500–600 ml. of hot water (the separation is slow). The yield of orange needles, dec. about 270°, is 0.4 g.

Moist II is satisfactory

PART II

Use of the Literature[1]   CHAPTER **43**

The most extensive survey of organic compounds is the great Beilstein "Handbuch der Organischen Chemie." It was originally a compilation of the growing literature meant as an aid for Beilstein's own researches, and then published in two volumes in 1881. Beilstein prepared, almost single-handedly, two later editions, and then the German Chemical Society acquired the rights and edited the last edition, the monumental fourth, composed of twenty-nine volumes, two of which are indexes. This great undertaking, completed in 1939, surveys the literature up to 1910. Since then the literature has been covered to 1919 in the first set of supplementary volumes ("Erstes Ergänzungswerk"), completed in 1938, and to 1929 in the second set of supplements ("Zweites Ergänzungswerk"), almost completed in 1954. Although the compounds are classified according to simple and rational principles, some difficulty was experienced in use of the books, and in 1929 the editors published a guide (246 pages!) to the use of Beilstein. However, both subject and formula indexes became available in 1940, and it is now a simple matter to locate a given compound. In addition, each volume contains an index, and it is generally fairly easy to guess which volume will contain a given substance. Thus all acyclic compounds are listed in volumes I–IV, the cyclic compounds in volumes V–XVI, and the heterocyclic compounds in volumes XVII–XXVII. In addition to the three main divisions, subclassifications are based on twenty-eight functional groups (with seven substituents considered as nonfunctional: the halogen atoms, —NO, —NO$_2$, and —N$_3$). For example, all cyclic hydroxylic compounds are covered in one volume and in the order of increasing number of oxygen

Beilstein

[1] By Mary Fieser

atoms. Within a given group of mono or di or tri hydroxylic compounds, the order is determined by increasing unsaturation, i.e., substances having the type formula $C_nH_{2n}O$ are listed before those of type $C_nH_{2n-2}O$. Compounds are grouped into various system numbers, given at the top of the page, and this number is retained through the supplements. Once a given compound is located it can be traced rapidly through the supplementary volumes by its system number.

The only disadvantage with the Beilstein system, simple and logical as it is, is that it is based primarily on structural formulas. Unfortunately the structures of many interesting compounds, particularly natural ones, are not known and hence these compounds are usually not included in Beilstein.

Elsevier

In 1940 the first volume of a new compendium appeared, "Elsevier's Encyclopedia of Organic Chemistry," under the general editorship of F. Radt. At the present time (1955) twelve sections have been published. The system used is similar to but less rigid than that of Beilstein; it also is based on structural formulas but compounds are grouped according to the carbon skeleton rather than the functional group. For example, in the Beilstein system all the cyclic carboxylic acids, both aromatic and nonaromatic, are grouped together; in the Elsevier system the acids are scattered in various volumes, depending upon the structural skeleton. This system has the great advantage that closely related compounds are grouped together. Thus all the compounds related to the steroids are contained in the volume which surveys tetracyclic compounds. Elsevier has not published the volumes in numerical order but rather on the basis of fields of particular current interest. Volumes covering the steroids and triterpenoids were among the first to appear. Another difference from Beilstein is that the literature is covered to within a few years, occasionally even less, of the date of publication. This lucid and critical survey of organic chemistry, when complete, may well surpass Beilstein, and in any case is an indispensable supplement.

Very recent literature

Literature more recent than Beilstein (1929) or Elsevier (no fixed date) can be traced through either "Chemisches Zentralblatt" or "Chemical Abstracts." Both have not only subject and formula indexes, but an author index as well.

Heilbron; Merck Index

When less detailed information about relatively well-known compounds is desired, Heilbron's "Dictionary of Organic Compounds" (four volumes, 1954) is a useful reference. Compounds are listed in alphabetical order. Chemical and physical properties are summarized, and the more important literature references, usually those pertaining to the preparation, are cited.

"The Merck Index" (Merck and Co., 1952) is more modest, both in scope and price, but it describes the more important properties and uses of a large number of both organic and inorganic compounds. A particularly useful section covers more than three hundred "name" reactions and includes original and review references.

Much useful information about laboratory methods can be found in Houben-Weyl's "Methoden der Organischen Chemie," of which seven volumes are now available (1954), and in H. Meyer's "Lehrbuch der Organisch-Chemischen Methodik. I. Analyse und Konstitutions-Ermittlung Organischen Verbindungen," six volumes (1938).

Two modern series of annual publications dealing with laboratory methods are those of Theilheimer[2] and of Velluz.[3] The former covers new or improved methods of synthesis scattered in the recent literature, often ones that might be overlooked unless experimental sections are read carefully. Reactions are classified according to the formation or splitting of particular bond types. The system is somewhat puzzling at times, but the indexes are extraordinarily complete and helpful. The Velluz series is not based on any system, but is nevertheless a gold mine of useful information. Each volume contains a detailed account of the preparation of about ten important natural products, such as amino acids, vitamins, and hormones. One or more of the methods used is then discussed fully, theory as well as practice being covered in an interesting way. The "Annual Reports of the Chemical Society (London)" usually contains a section entitled "General Methods," which covers the more important recent developments.

Laboratory methods

"Organic Syntheses" is an annual publication giving tested directions for the preparation of various compounds. The first twenty-nine volumes have been revised in two Collective Volumes. The procedures are not only useful for the preparation of specific compounds, but can serve as models for adaptation of known reactions to a new case. "Organic Reactions" is another publication that appears periodically and deals with better-known synthetic reactions. Detailed procedures are given, and extensive tables list all known examples of the reactions.

[2] *Synthetic Methods of Organic Chemistry*, S. Karger (Switzerland).
[3] *Substances Naturelles de Synthèse*, Masson (Paris).

Of the single volumes dealing with synthetic methods used in research perhaps the most useful is Weygand's "Organic Preparations," Interscience (1945). This book covers the more important reactions and gives enough details so that it can, at times, serve as a substitute to the original literature. "Newer Methods of Preparative Organic Chemistry" (Interscience, 1943) covers some useful reactions. Laboratory apparatus and techniques used in the isolation, purification, and characterization of compounds are discussed in Bernhauer's "Einführung in die organisch-chemische Laboratoriumstechnik," Springer, Vienna (1947). "Anleitung zur Darstellung organischer Präparate mit kleinen Substanzmengen" by Lieb and Schöniger, Springer, Vienna (1950) is an excellent introduction to semimicrotechniques used in organic preparations.

Temperature | CHAPTER **44**

1. Reaction Temperature and Time

In initial study of a new case it is advisable to try to effect reaction under the mildest conditions sufficient to effect a change. This may mean standing overnight at room temperature, reaction at a subzero temperature, or heating for a controlled period of time at a measured temperature, preferably with elimination of uncertain periods of warm-up and cooling so that the experiment can be duplicated exactly. Acetylation of DL-alanine (Chapter 22) in acetic acid-acetic anhydride requires a 1-min. reaction period at 100°, and overheating converts the product into the azlactone. The control required is achieved by warming a suspension of alanine in acetic acid a little above 100°, letting it cool to exactly 100°, adding acetic anhydride, waiting 1 min., and stopping the reaction by cooling and quenching. During the brief reaction period the temperature falls (95°) owing to addition of cold reagent, rises (103°, heat of reaction), and begins to fall.

Lower limit of reaction temperature

Once a lower limit of temperature has been found, higher reaction temperatures can be explored to define the upper limit of safe operation to shorten the time. Expedients for decreasing the working time are illustrated as follows. (1) The reaction time for nitration of benzene (Chapter 26.1) is reduced from 1 hr. to 20 min. by adding all the benzene at once and letting the exothermal reaction proceed at the highest temperature (60°) at which control is easy and dinitration is avoided. (2) The Huang-Minlon procedure of Wolff-Kishner reduction [1] utilizes high-boiling triethylene glycol as solvent for the carbonyl compound,

Upper limit

Expedients for shortening the reaction time

[1] Huang-Minlon, *J. Am. Chem. Soc.*, **68**, 2487 (1946); **71**, 3301 (1949). For the history of this discovery see *Ciba Foundation Colloquia on Endocrinology*, **7**, 102 (1953).

cheap aqueous hydrazine, and potassium hydroxide; once the hydrazone is formed, water and excess hydrazine are removed by distillation and the temperature raised to a point (200°) where decomposition with liberation of nitrogen takes place rapidly. The procedure (Chapter 35) for condensation of 3-nitrophthalic acid with hydrazine to form 5-nitro-1,4-phthalazdione utilizes this principle and cuts the reaction time from 4.5 hrs. to about 20 min. In the dehydrohalogenation of *meso*-stilbene dibromide (Chapter 31.7), substitution of triethylene glycol for ethanol and a small amount of potassium hydroxide for the large amount required to give a 43% solution permits raising the temperature from 140° to 160°, with reduction of the reaction time from 24 hrs. to 5 min. (3) Use of triphenylmethyl bromide in place of the chloride (Chapter 21.6) permits preparation of 6-tritylglucose tetraacetate in a few minutes instead of several hours, and acetolysis of *meso*-stilbene dibromide rather than the dichloride (Chapter 32) cuts the reaction time from 9 hrs. to 10 min.

2. Room Temperature

That laboratory working temperatures vary greatly with location and season is evident from the data of Table 44.1. The statement that a reaction was done at room temperature is not very definitive. If you routinely record the bench temperature in your notebook you can report "done at X°." "Steam bath temperature" is also variable. The determinations reported were made as described in the next section.

TABLE 44.1

WORKING TEMPERATURES

	Cambridge Mass.	London England	Kiel Germany	São Paulo Brazil	Mexico City	Bombay India	Stockholm Sweden	Dehra Dun India
Room temperature, winter	22–25°	18–21°	18–22°	19–23° [a]	10–15°	19–28°	20–23°	13–15° [b]
Room temperature, summer	26–33°	20–26°	18–25°		22–24°	26–33°	19–27°	
Flask on top of steam bath	87°	88°	86°	85°	81°	90°		
Flask in rings of steam bath	98°	97.5°	96°		89°	98°		

[a] Measurements (292) made from Dec. 1, 1950, to Nov. 30, 1951.
[b] Forest Research Laboratory; the building is not heated during the five-month period of cold weather.

3. Estimation of Temperature

Occasions arise where, for one's own purposes, estimation rather than measurement of temperature is adequate. Surprisingly accurate estimates can be made by practice of the following procedure.

Heat a 500-ml. Erlenmeyer flask containing 250 ml. of water on (not in) the steam bath and see if the maximal water temperature corresponds to an appropriate figure in Table 44.1; if not, extend the period of heating. If you like, check the maximal temperature obtainable by putting the flask within the rings of the steam bath and wrapping it with a towel. Remove the flask, wipe it dry, let it cool with occasional swirling to equalize the temperature, and estimate temperatures by touching the bottom walls of the flask firmly as follows. First touch the thumb and little finger of one hand and count the number of seconds that contact can be maintained without discomfort; check your counting against a stopwatch. Note the temperature at which the little finger tends to be withdrawn involuntarily but at which the thumb can stand the heat for five seconds, and record this as the thumb tolerance (Item 1, Table 44.2). Next find the temperature at which the little finger as well as the thumb can be kept in place for five seconds (Item 2). Then estimate the temperature at which you can touch the flask firmly to your cheek for just five seconds (Item 3). Then note the temperature at which the flask feels warm to the cheek but not to the palm of the hand (Item 4: cheek sensitivity).

TABLE 44.2

TEMPERATURE SCALE, °C.

No.			Your observation	Typical range
1	Tolerance to heat	Thumb		69–76
2		Little finger		64–69
3		Cheek		55–62
4	Sensitivity to heat	Cheek		34–36
5	Neutral	Cheek		30–32
6	Sensitivity to cold	Cheek		25–26
7		Palm		20–22
8		Little finger		10–15
9		Finger tips		4–8

Cool the flask under the tap and then by addition of ice as required, and establish the following calibration temperatures: (5) that at which the flask feels neither warm nor cold when pressed against the cheek; (6) that at which the sensation of coldness is apparent to the cheek but not to the palm of the hand; (7) where the palm registers a sensation of coldness; (8) where coldness is apparent when the pad of the little finger is pressed against the bottom of the flask; (9) where there is an immediate sensation of coldness when the finger tips are tapped lightly against the bottom of the flask. The temperature scale varies considerably from individual to individual, chiefly because of differences in the pressure exerted and in the interpretation of what constitutes discomfort.

After you have completed the calibration, test your ability to apply the experience gained by asking a laboratory partner to give you a series of unknowns. Average your results as follows:

$$\text{Score} = 100 - 5 \times \text{average deviation}$$

Average scores observed are: Ph.D. chemists, 75–95; beginners, 63–70.

4. Heating Baths

One inexpensive material commonly used for oil baths is stearic acid. Other materials often used are: hydrogenated oils, cotton seed oil, rape seed oil, lubricating oil, Nujol, paraffin. These substances begin to smoke at 250–300° and may catch fire. Both smoking and fire hazard are reduced by using as a cover an asbestos sheet with a hole in it to fit the vessel being heated. On removal from the oil bath the flask should be allowed to drain into the bath and then wiped.

A shallow iron dish filled with flaky graphite (or sand) is useful for higher temperatures; a beaker of iron filings can be used up to 350°. A bath of a fusible metal alloy allows better temperature control: *Wood's metal* (m.p. 71°): bismuth, 4; lead, 2; cadmium, 1; tin, 1; *Rose's metal* (m.p. 94°): bismuth, 9; lead, 1; tin, 1. The metal can be kept from sticking to a flask by coating the glass with graphite. Otherwise the metal is scraped from the flask with a rod when first removed from the bath and then wiped with a dry towel. Metal baths should not be used at temperatures above 350° on account of rapid oxidation of the alloy. When a temperature in the range 250–350° is to be maintained for some time, as in a pyrolysis or a selenium dehydrogenation, a mixture of 10 parts of potassium nitrate and 7 parts of sodium nitrite (m.p. 145°) is excellent. Care must be taken to avoid the spattering of the hot nitrate onto organic material or cracking of the reaction vessel. The container for the fused salt bath must be of metal (iron, stainless steel), for the melt expands sufficiently on solidification to crack glass or porcelain. A glass thermometer must be withdrawn before the melt solidifies, or it may be cracked. When not in use, the nitrate–nitrite bath is kept covered with a flat crystallizing dish; if left exposed it will absorb moisture and subsequently spatter when heated. A pot made from a block of aluminum may be used in place of a liquid heating bath.[2]

Glass-Col heaters are excellent but expensive. A boiling-water bath is easily constructed by providing a vessel of suitable size with one of the constant level siphons described in the literature.[3] A convenient way of heating a reaction mixture at a constant temperature for prolonged periods is to heat a small amount of some liquid of appropriate boiling point in a three-necked flask equipped with a condenser, and to insert test tubes containing the reaction mixture in the other two openings.[4]

5. Cooling Baths

The ordinary ice bath should consist of a slush of crushed ice covered with water. Thorough stirring of the mixture is required to maintain the lowest possible temperature. Temperatures below $0°$ are obtained with ice, water, and salt; with 1 part of sodium chloride and 3 parts of ice, temperatures to $-20°$ can be reached. A mixture of concentrated hydrochloric acid and ice (in a glass vessel!) provides still more effective cooling. Finely crushed ice with 1.5 parts of crystalline calcium chloride (powdered) gives temperatures to about $-50°$. If cooling is required when ice is not available, advantage can be taken of the cooling effect accompanying the solution of certain salts in water. A reduction from $10°$ to about $-20°$ can be obtained from 1 part each of ammonium chloride and sodium nitrate and 1–2 parts of water; also with sodium sulfate decahydrate, concd. hydrochloric acid, and water. Solid carbon dioxide, m.p. $-78.8°$, is used for temperatures as low as $-85°$. Bath temperatures in the range $0°$ to $-30°$ can be maintained by adding pieces of dry ice as required to alcohol; the evolution of gaseous carbon dioxide keeps the bath stirred. Effective cooling of a trap for a mercury vapor pump, or of a receiver in which a gaseous product is to be

[2] A. A. Morton, *Ind. Eng. Chem., Anal. Ed.*, **11**, 592 (1939).
[3] G. R. Yohe and C. G. Keckler, *J. Chem. Ed.*, **11**, 462 (1934); K. Bernhauer, "Laboratoriumstechnik," p. 9 (1947).
[4] A similar heating bath is described by J. Meisenheimer, W. Schmidt, and G. Schäfer, *Ann.*, **501**, 134 (1933).

condensed, is accomplished by adding dry ice cautiously to a mixture of equal parts (by weight or volume) of carbon tetrachloride and chloroform. An advantage is that solid carbon dioxide floats on the surface and does not tend to produce excessive initial frothing. Other solvents used: acetone, trichloroethylene,[5] methyl cellosolve.[6]

6. Pressure Reactions

Certain reactions proceed satisfactorily only at a temperature well above the boiling point of one or more of the reagents and must be carried out in a vessel capable of withstanding the sometimes excessive total pressure due to vaporized materials initially present and gaseous products. In exhaustive oxidations with nitric acid and high temperature reductions with hydriodic acid and red phosphorus, the only suitable vessel is a sealed glass tube. When the mixture is not corrosive to steel, a choice between an autoclave and a sealed tube depends on the scale of operation.

A stout tube of Pyrex glass is drawn out to a thick-walled, tapered capillary 4–5 cm. long. The heating is best done in an unoccupied bomb room. A steam bomb can be made from an iron tube mounted vertically and provided with steam inlet and outlet tubes inserted in rubber stoppers. Satisfactory control at other temperatures is best achieved with an electrically heated furnace. The entire unit must be allowed to cool to room temperature before the tube is opened. The proper method of opening the tube is to stand at the side of the furnace and in back of the front end and direct a Bunsen flame at the projecting tip of the capillary. If the tube is under pressure, a small hole is blown out at the end of the tip and the tube can be withdrawn. If the tip bends over, there is no excess pressure and the capillary can be filed and cut.

If one of the components of the reaction mixture is a gas at room temperature, the tube is cooled in a bath of ice or dry ice, the substance is poured or distilled into the chilled tube, and sealing is performed with the closed end still resting in the cooling bath. If some of the gaseous material is still present at the end of the reaction, the tube when cooled to room temperature will be under pressure. If the reaction is of a type which cannot produce a permanent gas, it is sometimes permissible to withdraw the thoroughly cooled tube (Pyrex), while keeping it covered with several layers of towelling, and insert it at once into a cooling

[5] *Org. Synth.*, **25**, 25 (1945).
[6] *Ibid.*, **32**, 43, note 4 (1952).

bath corresponding to that used in sealing. In the initial experiment the capillary of the chilled tube should be melted in a flame, as above.

An autoclave provides a safe method of conducting large-scale pressure reactions and is applicable to operations with small amounts of valuable materials, for methods are available for confining a small volume of reaction mixture and preventing losses. One is to seal the mixture into a glass tube, place the tube in an autoclave, and introduce nitrogen or other inert gas into the autoclave chamber sufficient to give a pressure substantially higher than that which will be developed in the sealed tube. Another method, introduced by Grosse,[7] consists in using a glass reaction flask having an outlet constructed of a long piece of capillary tubing wound into a spiral. Figure 44.1 illustrates a Grosse flask modified by inclusion of a ground joint of the ball and socket type held in place by a metal clamp. This joint has the advantage that it will not freeze at high pressures. The assembled flask containing the reaction mixture is placed in the autoclave in a beaker, and nitrogen is admitted very slowly, to avoid breaking the capillary, to give a pressure considerably higher than that anticipated from the reaction mixture. Gases under pressure diffuse through capillaries so very slowly that there is little chance for the escape of a volatile reagent or solvent into the autoclave chamber. With this device, autoclave heating can be extended to mixtures which are corrosive to metals, except in those cases where a considerable amount of gas is produced in the reaction. When a Grosse flask is used, the autoclave should be vented very slowly, for otherwise the capillary may be broken.

A method of conducting reactions at moderate temperatures and pressures is to use as container a bottle or tube closed with a metal bottle cap crimped in place with a capping machine. A thick-walled soda bottle has sufficient strength and capacity for many purposes; for example, for carrying out diene addition reactions in alcohol or benzene at 50–100°. Small amounts of materials are conveniently manipulated in the short pressure tube illustrated in Fig. 44.2. The tube is made of heavy-walled Pyrex glass and is provided with a thick rim to hold the cap. For capping, the tube is inserted in a hole in a wooden block of suitable height. Caps lined with various metal foils are available. In experiments with aluminum alkoxides, for example, a liner of aluminum foil can be used. The liner should extend only to about $\frac{1}{8}''$ of the edge of the cork disk.

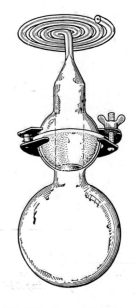

FIG. 44.1 **Pressure vessel for retaining gas or vapor**

Aluminum Foil Liner

FIG. 44.2 **Pressure tube and cap**

[7] A. V. Grosse, *J. Am. Chem. Soc.*, **60**, 212 (1938).

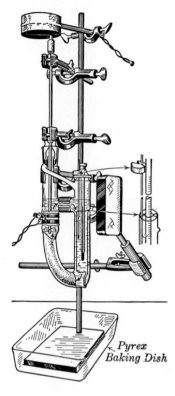

Pyrex Baking Dish

FIG. 44.3 Hershberg melting point apparatus

7. Melting Point Apparatus

Accurate corrected melting points can be determined with an apparatus designed to accommodate a set of short thermometers (Anschütz) which can be immersed in the heating bath over the entire length of the mercury column. The principle of total immersion is embodied in Hershberg's [8, 9] precision apparatus illustrated in Fig. 44.3. The heating fluid, preferably silicone oil,[9, 10] is circulated rapidly in an electrically heated Thiele tube by means of a glass stirrer driven by a shaded pole motor.[11] The propeller-type stirrer is mounted in the longer of the two vertical compartments. The thermometer and melting point capillary are inserted through holes drilled in a ground-glass cap and pass through guiding loops of platinum wire; in the body of the heating tube [12] they are surrounded by an insulating glass sleeve resting on a leg fitting into a depression at the bottom of the tube. The thermometer is supported by a permanent rubber disk and the capillary is held in the jaws of a fastener made by cutting slots in opposite sides of a section of a rubber stopper or heavy walled tubing (inset, Fig. 44.3). Features of the design are a mercury seal and a pressure-equalizing tube connecting the two arms; with this arrangement there is little escape of fumes and the liquid level remains the same in both arms. The apparatus is mounted in a Pyrex dish to catch the fluid in case of breakage. The Anschütz thermometers are conveniently mounted when not in use in a wire rack with provision for drainage (Fig. 44.4).

8. Melting Point Blocks

A metal block apparatus is useful for the determination of melting points above 400°. The block of Berl and Kullmann [13] consists of a copper cylinder with vertical holes for the ther-

[8] E. B. Hershberg, *Ind. Eng. Chem., Anal. Ed.*, **8**, 312 (1936).
[9] Modification: F. C. Merriam, *Anal. Chem.*, **20**, 1246 (1948).
[10] J. L. Hartwell, *ibid.*, **20**, 374 (1948).
[11] The Model 1 stirrer and rheostat of the Eastern Engineering Co., New Haven, Conn., is satisfactory. The unmounted motor may be obtained at low cost from the Barber-Colman Co., Rockford, Ill. (Model YAa No. 707, 0.0004 H.P.), and a 1000-ohm, 10- or 20-watt rheostat connected in series is suitable for speed control.
[12] A simplified method of winding the heating element is as follows. Two $\frac{1}{2}''$ strips of asbestos paper are wetted and stuck to the upper and lower walls of the curved part of the tube, leaving the side walls bare. The resistance wire is attached at one end to a stainless steel strap and wound over the partly dried asbestos strips with $\frac{1}{16}''$ spacings. When the lower end of the curve is reached, the winding is covered with a spiral of asbestos tape for insulation and the wire is returned in three or four turns to the second binding post. The wiring is then wrapped with a thin layer of asbestos paper, and this is moistened and worked into a smooth, adherent covering.
[13] E. Berl and A. Kullmann, *Ber.*, **60**, 811 (1927); see also W. L. Walsh, *Ind. Eng. Chem., Anal. Ed.*, **6**, 468 (1934).

mometer and the melting point capillary, and horizontal windows for illumination and observation. Modifications include illumination of the capillary from above at an angle [14] and by transmission of light through bent Pyrex tubes.[15]

A melting point block that has given good service in the author's laboratory is illustrated in Fig. 44.5.[16] The heating unit is made from a solid cylinder of aluminum, 11 cm. long and 9 cm. in diameter. A well is drilled in the center to a depth corresponding exactly to the immersion point of a 500° thermometer, and a second well of the same diameter is drilled close to this and at a slight angle sufficient to cause the two holes to meet, or nearly meet, at the bottom. The offset well is closed at the top with an aluminum plug drilled with two or three small holes for insertion of melting point capillaries. Observation is made through a horizontal hole drilled in the plane of the two vertical wells and extending just to the hole carrying the thermometer; the side hole is closed with a screw plug fitted with a mica window. Illumination is provided through a second horizontal hole drilled at an angle of 60° to the first and plugged with a piece of Pyrex rod. The sample in the capillary is seen clearly in its natural color. The large size of the block contributes to uniform distribution of the heat supplied by a Bunsen burner, and inclusion of the thermometer bulb and the sample in the same inner compartment causes them to reach the same temperature.

An alternative device for characterizing high-melting substances is the differentially heated melting point bar of Dennis and Shelton [17]; the substance is dusted onto the hot surface and the melting point determined from the line of demarcation between solid and liquid phases.

9. Microdetermination of Melting Point

Sometimes it is necessary to make accurate melting point determinations with a single tiny crystal. The micromethod of Kofler [18] consists in placing a minute fragment of material on a cover glass centered over a small hole in a metal stage of controllable temperature and establishing the point of melting by observation under the microscope. Determinations can be made rapidly and with high precision. Mixed melting point deter-

[14] F. W. Bergstrom, *Ind. Eng. Chem., Anal. Ed.,* **9,** 340 (1937).
[15] Eastman Kodak Co., *Synthetic Organic Chemicals,* **10,** No. 2 (1937).
[16] Designed by Dr. J. Cason and Dr. H. J. Creech.
[17] L. M. Dennis and R. S. Shelton, *J. Am. Chem. Soc.,* **52,** 3128 (1930).
[18] L. Kofler and H. Hilbck, *Mikrochemie,* **9,** 38 (1931); see F. Pregl, *Quantitative Organic Microanalysis,* 4th English Ed., pp. 185–186 (1946); E. M. Chamot and C. W. Mason, *Handbook of Chemical Microscopy,* I, pp. 200–204 (1938).

Temperature

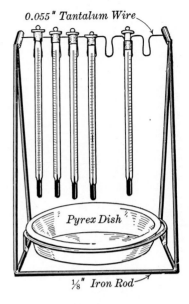

FIG. 44.4 Thermometer rack

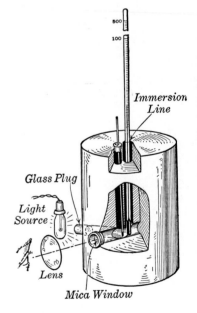

FIG. 44.5 Aluminum melting point block

minations can be made after rubbing minute amounts of the two substances together on a cover glass, without making a transfer. The original apparatus is elaborate, as are some of the later modifications designed for special studies. It is possible, however, to construct at moderate expense a simplified instrument suitable for general use which retains the chief advantages of the more complicated designs. A microscope is not necessary, for the observation can be made satisfactorily with an ordinary lens. A hot-stage assembly can be made by building an aluminum block, welled to accommodate a thermometer, along the lines of the simplified design described by Dunbar,[19] and equipping it with an electrical heating element of the type specified by Zscheile and White.[20] The thermometer used should have a rather short stem and should be provided with an armor. Calibration can be made with a series of compounds whose corrected melting points have been determined with a precision capillary-tube apparatus. The instrument can be made still more useful by providing it with facilities for optical polarization. This is done by interposing one piece of Polaroid in the eyepiece and another in the path of the light source, which is directed at the sample through the narrow hole in the hot-stage. When the optical axes of the two Polaroid pieces are crossed, a minute crystal of the sample gives a luminous image on a dark field, and the melting point is discerned by disappearance of luminosity.

Polarizing microscope

The usefulness of an inexpensive, low-power microscope can be increased by transforming it into a polarizing instrument as follows. A disk of Polaroid film is mounted in the eyepiece in a position near the uppermost lens and displaced from the focal point. A second sheet of Polaroid is mounted in a fixed position below the stage of the microscope in the path of the light source; this serves as the polarizer. The eyepiece can be rotated and functions as the analyzer of the improvised polariscope. In operation, the analyzer is turned to a position of minimum light transmission, indicating that the two Polaroid prisms are optically crossed. A doubly refractive crystal when examined between crossed prisms shows a white or colored image against a black field. Such behavior distinguishes between crystalline and amorphous substances and detects the presence of minute crystals in an oil. Nearly all organic crystals are doubly refractive, although a few are isotropic and do not give a lighted image. Observation of crystals under polarized light is sometimes im-

[19] R. E. Dunbar, *Ind. Eng. Chem., Anal. Ed.*, **11**, 516 (1939).
[20] F. P. Zscheile and J. W. White, *Ind. Eng. Chem., Anal. Ed.*, **12**, 436 (1940).

proved by suspending the crystals in a liquid vehicle such as aqueous glycerol or paraffin oil. Plates are sharply differentiated from needles, and a pure substance can be distinguished without difficulty from a mixture. When an oil has been inoculated with seed, one can determine by examination under polarized light if new crystals form, and if these correspond or not to the substance used as seed.[21]

21 E. M. Chamot and C. W. Mason, *Handbook of Chemical Microscopy*, I, pp. 261–326 (1938).

CHAPTER 45 | Distillation, Filtration, Evaporation

1. Vacuum Distillation

An improved method of mounting a thermometer in a distillation flask is illustrated in Fig. 45.1. The sealed-in thermometer well obviates contamination or leakage at this point. The flask shown has a conical bulb, and the capillary has been drawn out twice. The receiver is attached by a ground-glass joint to the side tube, which is provided with a simple cooling device. This apparatus is useful for distillation of high-boiling liquids and of substances that may solidify.

For a discussion of some of many ramifications of the technique of fractional distillation at atmospheric or reduced pressure see the manual by Morton.[1] Efficient and not too elaborate columns are: a modified Widmer column[2]; a simplified Podbielniak column[3] embodying features of a highly efficient apparatus for precise fractional distillation analysis,[4] a column of the partial condensation type designed for general laboratory use[5] (the column is packed with glass helices, as in the high-efficiency stills developed by Fenske[6]). Baker, Barkenbus and Roswell[7] describe a spinning-band column with very little holdup for fractionation of small quantities of liquid.

A number of satisfactory manometers are on the market, but

[1] A. A. Morton, *Laboratory Technique in Organic Chemistry*, pp. 73–123 (1938).
[2] M. E. Smith and H. Adkins, *J. Am. Chem. Soc.*, **60**, 662 (1938).
[3] T. L. Jacobs, *J. Am. Chem. Soc.*, **58**, 2272 (1936).
[4] W. J. Podbielniak, *Ind. Eng. Chem.*, *Anal. Ed.*, **3**, 177 (1931); **5**, 119 (1933); **13**, 639 (1941).
[5] K. C. Laughlin, C. W. Nash and F. C. Whitmore, *J. Am. Chem. Soc.*, **56**, 1396 (1934).
[6] M. R. Fenske, C. O. Tongberg and D. Quiggle, *Ind. Eng. Chem.*, **26**, 1169 (1934); C. O. Tongberg, D. Quiggle and M. R. Fenske, *ibid.*, **26**, 1213 (1934).
[7] R. H. Baker, C. Barkenbus and C. A. Roswell, *Ind. Eng. Chem.*, *Anal. Ed.*, **12**, 468 (1940).

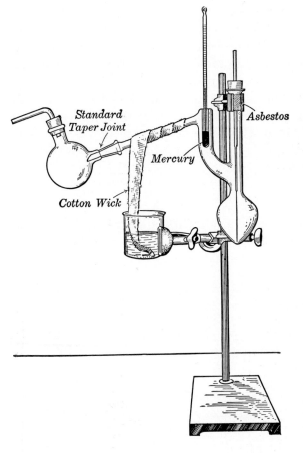

FIG. 45.1 Apparatus for the distillation of high-boiling substances

Standard Taper Joint

Asbestos

Mercury

Cotton Wick

Manometers

many are rather expensive, particularly if supplied filled with mercury. Where a general utility manometer is required, it is well to purchase or construct a simple and inexpensive U-tube and fill and mount it. One type is illustrated in Fig. 45.2; another has a constriction at the bottom of the bend in place of the sealed-in tip. The tube is cleaned in an acid bath, washed thoroughly, and dried in an oven. The closed arm is filled with mercury to the middle of the bend and the mercury is boiled out as follows. The tube is inverted and connected to the water pump, and it is then held in a nearly horizontal position with the closed end slightly depressed. A 2–3 cm. section of mercury at the closed end is heated in a Bunsen burner flame until it begins to boil, and the tube is given a sharp jerk or whip in the direction of its length to dislodge gas; the mercury on returning to its original position should click against the glass. A second short section of mercury immediately above the first is boiled as before and shaken free of gas, and the whole column is similarly treated.

255

CHAPTER 45

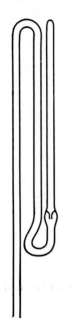

Sufficient mercury is eventually added to fill the bend and the boiling out at this point is completed by heating. The manometer is mounted on a wooden frame, with a backing of millimeter coordinate paper to serve as scale. Another simple manometer is described by Castro and Blood.[8]

The Zimmerli [9] manometer has certain desirable features but requires a large amount of mercury. Pressure regulators for precision work are of rather elaborate construction (see Morton, *loc. cit.*); simple and easily constructed regulating devices have been described recently.[10]

2. Steam Distillation

In steam distillation of a substance of low vapor pressure, for example nitrobenzene, the water-substance ratio is so unfavorable (4 g. H_2O : 1 g. $C_6H_5NO_2$) that the rate of steam flow has to be

FIG. 45.2 Manometer tube

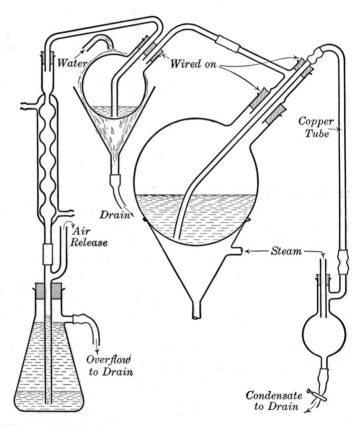

FIG. 45.3 Apparatus for steam distillation

---

[8] A. J. Castro and A. E. Blood, *J. Chem. Ed.*, **31**, 23 (1954).
[9] A. Zimmerli, *Ind. Eng. Chem., Anal. Ed.*, **10**, 283 (1938).
[10] M. S. Newmann, *Ind. Eng. Chem., Anal. Ed.*, **12**, 274 (1940); G. G. Lowry, *J. Chem. Ed.*, **28**, 535 (1951).

well beyond the capacity of ordinary condensers or else the distillation is very tedious. A condensing system of adequate capacity for very rapid steam flow (Fig. 45.3) works on the principle of a liquid seal or vapor trap. Some condensate is always retained in the small round bottomed flask, except when, for inspection or at the end, it is emptied by diverting the stream of cooling water. Nitrobenzene can be distilled at a rate of 400 g. per hr.

The assemblies shown in Figs. 45.4 and 45.5 are for steam dis-

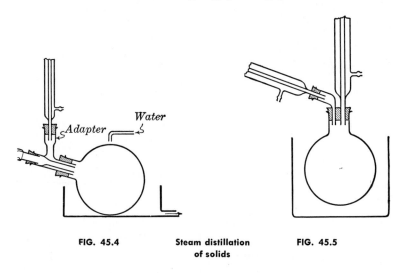

FIG. 45.4 **Steam distillation of solids** **FIG. 45.5**

tillation of compounds that solidify in the condensate. The receiver must be large enough to take the entire distillate and is cooled in a pan of water or ice. If solid condensate threatens to plug the system it can be dislodged by brief interruption of the cooling.

Steam distillation of small amounts of material can be done in a simple distilling flask without passing in steam (Chapter 8) or with a tube for admission of steam (Chapter 26.2). If a reaction mixture is already in a ground-glass flask, this may be equipped for steam distillation as in Fig. 45.6.

For substances of extremely low vapor pressure it may be necessary to resort to distillation with superheated steam or in vacuum, or both. Ordinary steam is conducted through a coil of 10–15 ft. of lead or copper tubing heated in an oil bath to a temperature 20–30° above the steam temperature desired. The temperature of the steam is read on a thermometer inserted in the line just before it enters the distillation flask, which is also heated in an oil bath.

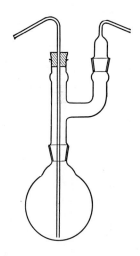

FIG. 45.6 Apparatus with interchangeable ground joints

257

3. Filtration

Although collection of a finely divided precipitate by suction filtration is often an unavoidably tedious operation, certain remedies sometimes help. It may be possible to coagulate the fine particles by digestion at or near the boiling point or by

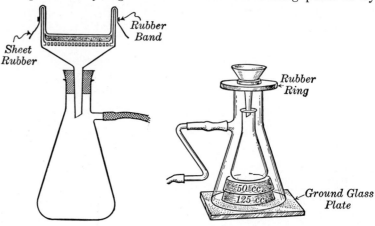

FIG. 45.7 Rubber dam for pressing the filter cake

FIG. 45.8 Suction filtration

stirring. If solid is obtained by precipitation, the rate and temperature may be controlling factors. When filtration requires many hours for completion the difficulty is increased by development of cracks in the filter cake which break the vacuum. In

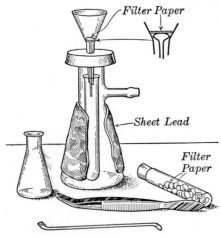

FIG. 45.9 Apparatus for suction filtration

such a case the rubber dam [11] is invaluable. After the suspension has been transferred to the Büchner funnel, a piece of rubber sheeting is laid over the top of the funnel and the edges folded over and held down by strong rubber bands to give an airtight fit. The unit is then allowed to stand for a few hours or overnight, with the suction pump running. As soon as a crack develops the rubber is drawn down onto the filter cake to the position shown in Fig. 45.7 and the vacuum is maintained. The solid is thus subjected to the full pressure of the atmosphere and a hard cake containing very little mother liquor results. For small funnels use a partially inflated toy balloon pressed down onto the top of the funnel by an iron ring.

A device for collecting the filtrate directly into an Erlenmeyer flask is shown in Fig. 45.8.[12] The flat rubber ring accommodates

[11] R. A. Gortner, *J. Am. Chem. Soc.*, **36**, 1967 (1914).
[12] Modification: I. A. Kaye and W. J. Burlant, *J. Chem. Ed.*, **31**, 127 (1954).

funnels of different sizes, and some range is also possible in the size of flask; a series of cork or wood supports can be kept on hand and labelled according to the size of flask with which they are to be used.

4. Filtration on a Micro Scale

A suction filter for collection of small amounts of solids is shown in Fig. 45.9. A slender filter rod long enough to project beyond the end of the funnel is provided with a flattened knob on which a circle of filter paper rests. These circles can be prepared in quantity with a cork borer or steel die and are manipulated with forceps. The drawing illustrates a method of weighting the suction flask to avoid its being tipped over. A small suction filter of another form is made by sealing a Witt porcelain plate into a Pyrex test tube, sealing a delivery tube to the bottom, and cutting off the top.[13] The filter illustrated in Fig. 45.10 is designed for the collection of very small amounts of solids. The capillary drainage tube is of such small diameter that no support is required for the filter paper, and the paper is of so limited an area that little product is lost by adherence to the paper. The construction permits filtration directly into a small Erlenmeyer flask or centrifuge tube.

Filtration of a small volume of solution can be done conveniently and with little loss of material by use of a filter stick. This is a capillary tube bent in the form of an inverted U. One leg, which is long enough to extend to the bottom of the vessel or tube containing the solution, is provided with a sintered glass disk, a filter paper held in place by a glass ring and a wire (Craig[14]), or other filtering device.[15] The second leg is shorter and delivers into a receiver to which suction can be applied by mouth or with a water pump. A suitable assembly is illustrated in Fig. 45.11. The filter stick[16] shown has the advantage of simplicity of construction and ease of cleaning. It is an adaptation of the Schwinger funnel[17] and is made by grinding the exposed ends of the sectioned limbs until a small circle of filter paper fits snugly between them; a short piece of rubber tubing is slipped over the joint to hold the ends.

Distillation, Filtration, Evaporation

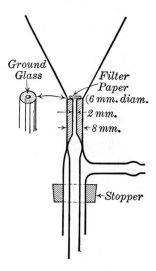

FIG. 45.10 Suction filter

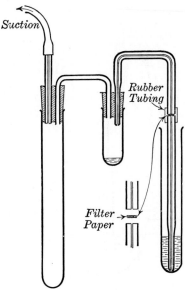

FIG. 45.11 Filter stick

[13] C. A. Roswell, *Ind. Eng. Chem., Anal. Ed.,* **12**, 350 (1940).
[14] L. C. Craig, *Ind. Eng. Chem., Anal. Ed.,* **12**, 773 (1940).
[15] A. A. Morton, *Laboratory Technique in Organic Chemistry,* pp. 166–167 (1938).
[16] Designed by W. von E. Doering.
[17] F. Emich, *Microchemical Laboratory Manual,* p. 30 (1932).

CHAPTER 45

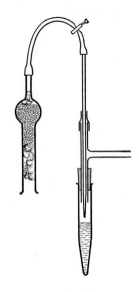

FIG. 45.12 Evaporation at reduced pressure in a centrifuge tube

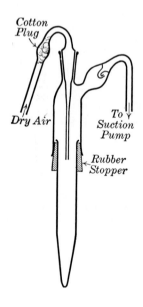

Cotton Plug

Dry Air

To Suction Pump

Rubber Stopper

FIG. 45.13 Evaporation head for a centrifuge tube

Small quantities of solids can be collected and washed by centrifugation rather than by suction filtration. The ordinary 15-cm. tapered centrifuge tube serves as a convenient crystallization vessel and indeed can be used for carrying out many small-scale operations. A solution can be evaporated quickly in a tared conical tube using the attachment shown in Fig. 45.12; a stream of dry air is admitted through a tube of easily adjustable height and directed at the surface of the liquid at a sufficient distance to produce a ripple. When a crystallizate or precipitate is obtained it can be packed down by centrifugation, and the clear liquid decanted into another tared tube for further concentration. The solid product can be washed, dried, and weighed in the original tube, and there is little loss of material. Various solvents can be tried in succession for crystallizing the substance, for a solvent which proves unsatisfactory can be evaporated quickly and replaced by another one.[18] The evaporation head shown in Fig. 45.13 is designed to prevent contamination of the contents of the tube from contact with rubber and is useful in preparation of an analytical sample. The convenient adapter arrangement can be combined with the adjustable gas inlet device of Fig. 45.12.

The technique of centrifuge filtration in a Skau tube [19] is useful for rapid collection of low-melting substances and for separation of a product that can be crystallized most advantageously from a small volume of a solvent in which it is readily soluble.[20] The Skau tube is a device for making a sharp separation of crystals and liquid in which the mixture is brought onto a filter in a tube permitting centrifugation. Modifications of the technique have been introduced by Hershberg,[21] Perrine and Kump,[22] and Craig.[20] The modified tube devised by Hershberg is shown in Fig. 45.14 in the position in which the filtering operation is performed. Initially, the unit is assembled in the inverted position, with the crystallization mixture contained in the rounded inner tube. The filter paper and plate are put in place and covered with the funnel tube with its attached receiver, and the whole unit is quickly inverted and filtration accomplished by centrifugation. The Craig tube employs the principle of centrifugation in the inverted position, but filtration occurs through crevices between a constricted neck and a loosely fitting glass plug.

[18] R. R. Williams and T. D. Spies, *Vitamin B₁*, 140–142 (1938).
[19] E. L. Skau, *J. Phys. Chem.*, **33**, 951 (1929); E. L. Skau and L. F. Rowe, *Ind. Eng. Chem., Anal. Ed.*, **3**, 147 (1931).
[20] L. C. Craig, *Ind. Eng. Chem., Anal. Ed.*, **12**, 773 (1940).
[21] A. A. Morton, *Laboratory Technique in Organic Chemistry*, 177–178 (1938).
[22] T. Perrine and W. Kump, *Ind. Eng. Chem., Anal. Ed.*, **11**, 658 (1939).

5. Evaporation of Solvent

A condenser with a take-off tube [23] is shown in Fig. 45.15. With this device it is possible to reflux a solution or distil the solvent. Use of a Nolub stopcock obviates contamination with stopcock grease, and a narrow loop in the delivery tube prevents escape of solvent vapor. The condenser shown can be fitted directly to a flask by a ground-glass joint or connected to a stoppered flask with an adapter. The drawing also illustrates a simple stand of adjustable height and shows the construction of a boiling tube. This is made by sealing an inverted glass cup to a rod which is provided with a hook to facilitate its withdrawal for rinsing. Applicator sticks are used for the same purpose.

The take-off condenser aids in carrying out crystallizations. A substance that dissolves slowly can be refluxed with excess solvent and the excess subsequently removed by distillation.

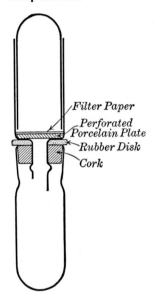

Filter Paper
Perforated Porcelain Plate
Rubber Disk
Cork

FIG. 45.14   Modified Skau tube

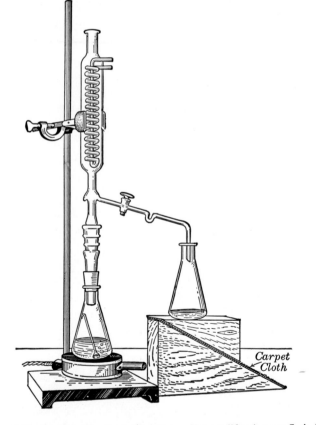

FIG. 45.15   Reflux condenser with a take-off tube

Carpet Cloth

[23] Designed by Dr. E. B. Hershberg. For modification see I. A. Kaye, *J. Chem. Ed.*, **30**, 521 (1953).

CHAPTER 45

The space-saving assembly is generally useful for distillation of solvent.

The apparatus shown in Fig. 45.16 is for rapid evaporation of a solution to dryness.[24] The tube at the right is connected to

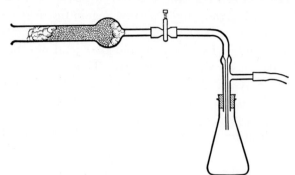

FIG. 45.16   Evaporation at reduced pressure

a suction pump and dry air or nitrogen is admitted at reduced pressure by operation of the screw clamp. The flask can be heated as required in a water bath. The gas stream should make a slight ripple on the surface of the liquid.

[24] R. R. Williams and T. D. Spies, *Vitamin B₁*, 141 (1938).

Accessories for Reactions | CHAPTER **46**

1. Stirring

An electric stirring motor of rugged construction which develops ample power at both low and high speeds is described by Hershberg.[1] Inexpensive motor units satisfactory for intermittent use with light and constant loads can be made from the motor of a discarded vacuum cleaner or fan. A speed regulator can be made from resistance coils and dials obtainable from a radio store. A discarded speedometer cable can be used as a flexible driving shaft. An easily constructed air-pump shaker driven by compressed air is described by Morton.[2]

Efficient agitation of even pasty mixtures can be accomplished with the Hershberg wire stirrer[3] illustrated in Fig. 46.1. A glass tube is used for the stirrer shaft in preference to a rod because of its light weight, strength, and straightness. A glass ring is sealed to the shaft and threaded with stiff wire; a second threaded ring placed at right angles to the first usually is not required. Smooth operation of a stirrer is obtained by using a ball-bearing mounting. A short piece of rubber tubing is inserted in the bearing, moistened with glycerol, and slid over the shaft (Fig. 46.1). It is generally advisable to use two ball bearings placed a few inches apart, as in the assembly shown in Fig. 44.3. Nichrome or chromel wire is satisfactory for use in condensations with sodium or in the Friedel and Crafts or Blanc reaction, but should be employed in Grignard reactions only when the stirrer is reserved exclusively for such use. Tantalum

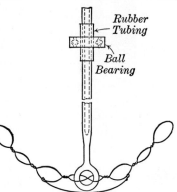

FIG. 46.1 Hershberg stirrer

---

[1] E. B. Hershberg, *Ind. Eng. Chem., Anal. Ed.*, **12**, 293 (1940).
[2] A. A. Morton, *ibid.*, **6**, 469 (1934).
[3] E. B. Hershberg, *ibid.*, **8**, 313 (1936).

CHAPTER 46

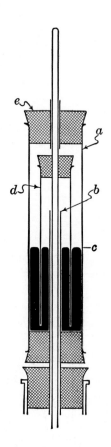

FIG. 46.2 Mercury seal for a stirrer

wire is better and can be used for all ordinary purposes; it resists corrosion by strong acids, bases, alkali metals, or chlorine. The wire threading is easily inserted through a narrow opening in a flask and in operation it follows the contour of the flask without scratching the glass.

Where only moderate agitation is required, stirrers of the bent rod and propeller type may be adequate. On occasion, mixing can be accomplished most satisfactorily by hand stirring with a glass rod or by swirling the flask; this may offer the best opportunity for control and observation, and also for inducing crystallization.

2. Stirrer Seals

To prevent escape of gas during mechanical stirring, a mercury seal of the form shown in Fig. 46.2 is useful. Mercury is poured into the space between the outer tube (*a*) and the bearing tube (*b*) up to the level *c*. Tube *d* revolves with the stirrer shaft in the mercury and entraps the gas. The stopper (*e*), with an additional glass bearing, prevents spattering and spilling of metal. The bearings are lubricated lightly with glycerol. Mercury-sealed stirrers made of stainless steel adapted for high-speed operation are described by Rogers.[4] A vapor-proof stirrer having an oil-impregnated bronze bearing is described by Calingaert.[5]

A mercury seal can be a needless complication. For elimination of noxious gas during stirring it is sufficient to run the stirrer through a close-fitting glass sleeve and to apply gentle suction to draw gases into a trap. Another method, useful where a gas is to be absorbed in a stirred liquid, is shown in Fig. 46.3. The stirrer sleeve (*a*) is extended well into the flask so that the liquid itself seals the stirrer. A rubber slip joint is also serviceable. A stirrer sleeve similar to tube (*a*) but extending only a short distance into the flask is provided with a 2-cm. section of rubber tubing which projects above the end of the tube and fits snugly around the stirrer shaft. The point of contact between the shaft and the rubber is lubricated with glycerol. The seal operates satisfactorily even in partial vacuum (10 mm.). Magnetic stirrers solve the problem of stirring in vacuum.

3. Addition Tubes

The assembly of Fig. 46.3 includes a gas-delivery tube (*b*) of useful construction: the glass rod (*c*) slips through a section of

[4] D. T. Rogers, *J. Am. Chem. Soc.*, **55**, 4901 (1933); *J. Chem. Ed.*, **11**, 427 (1934).
[5] G. Calingaert, *Ind. Eng. Chem., Anal. Ed.*, **12**, 51 (1940).

suction tubing and can be used to clear the lower end of the delivery tube in case it becomes plugged with solid.

For addition of a solid reagent in small portions to a reaction

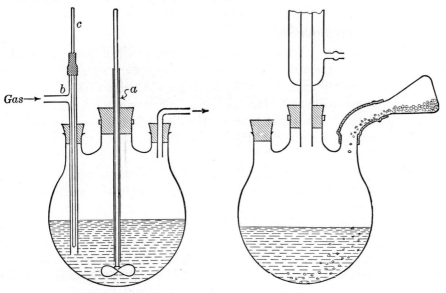

FIG. 46.3 Liquid-sealed stirrer and special gas-delivery tube

FIG. 46.4 Method of adding a solid reagent

mixture while this is refluxed or stirred, particularly if the reagent is sensitive to moisture (powdered potassium hydroxide, aluminum chloride), an Erlenmeyer flask fitted to one of the tubulatures of a three-necked flask by a section of rubber tubing can be used (Fig. 46.4). The intermittent addition of the solid is accomplished by raising the containing flask, which can then be cut off from the system by kinking the rubber tube.

A solid also can be added from a hopper provided with a glass valve.[6] A hopper-type tube for addition of a liquid can be made from a long-stem funnel stoppered by a rubber bung (small rubber stopper) on the end of a glass rod.[7]

When an ordinary dropping funnel is used for addition of a liquid, difficulty is often experienced in adjusting the stopcock to a sufficiently slow or steady rate of flow. The difficulty is obviated in the funnel designed by Hershberg[8] (Fig. 46.5). The flow of liquid is regulated by varying the distance to which the wire protrudes into the capillary. The rate of flow can be kept constant throughout the entire addition by connecting the funnel,

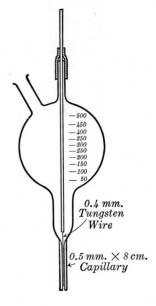

0.4 mm.
Tungsten
Wire

0.5 mm. × 8 cm.
← *Capillary*

FIG. 46.5 Hershberg dropping funnel

[6] S. H. Webster and L. M. Dennis, *J. Am. Chem. Soc.*, **55**, 3234 (1933).
[7] H. T. Clarke and W. W. Hartman, *Org. Synth., Coll. Vol.* **1**, 233 (1941).
[8] E. B. Hershberg, *Org. Synth.*, **18**, 16 (1938)

CHAPTER 46

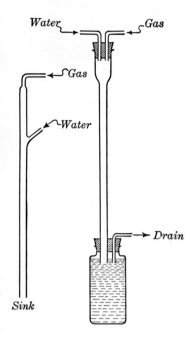

FIG. 46.6   Gas absorption
tubes

through the side opening, to a gas reservoir of constant positive pressure. In case the liquid is to be added extremely slowly, the funnel should be mounted in such a way that the tip touches a side wall and drop formation is prevented.

4. Gas Traps

When a gaseous reagent is absorbed in a reaction mixture, the excess gas can be caught in an absorption trap, such as one of those shown in Fig. 46.6. Another method is to attach a small rubber balloon to the gas-exit tube and run in gas until it is inflated. The slight pressure thus established assists absorption and the condition of the balloon indicates the course of absorption.

The evolution of gas from a reaction mixture can be followed with a bubbler connected either directly to the reaction vessel or to the top of a reflux condenser. A simple bubbler consists of an empty calcium chloride tube supported vertically with the small end dipping just below the surface of 5 ml. (no more) of water in a 10-ml. Erlenmeyer flask. Connection is made to a section of rubber tubing and suction is applied by mouth to make sure that the capacity of the calcium chloride tube cannot be exceeded.

A trap suitable for protection of an oil pump consists of a pair of glass towers connected near the bottom by a glass tube bent upward into a vertical loop about one fourth the height of the towers. The first tower is filled with pellets of potassium hydroxide and connected to the pump by a glass tube inserted in a rubber stopper. The second tower, which is closed with a rubber stopper making connection to the system to be evacuated, is filled with glass wool and provided at the bottom with a stopcock to permit draining. The filling is impregnated with concentrated sulfuric acid; from time to time, as this is observed to darken, the spent liquor is drawn off and fresh acid added.

5. Grignard Reaction

An assembly that meets most requirements is illustrated in Fig. 46.7. A three-necked flask with ground-glass openings is mounted on a removable steam cone and provided with a coil-type condenser, a dropping funnel with a pressure-equalizing side tube, and a mercury sealed Hershberg stirrer made of tantalum wire. Dry nitrogen is introduced at the top of the condenser and initially can be allowed to sweep through the apparatus and escape at the mouth of the dropping funnel; when the funnel is closed a slight positive pressure is maintained at the nitrogen

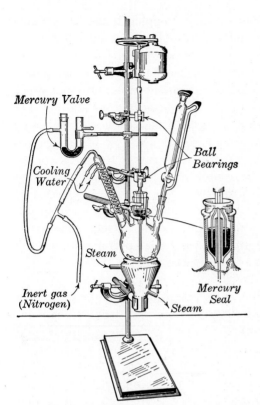

Mercury Valve

Ball Bearings

Cooling Water

Steam

Inert gas (Nitrogen)

Steam

Mercury Seal

FIG. 46.7 Apparatus for the Grignard reaction

tank, as indicated by the level of mercury in the escape valve. This gas-trap arrangement [9] is economical of nitrogen and has the further advantage over the use of a continuous stream of inert gas that it obviates evaporation of the solvent. Tank nitrogen can be used without purification if it is of the prepurified grade.

One reason for a nitrogen atmosphere is to prevent destruction of Grignard reagent by air oxidation. Both aliphatic and aromatic Grignard reagents interact with molecular oxygen in ether solution with formation of the hydroxy derivatives [10]:

$$2RMgX + O_2 \longrightarrow 2ROMgX$$

A beautiful demonstration of the chemiluminescent reaction is furnished by pouring a solution of p-chlorophenylmagnesium bromide from one flask to another in the dark.

Another reaction flask is illustrated in Fig. 46.8. The mercury seal and condenser are fitted into appropriate openings with

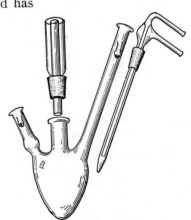

FIG. 46.8 Grignard reaction flask

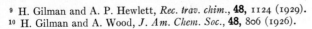

[9] H. Gilman and A. P. Hewlett, *Rec. trav. chim.*, **48**, 1124 (1929).
[10] H. Gilman and A. Wood, *J. Am. Chem. Soc.*, **48**, 806 (1926).

rubber stoppers, and an ordinary dropping funnel is mounted in the same way in the shorter side neck. Inlet and outlet tubes are provided for flushing the system with nitrogen.

In conducting a reaction, the required amount of magnesium [11] is placed in the flask and the apparatus is assembled and swept with nitrogen (flush both parts of the empty dropping funnel of Fig. 46.7). When the air has been displaced the flask is heated gently with a free flame under continued flow of nitrogen to insure elimination of any moisture adhering to the surface of the glass or the metal. Baking-out is more effective when conducted under a flow of dry gas than when done in a static system, and use of nitrogen prevents surface oxidation of the warm metal. When the flask has cooled completely, the nitrogen flow is reduced to a barely perceptible rate and small portions of the ether and halogen compound are introduced through the funnel. The stirrer is started, even though very little liquid is present, for the crushing of pieces of light magnesium foil in contact with the liquid is effective in initiating reaction. If stirring alone is insufficient, try the expedient of inserting a flattened stirring rod and crushing a piece of metal with a twisting motion against the bottom of the flask. If the reaction still fails to start, the addition of a small crystal of iodine or a few drops of methyl iodide may be effective. Gilman's catalyst [12] is prepared by interaction of magnesium and iodine in ether–benzene. An expedient for converting less reactive halogen compounds into their magnesio-halide derivatives introduced by Grignard [13] consists in adding one equivalent of ethyl bromide to the ethereal solution of the refractory halide and dropping this mixture slowly onto sufficient magnesium to react with both halides. The auxiliary halide keeps the magnesium clean and active, and functions by an exchange reaction. The resulting solution contains two Grignard reagents and when used in a synthesis must be treated with two equivalents of the second component. The presence of the reaction product from the ethylmagnesium bromide does not interfere with isolation of the desired product if this is of significantly higher molecular weight.

Difficulty experienced in starting a previously unexplored Grignard reaction may be due to inadequate purification of the

---

[11] Magnesium of high purity gives very clear Grignard solutions; with less pure metal the solutions are dark. Rods of pure metal can be turned in a lathe or reduced to granules in a grinding machine.
[12] H. Gilman and R. H. Kirby, *Rec. trav. chim.*, **54**, 577 (1935).
[13] V. Grignard, *Compt. rend.*, **198**, 625 (1934). See also H. Clément, *ibid.*, **198**, 665 (1934); E. Urion, *ibid.*, **198**, 1244 (1934).

halide rather than to its lack of reactivity. Traces of impurities not detectable by analysis or from the physical constants may exert a marked poisoning action. Possibly the impurity can be eliminated by washing with concd. sulfuric acid or by steam distillation, preferably from an alkaline medium. Certain halides will form Grignard derivatives if given sufficient time (1–2 days).

For preparation of small amounts of methylmagnesium bromide, a sealed vial of methyl bromide (b.p. 4.5°) is cooled in ice, opened, and fitted with a length of rubber tubing connected through a calcium chloride drying tube to a glass delivery tube leading into the reaction flask. The reagent is then introduced by warming the vial in the hand. Methyl chloride (b.p. −24°) is obtainable in steel cylinders from which it can be run directly into the mixture of magnesium and ether. Difficulty sometimes experienced in starting the reaction usually can be overcome by stirring and heating the mixture while passing in a slow stream of methyl chloride. Reagent can be conserved by providing the flask with a mercury valve or balloon, or with a cold-finger condenser inserted in a side tubulature consisting of a test tube filled with dry ice. The latter scheme avoids difficulty from back pressure and makes possible an initial high concentration of methyl chloride favorable for starting the reaction. A highly reactive halide such as allyl bromide is converted into the Grignard reagent in a very dilute solution to minimize coupling.

The solution can be analyzed by titration[14]: an aliquot (5 ml.) of solution is poured slowly into 20 ml. of water, excess standard hydrochloric acid is added (to react with the $Mg(OH)X$), and the excess acid titrated with standard sodium hydroxide solution (methyl orange). Gilman's test[15] for the presence of Grignard reagent is useful: about 0.5 ml. of the ethereal solution is pipetted and treated with an equal volume of a 1% solution of Michler's ketone in dry benzene, and then, slowly, with 1 ml. of water. Addition of several drops of a 0.2% solution of iodine in acetic acid then produces a characteristic greenish blue color if Grignard reagent was present.

Analysis and detection

Some addition reactions do not proceed satisfactorily at the boiling point of ether and require addition to the ethereal solution of Grignard reagent of solvent of higher boiling point (benzene, xylene) and removal of ether by distillation.

The reaction proper

A procedure for conducting an inverse Grignard reaction con-

[14] H. Gilman, P. D. Wilkinson, W. P. Fishel and C. H. Meyers, *J. Am. Chem. Soc.*, **45**, 150 (1923); J. Houben, J. Boedler and W. Fischer, *Ber.*, **69**, 1766 (1936). [15] H. Gilman and F. Schulze, *J. Am. Chem. Soc.*, **47**, 2002 (1925); H. Gilman and L. H. Heck, *ibid.*, **52**, 4949 (1930).

sists in preparing the reagent in the apparatus shown in Fig. 46.7, replacing the dropping funnel by a siphon tube held by a cork and bent to extend to the bottom of the flask, and transferring the solution under nitrogen pressure to a dry dropping funnel flushed with nitrogen. The funnel is then attached to a reaction flask containing a solution of the second component. Filtration, to remove traces of metal that might cause reduction of the carbonyl component, can be accomplished by introducing a plug of glass wool into the bottom of the siphon tube (5–7 mm. bore).

At the end of the reaction the MgX-derivative can be decomposed by adding 25% sulfuric acid dropwise with cooling under reflux, or by pouring the reaction mixture onto ice and dilute acid. If the reaction product is sensitive to the dehydrating action of mineral acids hydrolysis can be done with aqueous ammonium chloride solution. One procedure is to add a sufficiently large excess of the solution to bring precipitated basic salts into solution. A better method is to add just enough of the solution to precipitate the magnesium and leave a nearly anhydrous supernatant solution of the reaction product in ether. The reaction mixture is cooled and stirred under reflux in the original flask and a saturated solution of ammonium chloride in water (25°) is added slowly from the dropping funnel at a rate controlled by the rapidity of refluxing. Usually 150–170 ml. of saturated solution per mole of magnesium is required to reach a point where a clear separation occurs, and this point should not be passed. The solution at first becomes cloudy and opaque and then, when sufficient ammonium chloride has been added, the solution suddenly becomes clear and a white salt separates as a tough cake that is likely to stop the stirrer. The mixture is allowed to settle for several minutes, the supernatant solution is decanted, and the dense precipitate is washed with one or two portions of fresh ether. The ethereal solution requires no drying and can be evaporated directly for recovery of the product. The procedure is applicable to reaction mixtures in which as much as one third of the solvent is benzene.

Hydrolysis of the reaction mixture with ammonium chloride

Alkyl and aryl derivatives of lithium [16] are made by treating a halide with lithium metal in dry ether by essentially the same technique as employed in preparing a Grignard reagent, and yields are excellent.[17] The reaction with lithium starts more readily and proceeds at a greater rate than that with magnesium. Lithium metal should not be warmed in a nitrogen stream for

Lithium derivatives

[16] K. Ziegler and H. Colonius, *Ann.,* **479,** 135 (1930).
[17] H. Gilman and co-workers, *J. Am. Chem. Soc.,* **54,** 1957 (1932); **55,** 1262 (1933).

it tends to form the nitride. Lithium alkyls can be prepared not only in the presence of ether but also with low-boiling petroleum ether as sole solvent [18]; the hydrocarbon solvent has advantages over ether and makes possible preparation of organolithium compounds (e.g., isopropyllithium) otherwise difficultly obtainable.

The lithium derivatives are somewhat more reactive than the corresponding Grignard reagents [19] and, in the reaction with an α,β-unsaturated ketone, differ from the magnesiohalides in giving rise to a much higher proportion of the 1,2-addition product.[20] One application is in utilization of aromatic chloro compounds in syntheses which cannot be accomplished by the Grignard method.

Not all organic halides react satisfactorily with lithium, but often the desired lithium compound can be prepared indirectly by an exchange reaction with a readily available lithium compound such as phenyllithium:

$$C_6H_5Li + RX \longrightarrow RLi + C_6H_5X$$

The reaction was discovered in 1938 by Gilman [21] and by Wittig,[22] and has since found wide use.[23] The preparation of phenyllithium (*n*-butyllithium is also frequently used), the interchange step, and the Grignard reaction can all be carried out in the same apparatus; and only 30–60 min. need be allowed for formation of the intermediate RLi compound, which is not isolated. The lithium atom can be replaced by magnesium bromide and occasionally this route is the most expedient to a given Grignard reagent.[24]

Several procedures for manipulation of lithium are described by Gilman.[19] Another is as follows.[25] Lithium in the form of small blocks is pressed into a wire with a sodium press equipped with a 3-mm. die. The wire is collected under heavy paraffin oil and cut into uniform 12-cm. lengths which are placed in a test tube having a stopcock at the bottom and a nitrogen inlet near the rubber stopper. The sticks of metal are washed with successive portions of benzene and ether under nitrogen, and the wash liquor is drained out through the stopcock under nitrogen pressure. The average relationship of weight to length is determined by weighing a few of the wires, so that subsequently a given total length of wire can be measured for use in a reaction.

[18] H. Gilman, W. Langham and F. W. Moore, *J. Am. Chem. Soc.*, **62**, 2327 (1940).
[19] H. Gilman and R. H. Kirby, *J. Am. Chem. Soc.*, **55**, 1265 (1933).
[20] A. Lüttringhaus, *Ber.*, **67**, 1602 (1934).
[21] H. Gilman and A. L. Jacoby, *J. Org. Chem.*, **3**, 108 (1938).
[22] G. Wittig, U. Pockels and H. Dröge, *Ber.*, **71**, 1903 (1938).
[23] R. G. Jones and H. Gilman, *Organic Reactions*, VI, 339 (1951).
[24] H. Gilman and C. E. Arntzen, *J. Am. Chem. Soc.*, **72**, 3823 (1950).
[25] L. F. Fieser and E. B. Hershberg, *J. Am. Chem. Soc.*, **59**, 396 (1937).

Glass Blowing [1] | CHAPTER **47**

Laboratory tubing made of soft glass (soda-lime glass) softens at a comparatively low temperature (400–450°) and can be worked most satisfactorily using an air–gas blast lamp with a quiet blue flame just tipped with yellow. With soft glass, simple practice operations can be carried out in the flame of a Bunsen burner; a Cenco microburner is useful for learning the technique of joining pieces of 6–8 mm. tubing. Soft glass has a high co-efficient of expansion and must be brought to the working temperature slowly in a yellow flame to avoid cracking; the temperature during working should not be too high or the surface may become frosted as the result of volatilization of alkali. After the blowing operation has been completed, the glass should be annealed to relieve strains by rotating the piece in a luminous flame until it is coated evenly with a layer of soot.

Types of glass

Pyrex or other borosilicate glass has a higher softening point (820°) than soft glass and a lower coefficient of expansion. The proper working temperature is easily obtained with a blast lamp provided with valve-controlled inlets for gas, oxygen, and air; a gas–oxygen flame is preferred by some workers. A suitable gas mixture can be obtained by first adjusting the gas and air valves to give a soft, nonluminous flame and then feeding in enough oxygen to produce a sharp, light blue inner cone (considerable noise). The hottest part of the flame is at the tip of the blue cone, the diameter and length of which are determined by the size of the orifice of the burner and the composition of the gas mixture. A hand torch with a trigger-type gas regulator is useful in mounting and assembling apparatus; a satisfactory type which is quiet in operation is that fueled with premixed gas and oxygen

[1] By E. B. Hershberg

(without air). Pyrex glass tubes up to a diameter of 10 mm. can be plunged directly into the flame of the blast lamp without cracking; larger pieces are preheated with a soft gas–air flame. Less time and care are required at the beginning of the operation than when soft glass is used. Annealing is important and requires care and skill, for the annealing point (560°) is not much below the temperature of softening. The worked portion is rotated in a soft, bushy flame until it is heated uniformly to a just visible red, and the temperature is then gradually lowered by manipulating the glass in the cooler parts of the flame and by reducing the flame temperature.

Cutting glass tubing

Care is required in the initial operation of making a fine, straight scratch extending about a quarter of the way around the tube. A triangular file is unsatisfactory because after only brief use it becomes worn and produces too wide a scratch. Hardened steel knives and knives with tungsten carbide cutting edges are excellent but expensive. A 6-inch flat Swiss pattern pillar file (cut No. 4) is satisfactory and inexpensive. The four sharp edges formed at the junctions of the broad abrading surfaces and the smooth, narrow sides are all available for cutting and make clean, fine scratches in glass. The file is easily sharpened by light regrinding of the narrow edges. The scratch is best made by pressing one edge of the file firmly against the tube and slightly rotating the tube away from the body while filing in the same direction. Only one stroke should be made; a fine scratch gives a much better opportunity for a clean break than a wide groove sawed in the tube at the expense of dulling the file. After the scratch has been made, the tube (up to about 15 mm.) is grasped with the scratch away from the body and the thumbs pressed together at the near side of the tube just opposite the scratch. Slight pressure is exerted outward with the thumbs and at the same time the tube is forcefully pulled apart. A straight, clean break should result.

Tubing of larger sizes can be cut with an electrically heated wire [2] or by touching the scratch lightly but firmly with a hot

Hot-wire cutter

[2] A 6–8″ length of No. 22 chromel A wire is suspended in a loop from two supports and a 660-watt bowl heater element is partly unwound, a short section judged to be equivalent in resistance to the cutting wire is removed, and the remainder is connected in series with this wire. If the looped wire does not then reach bright red heat, the element is further shortened. The tube is scratched, laid firmly into the loop, and rotated until the entire circumference has been heated. Soft glass usually cracks at once; with Pyrex glass it is usually necessary to apply water to the heated portion with a small brush or dropper. Pyrex tubes of large diameter are best chilled by immersion in a stream of water. In another design the heated wire is suspended from the ends of a pair of tongs and can be made to encircle the tube (see glass blowing manual of the Corning Glass Works).

piece of glass rod. This produces a deep crack that can be led around the tube by further applications of the heated rod. With soft glass the rod should be of small diameter (2 mm.) and only moderately hot, for otherwise it may start a number of cracks radiating from the point of contact. In case of Pyrex tubing it is well to use a 2–4 mm. rod of soft glass heated at the tip to bright redness. A large bottle may be cut by the same method except that a slender flame is applied tangentially at right angles to the tube in order to lead the crack around the circumference.

A flaring tool is made from a $\frac{5}{8}'' \times 1'' \times 4''$ charcoal block by cutting it at one end to a smooth, uniform conical point, using a grinding wheel or a knife and sandpaper. Untreated charcoal does not tend to stick to glass as does a triangular metal reamer or an arc-light carbon rod, both of which must be rubbed while hot into beeswax prior to use. Charcoal is too fragile to be used for flaring tubes of small diameter and for this use carbon rods are preferable.

In forming a flare, the tube, stoppered or sealed at one end, is rotated in an oblique position in a rather narrow flame that impinges on both the front and the back edge at the same time without heating much of the body of the tube. When the glass is sufficiently plastic the tube is removed from the flame and the charcoal reamer is pressed lightly into the opening and rotated with sufficient pressure to turn out the edge. A reinforcing rim, such as that shown on the Pyrex pressure vial of Fig. 44.2, can be formed by reheating the flare in the same manner until the turned edge flows together into a rim, when the reamer is again applied. The process is repeated enough times to give a beaded edge of the desired thickness.

For production of a successful bend it is important to apply heat uniformly to the entire section of tubing necessary for the bend. The tube is grasped in the left hand with the palm down, and in the right hand with the palm up, for these positions make it possible to swing the right-hand end of the tube into a position for blowing without interruption of the steady process of synchronized rotation of the two ends. The rotating is best done in the direction in which the top of the tubing moves away from the body. Facility in rotation of the two ends at exactly the same rate is gained only with practice; in the beginning stages it may be helpful to make a chalk mark on each side of the heated portion in order to indicate the proper alignment. If a U-bend is to be made, one end of the tube is closed and the tube is heated to a higher temperature than required for a right-angle bend.

Flaring of glass tubing

Bends

With soft glass, the heating is best done with a Bunsen burner supplied with a fish-tail adapter; heating is continued until the tube begins to sag of its own weight and the flame has become strongly tinged with yellow (sodium light). To bend Pyrex glass, the section to be bent is rotated evenly in a long, bushy flame, and the tube held at a slight angle to the flame. Because of the higher temperature required and the narrower temperature range over which Pyrex retains plasticity, the operation must be carried out more rapidly than with soft glass. When the heated section has become thoroughly plastic, the tube is removed and bent in a vertical plane, with the ends upward and the central portion of the bend at the bottom. If the bend is sharp, the tube usually becomes somewhat constricted, and in this case pressure is applied by mouth to the open end of the tube immediately after completion of the bend until the tube is expanded to its full size and irregularities are eliminated. If a very sharp bend is to be made it is advisable to thicken a short section of the tubing to about two thirds its original diameter and, while forming the bend, to pull out the tube and apply air pressure.

The first step in closing a tube is to pull it down to a section of small diameter. This is known as a "point." A tube is often "pulled to a point" in order to provide a handle for its manipulation, and in this case a short section is heated strongly until pliable, and the tube is removed and pulled slowly, while being constantly rotated, to a length of about 8 inches. In making a round tube-end, the tube is heated in the same way but pulled out more rapidly, in order to produce greater constriction. The point *a* (Fig. 47.1) is then sealed with a sharp flame as in *b*. The thick lump is spread out evenly by heating the tip of the tube, blowing it out as in *c*, and heating the whole tube-end until a thick, even seal is produced (*d*); the tube is then blown to the final form *e*.

When two tubes of the same diameter are to be joined, one piece is stoppered[3] and held in the left hand with the palm over the tube and the open piece is held in the right hand with the palm upward. Both ends should be squared, if necessary, by making fresh cuts. The tubes are held at a slight angle from the horizontal and the ends are rotated simultaneously in opposite zones of the flame in such a way that only the cut edges are brought to the fusion point and very little constriction occurs. The tubes are removed a short distance above the flame (soft

Round ends

a

b

c

d

e

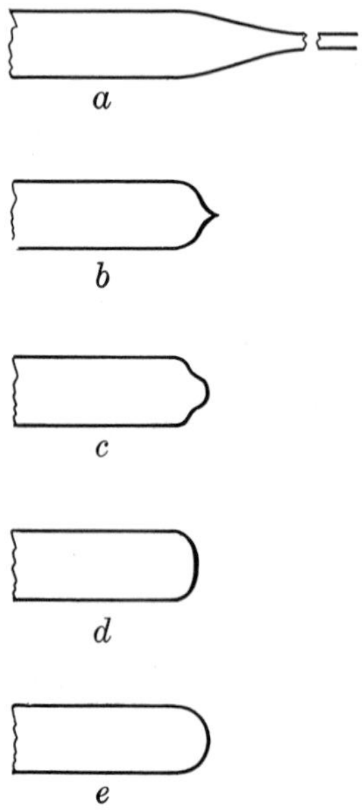

FIG. 47.1 Blowing a round end

---

[3] Tapered corks useful for stoppering small tubes are available in the following sub-sizes (below No. 1): o, oo, oo$\frac{1}{2}$, ooo, ooo$\frac{1}{2}$.

glass) and the ends pressed lightly and evenly together on the same axis and then pulled slightly to reduce the thick ring of glass at the joint. (With Pyrex glass these operations are performed without complete removal of the tube from the flame.) The flame is adjusted quickly to a narrow point and the tube is rotated in such a way as to heat only the welded section and cause it to shrink in diameter and increase in wall thickness. The tube is withdrawn and blown, without pulling, until the heated section is expanded slightly beyond the normal diameter. The bulbous part is heated in a softer flame and gently pulled enough to reduce the diameter of the seal to that of the tube. In order to secure the correct wall thickness it may be necessary to reheat the seal and repeat the shrinking and enlarging operations.

Tubes of unequal size can be joined by drawing out the larger tube, cutting it at a point where the diameter corresponds to that of the smaller tube, and making the seal essentially as described above. Another method is to make a round end on the larger tube, heat the central spot on the bottom with a sharp flame, and blow out a bulb of fragile glass which is brushed off with a file until a flared opening remains of diameter corresponding to that of the tube to be joined. By the same method, capillary tubing can be provided with a flared opening suitable for making a seal to a piece of ordinary tubing of the same diameter.

The tube that is to form the straight part of a T-seal is sealed or stoppered at one end and a small spot in the middle is heated with a sharp flame (Fig. 47.2) and blown out so as to form a bulge (b) of diameter somewhat less than that of the tube to be sealed on. The bulge is heated carefully at its tip and blown out to a thin-walled bulb (c). The thin glass is brushed away with a file until a short side tube is left which can be joined to the second tube by the method described above for making a straight seal (d and e).

Small flasks suitable for microdistillations can be blown from Pyrex tubing as follows. The tube is sealed at the bottom and the end is heated strongly until it shrinks and the glass thickens. It is blown out slightly, reshrunk, and the process is repeated until sufficient glass has been accumulated to produce the bulb. The thickened end is then heated until it is very soft, the tube is held in a horizontal position and rotated slowly and steadily, and a bulb is blown to the desired diameter. A tendency of the bulb to sink on one side can be corrected by quickly rotating this section to the opposite side and puffing. Similarly, a bulb can be formed at the middle of a piece of tubing by alternately

Glass Blowing

Straight seals

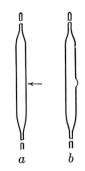

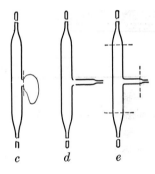

FIG. 47.2 Construction of a T-seal

Bulbs

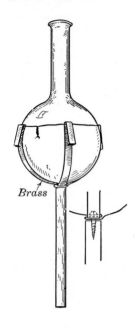

Brass

FIG. 47.3 Flask holder

Ring seals

---

shrinking and expanding a portion of the tube while pushing slightly on the ends. When a sufficiently thick section has been formed, the bulb is blown to final shape.

When bulbs of more than about 25-ml. capacity are required it is best to use the flasks available commercially in various sizes and shapes. The manipulation of a flask in a glass blowing operation is facilitated by having available a holder with which the bulb can be grasped firmly and rotated along the central axis. A flask holder can be made from a round piece of wood and flexible strips of brass as shown in Fig. 47.3. One of the brass strips is bent to a smooth hemisphere and the second strip is crimped around the first to maintain the right-angle position. The ends can be bent over at various positions to hold the tightening wire, and hence the holder is adjustable to flasks of different sizes.

One standard method of making ring seals can be illustrated by description of the blowing of an all-glass condenser of the cold-finger type. The method can be employed in the construction of thermometer wells (Fig. 45.1) and mercury seals (Figs. 46.7 and 46.8). The large tube that is to constitute the body of the condenser is provided with a rounded bottom (alternatively, this tube can be pulled to a point). The inner tube of the seal is flared slightly at the end, inserted in the larger tube, and maintained in a centered position by means of a smaller tube which slips into it and which is secured in a cork stopper, as shown in Fig. 47.4a. The assembled unit is rotated in a nearly horizontal position and a small, sharp flame is directed at the rounded bottom of the large tube at the point of contact between this and the flared tube. The two pieces of glass soon fuse and a clear ring can be discerned. The flame is then centered at the bottom of the large tube, and a bulb is blown, as in *b*. The thin glass is removed, the guide tube leading through the cork stopper is closed, and a terminal tube is sealed on as in *c*. As soon as this operation has been completed and before the ring seal has a chance to cool, a side tube is joined to the condenser body (*d*), and the lower part of the piece, including the ring seal, is annealed carefully. The stopper is then removed from the large tube, and this is sealed to a rounded end. The final operation consists in making a right-angle bend in the terminal tube, giving the completed condenser *e*. If the water inlet and outlet tubes are to be finished as shown in the drawing with slight bulges for retention of rubber tubing, these are best blown into the tubes before they are joined to the condenser body; sufficient tubing is left on both sides of the bulge for purposes of manipulation and the excess glass is cut off after the piece is assembled. The side tubes can be finished, also, after assembly of the piece, by flaring them slightly.

The ringed shaft of a wire stirrer of the type illustrated in Fig. 46.1 is constructed as follows. A glass rod is sealed to the end of a section of tubing that is to form the shaft of the stirrer and cut off at a length sufficient to make the ring. The rod is heated thoroughly and bent around with tweezers into a rough circle until the end meets the base of the rod, to which it is then fused. The crudely formed ring is softened uniformly, and a $\frac{1}{4}''$ carbon rod which has been rubbed in beeswax is inserted in the hole and employed to spread the ring evenly. The ring is reheated until it shrinks, and spread again, and the operations are repeated until a symmetrical ring of uniform diameter is obtained.

Asbestos, in the form of thin paper or special woven tape, is a useful accessory. A roll of $0.015'' \times 1''$ asbestos paper is satisfactory. When the paper is to be used in the dry form, traces of organic matter should be burned prior to use by passing the asbestos strip through a Bunsen flame until it is momentarily red. Standard taper joints can be held together securely during an operation by covering the male member with a strip of asbestos paper and thrusting it into the outer joint; without the paper the dry joint might be damaged. Another use is in making a holder for a short length of tubing which is to be heated close to the point of support (see pressure flask, Fig. 44.2). A tube of diameter slightly smaller than the tube to be supported is wrapped with one or two layers of asbestos paper and forced securely into the open end of the larger tube; the small tube forms a handle and the joint can be made tight enough for blowing.

Wet asbestos paper can be molded to fit a glass piece of irregular form and gives a protective covering which subsequently can be removed without damage to the glass. When a seal is to be made a short distance from a stopcock, this is first wrapped with a few layers of wet asbestos paper and the covering is molded with the fingers. When a reaction mixture is sealed into a rather short tube, it is often convenient to provide a collar of wet asbestos just below the portion to be heated.

Glass grinding is done by rubbing together two pieces of glass, or a piece of glass and one of metal, with an abrasive powder such as silicon carbide (carborundum, corundum) or fused aluminum oxide (alundum, aloxite). The grinding powder is wetted with

Rings

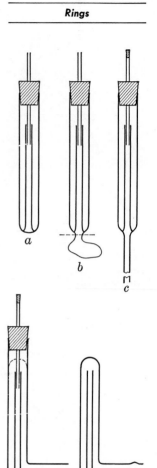

FIG. 47.4 Construction of a condenser with a ring seal

Glass grinding

279

a suitable fluid, which provides better distribution of the abrasive and helps dissipate the heat. Water serves satisfactorily in most operations; turpentine and other nonvolatile oils are used for drilling holes and in special polishing operations. The satiny finish on ground joints is achieved by performing the final grinding operation with fine powder (500–800 mesh), with water as the vehicle. A stopcock which will hold without lubricant or solvent is surfaced carefully in a final grinding with rouge as the abrasive.

The end of a glass tube can be squared by sprinkling a little 200- or 400-mesh grinding powder (0.2–0.4 g.) onto a flat piece of glass (preferably plate glass), moistening it with water, and grinding with a circular rubbing motion until the end is planar and smooth. An example of the process is in the construction of the suction filter flask and plate shown in Fig. 45.8. The plate is prepared by grinding together two squares of $\frac{1}{4}''$ plate glass, using 600-mesh aloxite as the abrasive, until a suitable finish is obtained. One of these plates is saved for the final apparatus and the other can be employed for the initially rough grinding of the flask. The filter flask (Pyrex) can be cut by making a scratch, starting the crack with a piece of hot rod, and continuing it around the flask with a long, sharp oxygen–gas flame. A satisfactory cut can be made more easily and surely with a hot-wire device. The grinding is started with 220-mesh carborundum and finished with 600-mesh aloxite. This gives a satin-smooth surface capable of holding a vacuum without use of lubricating grease.

It is sometimes desirable to square the jagged end of a tube roughly, or to smooth the uneven edge of a cut flask, in preparation for grinding or sealing. One method is illustrated in Fig. 47.5. A 5-inch square of heavy iron gauze (12-mesh) is held at an angle of slightly less than 90° to the axis of the tube, or nearly in the plane of the end to be formed, and the rough edge is hit with a quick striking and rubbing motion. The glass is removed partly as coarse chips and partly as dust; the refuse should be caught in a waste jar and care taken not to breathe the dust. Professional glass blowers often use a pair of iron tweezers for removing jagged ends. The operation, illustrated in Fig. 47.6, consists in grasping the wall of the tube firmly with the tweezers and withdrawing the tool with a quick motion.

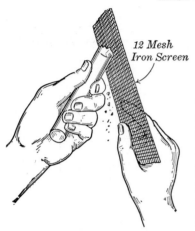

12 Mesh
Iron Screen

FIG. 47.5 **Chipping an edge with wire gauze**

FIG. 47.6 **Smoothing a surface with tweezers**

Solvents [1]

(Listed alphabetically)

CHAPTER **48**

Acetic Acid

M.p. 16.6°, b.p. 118°
Miscible with water

Commercial acetic acid contains traces of acetaldehyde and other oxidizable contaminants, which can be destroyed by refluxing the acid with 2–5% (by weight) of potassium permanganate for 2–6 hrs.; the acid is distilled and the fraction boiling at 117–118° collected.[2] An alternative procedure calls for refluxing acetic acid with chromic anhydride.[3] Traces of water can be removed from acetic acid by treatment with triacetyl borate; it reacts with water to form acetic acid and boric acid (insoluble). The reagent is prepared[4] by warming 1 part of boric acid with 5 parts (by weight) of acetic anhydride to 60°; on cooling, triacetyl borate separates and is collected by filtration. Acetic acid is treated with 2–3 times the amount of triacetyl borate estimated to be required for reaction with the water present, and anhydrous acetic acid is obtained by distillation.

Acetone

B.p. 56.5°
Miscible with water

Commercial acetone now available is sufficiently pure for nearly all uses. One use is as solvent for permanganate oxidations; in the absence of water the product formed from an alkene is the cyclic ether of the glycol. Acetone dissolves both the oxidizing agent and the substrate. If the solvent decolorizes a pinch of added permanganate at reflux temperature, add more reagent until the violet color persists, add potassium carbonate for drying,

[1] See chapter on pure solvents by L. Velluz, *Substances Naturelles de Synthèse*, **1**, 103–126 (1951).
[2] W. R. Bousfield and T. M. Lowry, *J. Chem. Soc.*, **99**, 1432 (1911); D. A. MacInnes and T. Shedlovsky, *J. Am. Chem. Soc.*, **54**, 1429 (1932); A. L. Wilds and C. H. Shunk, *ibid.*, **70**, 2427 (1948).
[3] W. C. Eichelberger and V. K. LaMer, *ibid.*, **55**, 3633 (1933).
[4] A. Pictet and A. Geleznoff, *Ber.*, **36**, 2219 (1903).

and distil. For special purposes purification can be accomplished through the addition compound $(CH_3)_2O \cdot NaI$, which crystallizes at $-10°$ and decomposes into the components at $25-30°$.[5]

Acetonitrile

B.p. 81.5°
Miscible with water

General solvent; solvent for amine hydrochlorides. A trace added to the reaction mixture of an aryl halide, cuprous cyanide, and pyridine destroys any water present.[6]

Alcohol   (See Ethanol)

Benzene, Thiophene-free

B.p. 80.1°
Immiscible

(a) Stir mechanically a mixture of crude benzene and crude concd. sulfuric acid (80 ml. per liter of benzene) in a separatory funnel at room temperature for one half hour, draw off the dark acid liquor, and repeat the process twice with fresh portions of acid. The acid should darken only slightly during the last agitation. Decant the benzene into a clean flask, without inclusion of any remaining acid, and distil.

(b[7]) Reflux 100 ml. of benzene (containing up to 1% thiophene) with 10 g. of Raney nickel[8] for 15 min. and remove the nickel by filtration or centrifugation.

Test for thiophene. Dissolve about 10 mg. of isatin in 1 ml. of concd. sulfuric acid (C.P.), shake the red solution with 3 ml. of benzene, and let the mixture stand. Thiophene if present produces a blue-green coloration. A more sensitive test is described by Holmes and Beeman,[9] together with a process for removal of thiophene by means of aluminum chloride.

Carbon Bisulfide

B.p. 46.3°
Immiscible

This common solvent (Friedel-Crafts reaction) and reagent is extremely flammable and has been known to ignite when overheated on the steam bath. For distillation of appreciable quantities use a pan of water warmed on the steam bath to just the required temperature. Purification (removal of odoriferous S-compounds) can be accomplished by shaking with mercury, then with a cold, saturated solution of mercuric chloride followed

[5] K. Shipsey and E. A. Werner, *J. Chem. Soc.*, **103**, 1255 (1913); R. Livingston, *J. Am. Chem. Soc.*, **69**, 1220 (1947); E. A. Werner, *Analyst*, **58**, 335 (1933); R. F. Hudson and J. E. Wardill, *J. Chem. Soc.*, 1729 (1950).
[6] L. F. Fieser and V. Desreux, *J. Am. Chem. Soc.*, **60**, 2261 (1938).
[7] R. J. Graul and J. V. Karabinos, *Science*, **104**, 557 (1946).
[8] A. A. Pavlic and H. Adkins, *J. Am. Chem. Soc.*, **68**, 1471 (1946).
[9] H. N. Holmes and N. Beeman, *Ind. Eng. Chem.*, **26**, 172 (1934).

by cold, saturated potassium permanganate solution, drying over phosphorus pentoxide, and distillation.[10]

Carbon Tetrachloride

B.p. 76.8°
Immiscible

Commercial material often contains carbon bisulfide, which can be removed by shaking at 60° with about one-tenth volume of a mixture of concd. potassium hydroxide solution and alcohol. After two or three repetitions the carbon tetrachloride is washed with water, stirred at 25° with small portions of concd. sulfuric acid until there is no further coloration, washed with water, dried over calcium chloride, and distilled. Phosphorus pentoxide can be used for final drying. Purification by distillation is reported.[11]

Carbon tetrachloride is a useful fire extinguisher but should not be applied to a sodium fire, for this may lead to an explosion. It is toxic and should be handled in a hood.

Chlorobenzene

B.p. 132°
Immiscible

Chlorobenzene has solvent action similar to that of benzene and toluene but considerably greater, and is used for crystallizing sparingly soluble substances. It has been recommended as a solvent for carrying out the Fries rearrangement of a phenol acetate with aluminum chloride.

Chloroform

B.p. 61.2°
Immiscible

Commercial chloroform contains 0.5–1% ethanol as stabilizer. It is purified by shaking with concd. sulfuric acid, washing with water, drying with calcium chloride, and distilling. (Do not dry with sodium as there is danger of an explosion.)

α-Chloronaphthalene

B.p. 259°
Immiscible

The anthraquinone ring closure reaction has been conducted in this solvent with benzoyl chloride as the dehydrating agent.[12]

o-Dichlorobenzene

B.p. 179°
Immiscible

o-Dichlorobenzene is a good solvent for conversion of hydrocarbons into aldehydes by interaction with methylformanilide and phosphorus oxychloride.[12, 13]

Diethylene Glycol Monomethyl Ether and Diethylene Glycol Monobutyl Ether (Methyl and Butyl Carbitol), $ROCH_2CH_2OCH_2CH_2OH$

B.p. 194.1° and 230.7°
Miscible with water

[10] H. Wieland and L. Bettag, *Ber.*, **55**, 2249 (1922).
[11] E. H. Waters, *Chem. Ind.*, 742 (1953).
[12] H. Vollmann, H. Becker, M. Corell and H. Streeck, *Ann.*, **531**, 1 (1937).
[13] L. F. Fieser, J. L. Hartwell and J. E. Jones, *Org. Synth.*, **20**, 11 (1940).

CHAPTER 48

Dimethylformamide, HCON(CH₃)₂

This solvent is used as the medium for a variety of reactions, e.g., debromination,[14] decarboxylation,[15] desulfuration,[16] condensation [17] (Ullmann reaction), Gabriel synthesis [18] (it dissolves potassium phthalimide), and to replace part of the more costly pyridine in acylations. It can be purified by shaking with solid potassium hydroxide and then lime, followed by distillation at atmospheric pressure.[19]

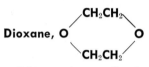

Dioxane, O

Dioxane is an effective solvent for a wide variety of organic compounds; the solvent action is similar to that of ether but more pronounced. The fact that the substance is also miscible with water renders it useful for a number of special purposes. Although dioxane usually behaves as a neutral, indifferent solvent, it can form complexes of considerable stability, which in some instances may interfere with the normal course of a reaction. Thus dioxane added to an ethereal solution of a Grignard reagent quantitatively precipitates the RMgX and MgX₂ components as complexes and leaves a solution of the MgR₂.[20] Phenolic substances when crystallized from dioxane frequently separate as more or less stable solvated complexes.

Commercial dioxane usually contains a certain amount of glycol acetal, $CH_3CH \begin{array}{c} OCH_2 \\ | \\ OCH_2 \end{array}$, and some water. On storage the acetal tends to undergo hydrolysis, and the liberated acetaldehyde gives rise to rapid peroxide formation. Although the commercial solvent is adequate for some purposes, other uses call for anhydrous, peroxide-free dioxane (high-pressure hydrogenations, sodium reactions). If the material contains only small amounts of impurities, it may be possible to effect satisfactory purification by refluxing the solvent for a day or two with adequate amounts of sodium, but if some of the glycol acetal escapes conversion into aldehyde gum, it may subsequently give rise to peroxide formation. Purification processes are as follows.

[14] R. P. Holysz, *J. Am. Chem. Soc.*, **75**, 4432 (1953).
[15] O. Süs, *Ann.*, **579**, 133 (1953).
[16] E. C. Taylor, Jr. and A. E. Martin, *J. Am. Chem. Soc.*, **74**, 6295 (1952).
[17] N. Kornblum and D. L. Kendall, *ibid.*, **74**, 5782 (1952).
[18] J. C. Sheehan and W. A. Bolhofer, *ibid.*, **72**, 2786 (1950).
[19] G. R. Leader and J. F. Gormley, *ibid.*, **73**, 5731 (1951).
[20] W. Schlenk and Wilh. Schlenk, *Ber.*, **62**, 920 (1929).

(**a** [21]) A mixture of 2 l. of commercial dioxane, 27 ml. of concd. hydrochloric acid, and 200 ml. of water is refluxed for 12 hrs., during which time a slow stream of nitrogen is bubbled through the solution to entrain acetaldehyde. The solution is cooled, and potassium hydroxide pellets are added slowly with shaking until they no longer dissolve and a second layer has separated. The dioxane is decanted, treated with fresh potassium hydroxide pellets to remove adhering aqueous liquor, decanted into a clean flask, and refluxed with sodium for 10–12 hrs., when the metal should remain bright. The solvent is then distilled from the sodium and stored out of contact with air.

(**b** [22]) Peroxides are removed and the aldehyde content decreased by passing the solvent through a column of alumina (80 g. for 100–200 ml. of solvent). The method is applicable to ether and other anhydrous solvents.

Ethanol, Absolute

B.p. 78.4°
Miscible with water

Complete dehydration of the constant-boiling mixture containing 95.5% ethanol by weight is best accomplished in two steps. The bulk of the water can be removed by reaction with quicklime, which gives a product containing about 99.5% ethanol. Commercial grades of absolute ethanol likewise may contain traces of water, for pure ethanol is extremely hygroscopic and easily picks up moisture during transfer. (The industrial method consists of distillation of the azeotropic mixture: ethanol, water, benzene. A mixture of all three components distils first, then benzene and ethanol, then absolute ethanol.) Of the many methods which have been suggested for removal of last traces of water the two outlined below appear to be the simplest and most reliable.

(**a**) Ethanol of approximately 99.5% purity is prepared as follows: A round bottomed flask is charged about two thirds full with 95% ethanol and (fresh) quicklime broken into lumps, using enough lime so that the pieces project above the surface of the ethanol. A reflux condenser equipped with a calcium chloride tube is attached and the mixture is refluxed gently for about 1 hr. and then allowed to stand for 2 or 3 days, when the lumps should have largely disintegrated to a powder. The ethanol is then refluxed for 1 hr. and distilled into a suction flask fitted by means of an adapter and protected with a calcium chlo-

[21] K. Hess and H. Frahm, *Ber.*, **71**, 2627 (1938); see also E. Eigenberger, *J. prakt. Chem.*, **130**, 75 (1931).
[22] W. Dasler and C. D. Bauer, *Ind. Eng. Chem., Anal. Ed.*, **18**, 52 (1946).

ride tube. The distillation is rather slow and considerable ethanol is retained by the solid residue.

Further dehydration of this material or of commercial ethanol is accomplished by a method which makes use of the irreversible reaction of an ethyl ester with sodium ethoxide and water [23]:

$$RCOOC_2H_5 + C_2H_5ONa + H_2O \longrightarrow RCOONa + 2C_2H_5OH$$

The ester must be one of low volatility so that it will not distil with the ethanol when used in excess. Smith selected ethyl succinate and Manske [24] substituted the still higher-boiling and less expensive ethyl phthalate. Thus 7 g. of sodium is dissolved in small portions in 1 liter of "absolute" ethanol, 27.5 g. of ethyl phthalate (or 25 g. of ethyl succinate) is added, and the solution is refluxed for 1 hr. in a system protected from moisture. The anhydrous alcohol is then distilled through a short column with exclusion of moist air. Ethanol containing less than 0.05% of water can be obtained by this method.

(b) In the process of Lund and Bjerrum [25] water is removed by reaction with magnesium ethoxide:

$$Mg(OC_2H_5)_2 + 2H_2O \longrightarrow Mg(OH)_2 + 2C_2H_5OH$$

Since the magnesium hydroxide formed is insoluble in ethanol the reaction proceeds to completion. A mixture of 5 g. of magnesium turnings, 60 ml. of absolute ethanol, and a few drops of carbon tetrachloride is refluxed in a large flask until a vigorous reaction ensues and until the magnesium nearly all has been converted into the ethoxide. (If the reaction is slow in starting more catalyst is added.) Nine hundred ml. of absolute ethanol is added, the mixture is refluxed for 1 hr. and the anhydrous ethanol is distilled. The quality of the product depends upon the success with which moisture is excluded from the apparatus. If the presence of carbon tetrachloride in the distillate is objectionable, ethyl bromide is used as catalyst since this halide is so volatile that it is removed in the first few milliliters of distillate.

A test capable of detecting 0.05% of water in ethanol is a voluminous precipitate formed on adding a solution of aluminum ethoxide in benzene to a test portion of the ethanol. [26]

[23] E. L. Smith, *J. Chem. Soc.*, 1288 (1927).
[24] R. H. Manske, *J. Am. Chem. Soc.*, **53**, 1106 (1931).
[25] H. Lund and J. Bjerrum, *Ber.*, **64**, 210 (1931); H. Lund, *ibid.*, **37**, 936 (1934); *J. Am. Chem. Soc.*, **74**, 3188 (1952).
[26] F. Henle, *Ber.*, **53**, 719 (1920).

Ether, Anhydrous

Ether available commercially contains so little water and ethanol that it can be treated with sodium without preliminary drying (by shaking with 1:1 sulfuric acid and drying over calcium chloride or by distillation from concd. sulfuric acid). It is placed in a dry bottle or flask connected by an inverted U-tube to a drying tube containing calcium chloride or anhydrous calcium sulfate, and sodium wire (2–3 g. per kg.) is run in from a press. If there is an appreciable evolution of hydrogen, fresh sodium wire is added after an interval of about 12 hrs. When all reaction has ceased and the wire remains bright, the bottle is stoppered with a cork and stored in a cool place remote from flames.

Peroxide-free ether. Ether exposed to the air is liable to contain enough peroxide to destroy significant amounts of oxidizable substances or to cause an explosion if not removed before solvent used for an extraction is evaporated to dryness. To *detect peroxide* dissolve 1 mg. of sodium dichromate in 1 ml. of water in a test tube, add a drop of dil. sulfuric acid, and fill the tube with ether and shake. A blue color in the ether layer (perchromate) indicates the presence of peroxide. (For determination of peroxide, see ref. 22.) If the ether is to be used for extraction from an aqueous solution it can be freed of peroxide by shaking with 5% ferrous sulfate solution weakly acidified with sulfuric acid or by dissolving a little water in the ether and adding calcium hydride. The reagent is also used to remove last traces of moisture from ether (let stand overnight, add a little more hydride, and see if bubbles of hydrogen are still evolved).

Ether can be freed of peroxide without getting it wet by chromatography on alumina [22]; the peroxide is adsorbed, not destroyed. Moisture decreases the efficiency of peroxide removal. Over 700 ml. of anhydrous ether can be freed of peroxide with 80 g. of alumina.

Ethyl Acetate

Commercial material may contain traces of water, ethanol, and acetic acid. Purification is accomplished by washing with an equal volume of 5% sodium carbonate solution, then with saturated calcium chloride solution, drying over anhydrous potassium carbonate, and distilling. Phosphorus pentoxide can be used for a final drying, after which the ethyl acetate is filtered and distilled with protection from moisture.

Another procedure involves conversion of the ethanol into ethyl acetate. One liter of ethyl acetate (98%) is refluxed with

B.p. 34.6°
Immiscible

B.p. 77.1°
Immiscible
8.5g/100 $H_2O^{15°}$

55 ml. of acetic anhydride and then distilled through a fractionating column. The distillate is shaken with anhydrous potassium carbonate and redistilled (purity 99.6%). The same method is applicable to methyl acetate.[27]

Ethylene Dichloride, CH_2ClCH_2Cl [28]

B.p. 83.8°
Immiscible

Ethylene dichloride is used for extraction of various natural products (steroids, Vitamin A, caffeine, nicotine). Its toxicity is comparable to that of chloroform. Most of the water can be removed by distillation (the solvent forms an azeotrope containing 8.9% water). The remainder can be removed by distillation from phosphorus pentoxide. The commercial product can be purified by washing with concd. sulfuric acid and then with water.

Ethylene Glycol Dimethyl Ether, $CH_3OCH_2CH_2OCH_3$

B.p. 83°
Miscible with water

Like the analogously constituted dioxan, this substance is an effective solvent for water-insoluble organic compounds and is at the same time miscible with water. Interaction of aromatic hydrocarbons with metallic sodium is facilitated by employing either this solvent or dimethyl ether (less conveniently handled, b.p. $-25°$).[29] Even naphthalene and diphenyl will add sodium in the presence of either of these special solvents, whereas no reaction occurs when diethyl ether is used.

Ethylene glycol diethyl ether (diethyl cellosolve), b.p. 121.4°, dissolves in water to the extent of 21% at 20°.

Ethylene Glycol Monomethyl Ether (Methyl Cellosolve), $CH_3OCH_2CH_2OH$

B.p. 125.0°
Miscible with water

Ligroin and Petroleum Ether

B.p. 20–120°
Immiscible

These refined fractions from petroleum usually contain unsaturated hydrocarbons which ordinarily do not interfere with use of the solvents for crystallizations but which are sometimes undesirable because of their reactivity. The bulk of the unsaturated substances can be removed by shaking with concd. sulfuric acid, after which a test should be made with acid permanganate and, if there is any reaction, the hydrocarbon fraction should be shaken with a solution of potassium permanganate and sulfuric acid until oxidizable substances have been destroyed. The solvent is then washed with water, dried over calcium chloride, and distilled. It is not advisable to use a fraction boiling

[27] C. D. Hurd and J. S. Strong, *Ind. Eng. Chem., Anal. Ed.*, **23**, 542 (1951).
[28] R. E. Buckles and J. F. Mills, *J. Am. Chem. Soc.*, **75**, 552 (1953).
[29] N. D. Scott, J. F. Walker and V. L. Hansley, *J. Am. Chem. Soc.*, **58**, 2442 (1936).

over a range of more than 30° because in dissolving a solid there is some loss of the more volatile part of the solvent, and the substance, being more soluble in the higher-boiling residue, may not crystallize. Hexane fractions of narrow boiling range are available commercially. Peroxides can be removed by chromatography on alumina.[22]

Methanol

B.p. 64.7°
Miscible with water

Because of its lower cost, methanol is preferred to ethanol except where a higher reflux temperature or greater solvent power is essential. Many workers prefer methanol for crystallizations. Synthetic methanol is suitable for most purposes without purification but usually contains traces of acetone (less than 0.1%) and formaldehyde. Acetone can be eliminated by treatment with a hypohalite and formaldehyde presents no difficulties. An interesting method of purification has been developed by Morton and Mark [30]: methanol (500 ml.) is refluxed for several hours with furfural (25 ml.) and 10% sodium hydroxide solution (60 ml.), thereby forming a resin which carries down all carbonyl compounds present. The alcohol is then fractionated and separated from water and furfural with 95% recovery. A highly sensitive test for acetone with Nessler's reagent is described in this paper.

When water is the chief objectionable impurity, and when it is present in quantities of only 1–2%, a process similar to that of Lund and Bjerrum [25] is useful. The methanol is placed in a large flask provided with an efficient condenser and 5–15 g. of magnesium turnings is added (adjust the amount according to the quantity of water probably present). If there is but little water the reaction will start after a short time and may require cooling (do not heat at the outset). If much water is present and the reaction is slow in starting, treat a small amount of magnesium with purer methanol in a small vessel, and after the formation of magnesium methoxide has commenced, pour the solution into the main reaction flask. Once the first vigorous reaction is over and the magnesium has been largely dissolved, the mixture is refluxed for 2–3 hrs. and the dry alcohol is distilled from the residue of magnesium hydroxide and magnesium methoxide.

Methylcyclohexane

B.p. 100.9°
Immiscible

This (a good lighter fluid) has much greater solvent power (e.g., for steroids) than ligroin of comparable boiling point.

[30] A. A. Morton and J. G. Mark, *Ind. Eng. Chem., Anal. Ed.*, **6**, 151 (1934).

B.p. 40.8°
Immiscible

B.p. 79.6°
Partly miscible

CH_3NO_2, b.p. 101.2°
$C_2H_5NO_2$, b.p. 114.0°
Immiscible

B.p. 210°
Immiscible

Methylene Chloride, CH_2Cl_2

Methylene chloride is a convenient substitute for ether where it is desired to employ an extraction solvent heavier than water.

Methyl Ethyl Ketone

Methyl ethyl ketone is available in 99% purity and can be purified through the bisulfite addition compound. It forms an azeotrope with water, b.p. 73.4°, containing 88.7% of the ketone. Anhydrous material can be made by salting with sodium chloride.

Nitroalkanes

Nitroalkanes became available commercially in 1940 and have found increasing use as solvents for a wide range of compounds. They have relatively high boiling points, comparatively low toxicities, and low flammabilities. They are useful in Friedel-Crafts reactions, since they dissolve aluminum chloride and thus furnish homogeneous reaction mixtures. Those most commonly used, nitromethane and nitroethane, should be handled with caution because they can explode when heated above the boiling point. A method of purification described [31] requires a rather elaborate distillation technique.

Nitrobenzene

Nitrobenzene is useful as solvent for crystallization of substances that dissolve to only a slight extent in usual solvents. After the crystalline product is collected it should be washed thoroughly with ether to remove the nitrobenzene, which otherwise adheres tenaciously to the crystals. The vapor of the solvent is poisonous. A limitation to use of this solvent is that at the boiling point it has a pronounced oxidizing action. Aluminum chloride is moderately soluble in nitrobenzene (labile molecular compound), which is thus a good solvent for Friedel-Crafts reactions, particularly at temperatures ranging from −15° to 25°.

Crude nitrobenzene may contain dinitrobenzene, and recovered solvent may contain aniline. Both substances, along with other impurities, are removed by steam distillation from a mixture with dilute sulfuric acid. The solvent is then dried over calcium chloride and distilled.

Petroleum Ether   (See Ligroin)

[31] C. J. Thompson, H. J. Coleman and R. V. Helm, *J. Am. Chem. Soc.*, **76**, 3445 (1954).

Pyridine

Commonly used as solvent and base in acetylations; also useful because of its great solvent power. It is used in Zerewitinoff determination of the number of active hydrogen atoms in a compound through measurement of the methane evolved on reaction with methylmagnesium iodide, or in the modified method [32] in which the amount of Grignard reagent consumed by an addition reaction is also determined. An alternate solvent for use in determination of sparingly soluble substances is a mixture of diphenyl ether (solid) and xylene.[33] Anhydrous pyridine can be prepared by distillation of commercial material from barium oxide with exclusion of moist air. Another method is to add phenylmagnesium bromide solution, evaporate the ether, and distil the pyridine.

B.p. 115°
Miscible with water

Quinoline Substitute

Because it is basic and has a high boiling point (238°), quinoline is useful as solvent for decarboxylations [34] and in purification of low-boiling liquids containing traces of acids (e.g., thionyl chloride). The same purposes are well served by the less expensive coal tar base fractions of suitable boiling point range supplied by the Barrett Co., Philadelphia.

s-Tetrachloroethane, CHCl₂CHCl₂

This is an excellent solvent for many substances which dissolve with difficulty in benzene, glacial acetic acid, etc., although it does not equal nitrobenzene. The pure liquid is inert to aluminum chloride and it serves as solvent for the Friedel-Crafts reaction, particularly since it is easily volatile with steam. A convenient method of removing a trace of colored impurity often persisting through several crystallizations of a higher aromatic hydrocarbon (e.g., chrysene) is to shake a solution of the substance in tetrachloroethane (warmed if necessary) with successive portions of concd. sulfuric acid until no further color is extracted. A crude reaction product that does not dissolve well in commoner solvents and is likely to contain char is conveniently purified by dissolving it in s-tetrachloroethane, clarifying the solution with Norit, and removing the solvent by steam distillation (example: benzanthrone prepared by the Bally-Scholl method).

B.p. 146.3°
Immiscible

[32] E. P. Kohler and N. K. Richtmeyer, *J. Am. Chem. Soc.*, **52**, 3736 (1930).
[33] O. Schmitz-Dumont and K. Hamann, *Ber.*, **66**, 71 (1933).
[34] A. F. Shepard, N. R. Winslow and J. R. Johnson, *J. Am. Chem. Soc.*, **52**, 2083 (1930).

For purification the crude liquid is warmed on the steam bath with crude, concd. sulfuric acid (80 ml. per liter) and either shaken or stirred mechanically for one half hour. After decanting the upper layer, the process is repeated once or twice until the acid liquor does not become discolored. The solvent is then separated, washed with water (or steam distilled), dried with calcium chloride, and distilled.

Tetrahydrofuran

B.p. 65.4°
Miscible with water

Tetrahydrofuran has high solvent power and is a useful solvent for reductions with lithium aluminum hydride that proceed slowly in ether. For this purpose, it should be purified by treatment with solid potassium hydroxide, followed by distillation over lithium aluminum hydride. Tetrahydrofuran is also a useful solvent for Grignard reactions, Friedel-Crafts reactions, and for various alkylation reactions.

Toiuene, Free from Sulfur Compounds

B.p. 110.6°
Immiscible

Crude toluene may be purified with sulfuric acid as in the case of benzene but is more subject to sulfonation, and some control of the temperature is required. Stir mechanically for one half hr. a mixture of 1 l. of toluene and 80 ml. of crude, concd. sulfuric acid, keeping the temperature about 30° by occasional cooling. Decant from the acid layer, repeat the process once or twice, separate the acid, and proceed as in the purification of benzene.

1,2,4-Trichlorobenzene

B.p. 213°
Immiscibla

This has been used as solvent in chlorination of sparingly soluble pyrene derivatives.[12]

Triethylene glycol (triglycol), $HOCH_2CH_2OCH_2CH_2OCH_2CH_2OH$

B.p. 287.3°
Miscible with water

Because of its high solvent power this is useful for dissolving organic compounds and potassium hydroxide (Chapter 44.1).

DRYING AGENTS [35]

Calcium Chloride

Large capacity for the absorption of water (forms the hexahydrate below 30°), not very efficient, particularly useful for preliminary drying. *Usually unsuitable for drying:* alcohols and amines (forms molecular compounds), phenols, esters, acids (contains lime).

[35] See L. Velluz, *Substances Naturelles de Synthèse*, **1**, 123–126 (1951).

Calcium Hydride (See Ethanol, this chapter)

Cotton, Absorbent

An excellent drying agent [36] well suited for use in drying tubes placed at the top of reflux condensers or dropping funnels. The cotton can be dried by heating it in an oven at 100°.

Phosphorus Pentoxide

Very efficient and rapid; for hydrocarbons, ethers, esters, nitrites, alkyl halides; not for alcohols, acids, amines, ketones.

Potassium Carbonate

Fair efficiency and capacity (forms the dihydrate); for esters, nitriles, ketones; not for use with acidic substances.

Potassium Hydroxide (solid)

Very efficient and rapid, but limited almost entirely to use with amines.

Salts: Na_2SO_4, $MgSO_4$, $CaSO_4$

Being neutral, inert, and insoluble in organic liquids, these salts can be used for all types of compounds, including those sensitive to other drying agents. *Sodium sulfate* is inexpensive and has a high capacity of absorption because at temperatures below 33° it forms the hydrate $NaSO_4 \cdot 10H_2O$, but the drying action is slow and not thorough. Anhydrous *magnesium sulfate* is somewhat more rapid and effective, forms the heptahydrate below 48°, and is thus capable of absorbing considerable quantities of water. It is less easily poured into a funnel than sodium sulfate. Both the sodium and the magnesium salts can be obtained in anhydrous condition by heating hydrated or partially hydrated material in a casserole over a wire gauze. Anhydrous *calcium sulfate* prepared in a special way [37] is marketed under the trade name Drierite. An indicating form is available which turns from blue to red when exhausted. The reagent, called "soluble anhydrite" to distinguish it from the insoluble mineral of the same composition but different behavior, is prepared by heating either the dihydrate or the hemihydrate in an oven at 235° for 2-3 hrs., and used material can be regenerated by the same process. The soluble salt reverts in drying to the hemihydrate, $CaSO_4 \cdot \frac{1}{2}H_2O$, and its capacity is limited to the ab-

[36] F. P. Pingert, *Org. Synth.*, **20**, 9 (1940).
[37] W. A. Hammond and J. R. Withrow, *Ind. Eng. Chem.*, **25**, 653, 1112 (1933).

sorption of only 6.6% of its weight of water. The rapidity and efficiency of drying, however, are both very great. Added to a moist liquid such as ordinary alcohol, the salt produces a marked rise in temperature. In completeness of drying Drierite stands between phosphorus pentoxide and concd. sulfuric acid, and it is surpassed only by the former. The reagent should find many uses, particularly when employed in combination with a primary drier.

Sodium (wire)

Very efficient but of use only with inactive, neutral compounds (ethers, saturated and aromatic hydrocarbons). The liquid or solution should be dried first with calcium chloride to remove the bulk of the water.

Caution: Every precaution must be taken in using sodium for drying purposes or as a reagent; on no account must the metal come in contact with water. A serious explosion can result from a leaky condenser or a flask which cracks when heated over a steam or water bath, and the apparatus must be tested in advance as to soundness. Sodium residues and cuttings should be transferred at once to a bottle provided for the purpose and filled with kerosene; scraps must not be allowed to remain exposed and on no account are they to be thrown into the sink or the waste jar. From time to time the residues accumulating should be destroyed by adding the scraps in *small* portions to a rather large quantity of alcohol. After *all* the metal has reacted the solution is washed down the drain. Wire remaining after a drying operation is destroyed in the same way and *not* by pouring alcohol onto the wire.

Lead–sodium alloy [38] can be used in place of sodium for drying ether and other flammable liquids. The alloy is easily prepared in a finely divided form and is less hazardous to handle than sodium.

[38] H. Soroos, *Ind. Eng. Chem., Anal. Ed.,* **11,** 657 (1939).

Ammonia

The gas can be obtained from a cylinder of liquid ammonia or generated in the apparatus shown in Fig. 49.1. Concd. ammonia water (sp. gr. 0.89) is heated in *a* with a very small flame at first and then more strongly and the gas evolved is dried in

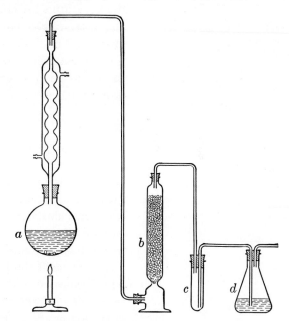

FIG. 49.1 The preparation of dry ammonia

a tower of soda lime (*b*). A trap (*c*) is introduced just before the flask (*d*) in which the ammonia is to be absorbed in a reaction mixture or in solvent, and the tubes are so arranged that any liquid sucked back into the trap will eventually find its way again into the absorption vessel.

Carbon Dioxide

Gaseous carbon dioxide containing air but suitable for some purposes may be obtained from a cylinder of the liquid material or by evaporation of dry ice from a bottle wrapped with a towel and fitted with a stopper carrying a gas outlet and a Bunsen valve for release of excess pressure. The gas also may be generated by dropping hydrochloric acid (1 : 1) onto lumps of marble, as shown in Fig. 49.2, or, where small amounts of gas are required over a long period, with the use of a Kipp, Ostwald, or other standard form of generator. For use in the Dumas method for the determination of nitrogen, where traces of air are objectionable, the marble is boiled with water before use or replaced by either potassium carbonate or sodium bicarbonate. A dry ice generator suitable for use in micro-Dumas determination of nitrogen is described by Hershberg and Wellwood.[1]

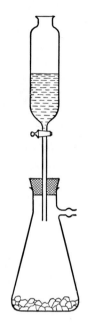

FIG. 49.2 Carbon dioxide generator

Carbon Monoxide

Carbon monoxide is prepared by dropping 85–90% formic acid into concd. sulfuric acid contained in a 1-liter distilling flask as the generator. A condenser tube fitted with a dropping funnel and extending 2 cm. below the surface of the acid promotes mixing. The flask is heated in a water bath kept at 60–70° to promote an even flow of gas on dropping in the formic acid. The gas is passed through a drying tower filled with potassium hydroxide pellets.

Chlorine

When 25–50 g. of gaseous chlorine is to be passed into a reaction mixture use one of the small cylinders of liquid chlorine and follow the addition by the loss in weight of the cylinder. For smaller quantities, or where more exact control is required, generate the chlorine according to Graebe.[2] The calculated amount of solid potassium permanganate is placed in a distilling flask with a high side arm, which serves as gas exit tube. Concd. hydrochloric acid diluted with one fourth its volume of water is added from a dropping funnel, the stem of which runs nearly to the bottom of the flask and is drawn down and bent upward at the extremity. The chlorine evolved is passed through a wash bottle containing water to remove hydrogen chloride and then it is dried in a sulfuric acid wash bottle. A safety trap to relieve excessive gas pressure, consisting of a T-tube with a long arm

[1] E. B. Hershberg and G. W. Wellwood, *Ind. Eng. Chem., Anal. Ed.*, **9**, 303 (1937).
[2] C. Graebe, *Ber.*, **35**, 43 (1902).

dipping into concd. sulfuric acid, comes next in line and the gas is then passed into the reaction vessel. The acid solution is run in slowly at room temperature until about half of it has been added; when gas evolution begins to slacken, the mixture in the generating flask is heated with a small flame at first and then nearly to boiling to complete the reaction. For each gram of potassium permanganate 6.2 ml. of concd. hydrochloric acid is used (excess); the theoretical yield is 1.12 g. of chlorine. The actual yield does not fall far short of this amount and the recovery is practically quantitative if the chlorine is swept out of the flask and bottles with a stream of carbon dioxide.

Hydrogen Bromide

Gaseous hydrogen bromide can be prepared by direct combination of the elements. Claisen and Eisleb [3] heated bromine to a temperature of about $40°$, where the vapor pressure is 0.5 atmosphere, and passed in a stream of hydrogen. The gas mixture issuing from the flask contained approximately equimolecular quantities of the two elements, and combination was effected by passing the mixture through a hot tube packed with platinized quartz or asbestos. Any excess bromine was removed in a tube charged with beads moistened with red phosphorus. The method has been improved by Ruhoff, Burnett and Reid,[4] whose description should be consulted for details. These authors find the catalyst to be unnecessary and simply pack the combustion tube with clay chips and heat it with the full force of a burner. Excessive bromine is removed in a tube filled with copper turnings. According to Ionescu and Radulescu,[5] pure dry hydrogen bromide can be prepared in 80–90% yield by dropping bromine onto petroleum ether in the presence of aluminum bromide.

Hydrogen Chloride

Hydrogen chloride is available in cylinders. Small quantities of the gas can be generated by dropping concd. sulfuric acid from a separatory funnel mounted in a distilling flask onto solid ammonium chloride.[6] When the initial reaction slows down, a very small flame at the side of the flask close to the surface of the powder continues the action, which soon stops when the flame is removed. The reaction mixture remains liquid in the

[3] L. Claisen and O. Eisleb, *Ann.*, **401**, 28 (1913).
[4] J. H. Ruhoff, R. E. Burnett and E. E. Reid, *Org. Synth., Coll. Vol.* **2**, 338 (1943).
[5] C. N. Ionescu and V. Radulescu, *Bul. soc. chem. România*, **17**, 309 (1935).
[6] Method suggested by W. Rigby.

warmed zone (NH₄HSO₄, m.p. 147°), and as the flame is moved lower more of the mass liquefies. A flask of moderate size can cope with foaming that may occur if gas evolution is brisk.

In the generator shown in Fig. 49.3 a charge of concd. sulfuric acid is run into the large separatory funnel and the concd. hydrochloric acid is placed in the dropping funnel and run in when required through the long stem. Entering in this way at the bot-

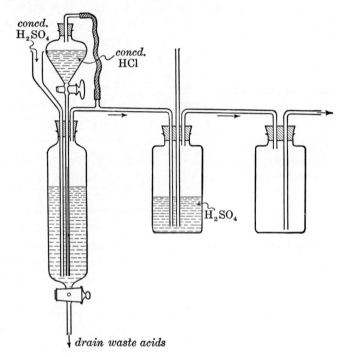

FIG. 49.3 Hydrogen chloride generator

tom of the layer of heavier liquid, the hydrochloric acid becomes thoroughly mixed with it. The capillary construction permits the stem to remain filled with liquid so that the flow is continuous. The connection between the gas exit and the top of the dropping funnel equalizes the pressure in the system and allows hydrochloric acid to flow in under gravitational pressure. The sulfuric acid wash bottle is provided with a safety tube to prevent a suck-back. The empty bottle next in line is a trap to catch any liquid which may suck back from the absorbing flask, and it will return such liquid to the flask when the flow of hydrogen chloride is resumed. The spent acid liquor can be run out and the separatory funnel recharged without disassembling the apparatus. If the rubber stopper at the top of the separatory funnel is coated heavily with varnish after it has been put in place it will remain gas-tight for many months; after the surface of a

stopper has been corroded by hydrogen chloride the rubber becomes impervious to further attack.

Nitrogen

For many purposes prepurified nitrogen containing less than
0.1% oxygen is satisfactory as an inert gas. If nitrogen of this
quality is not available, or if a still purer gas is required, the
oxygen can be removed by absorption in Fieser's solution [7]:
an alkaline sodium hydrosulfite solution to which sodium β-an-
thraquinone sulfonate is added as catalyst. The quinone is at
once reduced to the hydroquinone, which absorbs oxygen with
rapidity and which is kept in the reduced condition by the re-
serve of hydrosulfite present. The solution is prepared by dissolving 20 g. of potassium hydroxide in 100 ml. of water and
adding 2 g. of sodium anthraquinone β-sulfonate and 15 g. of
sodium hydrosulfite ($Na_2S_2O_4$) to the warm solution. The mixture is stirred until a clear, blood-red solution is obtained; this
is ready for use after it has been cooled to room temperature.
Nitrogen from the tank is passed through two or three wash
bottles containing this solution and then into a wash bottle of
saturated lead acetate solution, which absorbs traces of hydrogen
sulfide sometimes present. Since the absorbent functions on a
catalytic principle the original efficiency is retained to the point
of exhaustion and the wash bottles do not require refilling as
long as the solution remains clear and bright. When the color
changes to dull red or brown, or when a precipitate appears, the
solution should be replaced. With fresh commercial hydrosulfite
the efficient capacity of the above quantity of solution is 788 ml.
of oxygen.

For some purposes, as in working with free radicals, completely
dry, oxygen-free nitrogen is required. Nitrogen purified as described above and dried with sulfuric acid will often give satisfactory service, but as an added precaution the gas can be washed
with a solution in absolute ether of the metal ketyl from benzophenone and sodium, $(C_6H_5)_2CONa$ (or the bimolecular form).
This substance is extremely sensitive to both oxygen and moisture. If the vapor of ether in the gas stream is objectionable a
higher-boiling liquid such as xylene can be employed in combination with liquid sodium–potassium alloy. To fill a wash bottle
of ordinary size 5 g. of sodium is covered with a little xylene and
5 g. of potassium is dropped in. If the metals do not alloy they
are pushed together with a glass rod until liquefaction occurs.

[7] L. F. Fieser, *J. Am. Chem. Soc.*, **46**, 2639 (1924).

The liquid alloy is transferred with a pipette under a layer of solvent to a suitable amount of xylene contained in the wash bottle. Ten grams of benzophenone is added and the bottle is sealed with wax at the top. Before each period of use the bottle should be shaken vigorously. To remove the small amount of hydrocarbon vapor and to seal the metal ketyl bottle from the air, the gas is next passed into a wash bottle containing liquid paraffin.

Sulfur Dioxide

Sulfur dioxide is available in cylinders; it can be generated by dropping 1 : 1 hydrochloric acid onto sodium bisulfite (Fig. 49.2).

INTRODUCTION

This chapter lists some of the reagents that are of general use in the organic laboratory and some of those that have found application in only one specialized field. The citation usually includes the molecular weight, physical constants pertinent to use of the reagent, name of a supplier or reference to a method of preparation of a less common chemical, and leading references to literature pertaining to reactions and uses of the reagent. Reagents whose properties and chief uses are well known usually are not included.

Although the reagents are listed alphabetically, they are also included in the general index of the book. The entries are further classified as to type in the index that follows. For identification in this index, the reagents in each letter-group are numbered serially. Thus A 1 identifies acetaldehyde, B 2 benzaldehyde. Some reagents appear in two or more classifications; e.g., N-bromosuccinimide (B 16) is used for both halogenation and oxidation.

INDEX OF TYPES

ACIDS, inorganic: H 6, 7, 8, 9, 11,   M 10, 14,
  N 4,   P 11, 12, 23

ACYLATING AGENTS
  Accessory, M 16
  ArCO—, B 5,   D 26
  RCO—, A 4, 6,   C 4, 5,   I 14,   K 1,
    T 4, 17
  ROCO—, B 14, 21,   C 2,   E 3,   N 2, 5
  S-compounds, B 3, 4, 6,   M 12, 13,   T 9
  Unclassified, C 21,   D 15,   F 8,
    M 11,   O 3

ALKYLATING AGENTS, A 10, 12,   B 19,   D 2,
  4, 22,   E 4,   M 18, 19,   T 29, 30

CARBONYL COMPOUNDS, reagents for
  Acetal formation, E 1, 6,   M 5,   P 38
  Hydrazine, hydrazide, D 21, 29, 33,   G 1,
    2,   H 5,   L 11,   N 3,   O 2 (accessory),   P 8, 46 (accessory), S 2, 28 (accessory),   T 10
  Other, A 5,   B 18,   D 3, 4,   F 1,   H 3,
    L 5,   P 7,   T 24

CATALYSTS (and reagents) for acylation, alkylation, condensation, dehydration

[1] By Mary Fieser and Louis F. Fieser

INDEX OF TYPES

REAGENTS

1. **Acetaldehyde.** Mol. wt. 44.05, b.p. 20.8°, sp. gr. 0.78. Pour 20 ml. (20 g.) of paraldehyde into a 100-ml. round bottomed flask fitted with a fractionating column and add a mixture of 0.5 ml. each of concd. sulfuric acid and water. Attach the column and warm the flask very gently over an asbestos-wire gauze with a small flame at such a rate that acetaldehyde distils at a temperature not higher than 35°. To avoid charring of the mixture, continue only until about half the material has been converted into acetaldehyde, collected in an ice-cold receiver.

2. **Acetaldoxime,** $CH_3CH{=}NOH$; **formaldoxime,** $HCH{=}NOH$. These reagents react with diazonium salts to form arylated oximes, which on acid hydrolysis yield an aryl methyl ketone or an aryl aldehyde,[1] e.g.,

$$ArN_2Cl + CH_3CH{=}NOH \rightarrow$$
$$ArC(CH_3)N{=}OH \rightarrow ArCOCH_3$$

[1] W. F. Beech, *J. Chem. Soc.*, 1297 (1954).

3. **Acetamide.** Mol. wt. 59.07, m.p. 82°. This substance is useful in bromination of acid-sensitive compounds since it forms a stable complex with hydrogen bromide, $(CH_3CO-NH_2)_2 \cdot HBr$, which is insoluble in common bromination solvents.[1]

[1] K. Zeile and H. Meyer, *Ber.*, **82**, 275 (1949).

4. **Acetic anhydride.** Mol. wt. 102.09, b.p. 139.6°, sp. gr. 1.08. The reagent often deteriorates as the result of improper storage, and it is well to test it either in a preliminary, small-scale run or by shaking a sample with ice water and rapidly titrating the free acetic acid. A satisfactory purification can be effected by fractionation; material of practical grade can be first distilled from fused sodium acetate to eliminate halogen compounds and metals.

Procedures for acetylation: DL-alanine (Chapter 22); reductive acetylation (Chapter 31.4); salicylic acid, catalysis by H_2SO_4, BF_3, pyridine, NaOAc (Chapter 37); of amines in aqueous solution (Chapters 26.3b, 42.4).

5. **Acetone cyanohydrin,** $(CH_3)_2C(OH)CN$. Mol. wt. 85.10, b.p. 80°/15 mm. Preparation.[1] Use for transcyanohydration[2]: preparation in good yield of the 17-monocyanohydrin of a 3,17-diketo steroid by hydrogen cyanide exchange with the reagent.

[1] *Org. Synth., Coll. Vol.*, **2**, 7 (1943); **20**, 43 (1940).
[2] A. Ercoli and P. de Ruggieri, *J. Am. Chem. Soc.*, **75**, 650 (1953).

6. **Acetyl chloride.** Mol. wt. 78.50, b.p. 52°, sp. gr. 1.10. Preparation from acetic anhydride and calcium chloride.[1]

[1] J. Gmünder, *Helv. Chim. Acta*, **36**, 2021 (1953).

7. **Acetylene.** Mol. wt. 26.04, b.p. −83°. Purification and technique of handling.[1]

[1] *Org. Synth., Coll. Vol.*, **1**, 229 (1941).

8. **Acrylonitrile,** $CH_2{=}CHCN$. Mol. wt. 53.06, b.p. 77°, sp. gr. 0.81. Used in cyanoethylation.[1]

[1] H. A. Bruson, *Org. Reactions*, **5**, 79 (1949).

Acyl peroxides, see Diacyl peroxides.

9. **Alkyl hydroperoxides,** ROOH. See also *t*-Butyl hydroperoxide. Preparation (a) Baeyer and Villiger's method[1] of treating 30% hydrogen peroxide with a dialkyl sulfate gives in low yield impure and dangerously unstable preparations of methyl, ethyl, *n*-propyl, and *n*-butyl hydroperoxide. An improved procedure[2] utilizing methanol as solvent affords pure *n*- and *s*-butyl hydroperoxide in yields of 20 and 40%. (b) A synthesis by the reaction of an *n*-alkyl methanesulfonate (CH_3SO_3R) with hydrogen peroxide in methanolic potassium hydroxide solution affords pure *n*-alkyl[3] hydroperoxides (propyl through decyl) in 70–80% yield (secondary, 20–25%). These hydroperoxides are of the same order of stability as the *t*-butyl derivative. (c) Pure alkyl hydroperoxides are obtainable by slow addition of alkyl Grignard reagents to oxygen-saturated ether at −75°.[4]

[1] A. Baeyer and V. Villiger, *Ber.*, **33**, 3387 (1900); **34**, 738 (1901).
[2] E. G. Lindstrom, *J. Am. Chem. Soc.*, **75**, 5123 (1953).

³ H. R. Williams and H. S. Mosher, *ibid.*, **76**, 2984, 2987 (1954).

⁴ C. Walling and S. A. Buckler, *ibid.*, **75**, 4372 (1953).

10. Alkyl iodides. Methyl and ethyl iodide deteriorate rapidly with liberation of iodine if exposed to light, and commercial preparations which have been kept long in storage are often dark and unsuitable for use. Such material can be purified by shaking it with successive portions of a dilute solution of either sodium thiosulfate or sodium bisulfite until the color is bleached, washing with water, drying over calcium chloride, and distilling the product. The colorless distillate should be stored in a brown bottle and kept out of sunlight. As a further protective measure a few drops of clean mercury can be added, for the alkyl iodide will then keep almost indefinitely without becoming discolored if not exposed to light for long periods. Prolonged exposure presents a certain danger, for appreciable quantities of the poisonous methylmercuric iodide may result from photochemical reaction. A little mercury can be used also to remove a slight purple or pink color from a sample of an iodide which has begun to decompose.

11. Alkyl methanesulfonates, CH_3SO_3R. Preparation by reaction of mesyl chloride with alcohols in pyridine solution.[1]

¹ V. C. Sekera and C. S. Marvel, *J. Am. Chem. Soc.*, **55**, 345 (1933).

12. Alkyl sulfates. Discolored samples of dimethyl or diethyl sulfate can be purified by slow distillation at the water pump ($ROSO_2OH$ if present decomposes to R_2SO_4 and H_2SO_4). Higher alkyl sulfates are conveniently made through the sulfites.[1]

¹ *Org. Synth., Coll. Vol.*, **2**, 111, 112 (1943).

13a. Alumina for chromatography. The equivalent of *acid-washed* material can be prepared by stirring ordinary alumina with ethyl acetate, letting the mixture stand for 1–2 days, filtering, and drying at 80°. Alumina washed with 5-10% acetic acid in water is suitable for adsorption of base-sensitive substances (enol acetates, α,β-unsaturated acetates).[1] For chromatography of β,γ-unsaturated ketones without isomerization, the alumina can be washed with warm aqueous alkali, then warm acetic acid followed by water (to neutrality); it is then reactivated at 200° for 30 hrs.[2]

¹ K. R. Farrar, J. C. Hamlet, H. B. Henbest and E. R. H. Jones, *J. Chem. Soc.*, 2657 (1952); R. B. Clayton, A. Crawshaw, H. B. Henbest, E. R. H. Jones, B. J. Lovell and G. W. Wood, *ibid.*, 2009 (1953).

² C. W. Shoppee and G. H. R. Summers, *J. Chem. Soc.*, 689 (1950).

13b. Alumina, morin-dyed.[1] Morin, 2′,3,4′,5,7-pentahydroxyflavone, is supplied by Eastman. A solution of 300 mg. of morin in 500 ml. of methanol is added with stirring to a slurry of 500 g. of alumina in 500 ml. of methanol. When the supernatant liquor is decolorized, the alumina is collected and dried at 150° for 2 hrs., when the citrone-yellow preparation has grade II activity.[2] A column of this adsorbent fluoresces in ultraviolet light (ca. 360 mμ) and colorless substances that absorb in the near ultraviolet show up on the column as dark bands on a luminous background. It proved useful for separation of naturally occurring polyunsaturated diols.[3]

¹ H. Brockmann and F. Volpers, *Ber.*, **80**, 77 (1947).

² H. Brockmann and H. Schodder, *ibid.*, **74**, 73 (1941).

³ E. F. L. J. Anet, and others, *J. Chem. Soc.*, 309 (1953).

14. Aluminum amalgam. Useful for desulfurization, particularly where Raney nickel leads to overreduction.[1]

¹ J. D. Dutcher, J. R. Johnson and W. F. Bruce, *J. Am. Chem. Soc.*, **67**, 1736 (1945); J. R. Johnson and J. B. Buchanan, *ibid.*, **75**, 2103 (1953).

15. Aluminum *t*-butoxide.[1] Mol. wt. 246.32. Preparation.[2]

¹ A. L. Wilds, "Reduction with Aluminum Alkoxides," *Org. Reactions*, **2**, 178 (1944); C. Djerassi, "The Oppenauer Oxidation," *ibid.*, **6**, 207 (1951).

² *Org. Synth.*, **21**, 8 (1941).

REAGENTS

16. Aluminum chloride. Mol. wt. 133.35. Friedel-Crafts reactions: Chapters 28, 29.1. See Sodium aluminum chloride. Catalyst for esterification of hindered alcohols with acid chlorides.[1]

> [1] M. E. Hill, *J. Am. Chem. Soc.*, **76**, 2329 (1954).

17. Aluminum isopropoxide.[1] Mol. wt. 204.24. Supplier: Eastman. Preparation.[1]

> [1] A. L. Wilds, "Reduction with Aluminum Alkoxides," *Org. Reactions*, **2**, 178 (1944); C. Djerassi, "The Oppenauer Oxidation," *ibid.*, **6**, 207 (1951).

Ammonium persulfate. Mol. wt. 228.21. See Potassium persulfate.

18. n-Amyl nitrite (or isoamyl nitrite) in the presence of potassium *t*-butoxide[1] or hydrochloric acid[2] reacts with a ketone having an adjacent methylene group to give an α-oximino ketone, $RCOC(=NOH)R'$. This on hydrogenation yields the α-amino ketone[3] and on reduction with zinc and acetic acid yields the α-ketol. Hydrolysis with dilute hydrochloric acid in the presence of formaldehyde leads to the α-diketone.[4] See Nitrosyl chloride.

> [1] F. Litvan and R. Robinson, *J. Chem. Soc.*, 1997 (1938).
> [2] J. A. Barltrop, A. J. Johnson and G. D. Meakins, *ibid.*, 181 (1951).
> [3] D. Caunt, and others, *ibid.*, 1631 (1950).
> [4] F. H. Stodola, E. C. Kendall and B. F. McKenzie, *J. Org. Chem.*, **6**, 841 (1941).

19. Aniline. Mol. wt. 93.12, b.p. 184°, sp. gr. 1.02, pK_b 9.30. The color can be removed from old samples by distillation from a small amount of zinc dust.

1. Barium permanganate. Mol. wt. 375.22, 205.8 g./100 g. $H_2O^{0°}$. Preparation.[1] Oxidation: $-SH \rightarrow -SO_3H$.[2]

> [1] L. Vanino, "Handbuch der Präparativen Chemie," 3rd ed., 479 (1925).
> [2] K. Hofmann, A. Bridgwater and A. E. Axelrod, *J. Am. Chem. Soc.*, **71**, 1253 (1949).

2. Benzaldehyde. Mol. wt. 106.12, b.p. 179°, sp. gr. 1.05. Eastman's material is satisfactory, but if a bottle has been opened and let stand for long the material should be redistilled in vacuum.

3. Benzenesulfonic anhydride, $(C_6H_5SO_2)_2O$. Mol. wt. 298.33, m.p. 90°. Preparation and use in Friedel-Crafts synthesis of sulfones and for preparation of benzenesulfonates of phenols.[1]

> [1] L. Field, *J. Am. Chem. Soc.*, **74**, 394 (1952).

4. Benzenesulfonyl chloride. Mol. wt. 176.62, m.p. 14.4°, b.p. 251.5°/760 mm., 120°/10 mm., sp. gr. 1.38. Impure material should be distilled at the water pump. Used in pyridine or 2,6-lutidine for cyclization of 1,4- and 1,5-glycols.[1]

> [1] D. D. Reynolds and W. O. Kenyon, *J. Am. Chem. Soc.*, **72**, 1593 (1950).

5. Benzoyl chloride. Mol. wt. 140.57, b.p. 197°, sp. gr. 1.21. A mixture of a C_{2-6} aliphatic acid with excess benzoyl chloride on rapid distillation affords $RCOCl$ in 80–90% yield.[1] Other examples: acrylyl chloride (70%),[2] propionyl chloride (80%).[3]

> [1] H. C. Brown, *J. Am. Chem. Soc.*, **60**, 1325 (1938).
> [2] G. H. Stempel, Jr., and others, *ibid.*, **72**, 2299 (1950).
> [3] J. Forrest, and others, *J. Chem. Soc.*, 454 (1946).

6. Benzoyl isothiocyanate, C_6H_5CONCS. Mol. wt. 163.19. Prepared *in situ* by reaction of benzoyl chloride with ammonium thiocyanate (mol. wt. 76.11).[1] Reacts with a primary or secondary amine to form a benzoyl thiourea, which is readily hydrolyzed by base to the free thiourea.

$$C_6H_5CONCS \xrightarrow{C_6H_5NH_2} C_6H_5CONHCSNHC_6H_5$$
$$\longrightarrow H_2NC(=S)NHC_6H_5$$

> [1] I. B. Douglass and F. B. Dains, *J. Am. Chem. Soc.*, **56**, 1408 (1934); *Org. Synth.*, **28**, 89 (1948).

7. Benzoyl peroxide, $(C_6H_5CO)_2O_2$. Mol. wt. 242.22, m.p. 107°. Commercial material can be purified by dissolving it in the least amount of cold chloroform and adding methanol.

Benzyl chloroformate. See Carbobenzoxy chloride.

REAGENTS

8. O-Benzyl phosphorus O,O-diphenylphosphoric anhydride,

$$(C_6H_5O)_2\overset{\overset{O}{\|}}{P}\cdot O\cdot \overset{\overset{O}{\|}}{P}HOCH_2C_6H_5$$

Mol. wt. 404.28. Preparation.[1] Reacts with the free hydroxyl group of a sugar derivative (catalyst: 2,6-lutidine) to form a benzyl phosphite, which can be chlorinated (N-chlorosuccinimide). Hydrolysis then gives the benzyl hydrogen phosphate, and the benzyl group is removed by hydrogenation[2]:

$$\begin{array}{ccc} & \overset{H}{\cdot} & \\ -CHOH & -CHOPOOCH_2C_6H_5 & \\ | & \to & | & \to \\ -CHOAc & -CHOAc & \end{array}$$

$$\begin{array}{ccc} \overset{Cl}{\cdot} & & \\ -CHOPOOCH_2C_6H_5 & -CHOPO(OH)OCH_2C_6H_5 & \\ | & \to & | \\ -CHOAc & -CHOAc & \end{array}$$

$$\begin{array}{c} -CHOPO(OH)_2 \\ \to \quad | \\ -CH_2OAc \end{array}$$

> [1] N. S. Corby, G. W. Kenner and A. R. Todd, *J. Chem. Soc.*, 3669 (1952).
> [2] D. M. Brown, G. D. Fasman, D. I. Magrath and A. R. Todd, *ibid.*, 1448 (1954).

9. Bistriphenylphosphinedicarbonylnickel, $[(C_6H_5)_3P]_2Ni(CO)_2$.

This complex catalyzes trimerization of acetylenes to aromatic compounds,[1] and in the presence of acetylene promotes dimerization of butadiene to cyclooctadiene-1,5.[2]

> [1] W. Reppe and W. J. Schweckendiek, *Ann.*, **560**, 104 (1948).
> [2] H. W. B. Reed, *J. Chem. Soc.*, 1931 (1954).

10. Blue tetrazolium.

Mol. wt. 658.74, m.p. 244°. Supplier: Monomer-Polymer, Inc., Leominster, Mass. Preferred to red tetrazolium: Chapter 21.3. Purified by crystallization from pyridine.[1]

> [1] W. Ried and H. Gick, *Ann.*, **581**, 16 (1953).

11a. Boron fluoride.[1]

B.p. −101°. Available in cylinders and can be bubbled into a reaction mixture. Boron fluoride, alone or as acetic acid complex, is recommended as catalyst for acylation of ketones to form β-diketones.[2]

> [1] D. Kästner and J. E. Jones, "Catalysis of Organic Reactions by Boron Fluoride," *Newer Methods of Preparative Organic Chemistry*, p. 249, Interscience (1948).
> [2] R. M. Manyik, F. C. Frostick, J. J. Sanderson and C. R. Hauser, *J. Am. Chem. Soc.*, **75**, 5030 (1953).

The solid monoacetic acid complex (hygroscopic) can be made by saturating an ethylene chloride solution of acetic acid with boron fluoride, filtering, and washing the precipitate with more solvent; the liquid diacid complex remains in solution.

11b. Boron fluoride etherate, $BF_3\cdot 2(C_2H_5)_2O$.

B.p. 126°. Commercial material darkens rapidly owing to air oxidation. Redistillation gives water-white material. Use as catalyst in acetylation (Chapter 37) and in alkylation (Chapter 38.4). Use of boron fluoride etherate as catalyst for dehydration,[1] in condensation of ketones with ethanedithiol[2] and with thiols,[3] and in Thiele addition of acetic anhydride to a quinone.[4]

> [1] H. Heymann and L. F. Fieser, *ibid.*, **73**, 5252 (1951); H. L. Herzog, C. P. Payne and E. B. Hershberg, *ibid.*, **76**, 930 (1954).
> [2] L. F. Fieser, *ibid.*, **76**, 1945 (1954).
> [3] A. Schöberl and G. Wiehler, *Angew. Chem.*, **66**, 273 (1954).
> [4] L. F. Fieser, *J. Am. Chem. Soc.*, **70**, 3165 (1948).

12. Bromine–dioxan complex, $C_4H_8O_2\cdot Br_2$.

Mol. wt. 247.94, m.p. 64°. Prepared by mixing equimolecular amounts of the components and cooling; the orange-yellow solid or a solution prepared by adding bromine to excess dioxan is useful for bromination of sensitive compounds (aniline → p-bromoaniline, 68% yield).[1]

> [1] G. M. Kosolapoff, *J. Am. Chem. Soc.*, **75**, 3596 (1953).

13. N-Bromoacetamide, $CH_3CONHBr$.

Mol. wt. 137.98, m.p. 102–105°. Supplier: Arapahoe Chemicals, Inc. Preparation.[1] Oxidation of secondary alcohols.[2] Partial oxidations.[3] Source of HOBr.[4]

> [1] *Org. Synth.*, **31**, 17 (1951).
> [2] B. A. Koechlin, T. H. Kritchevsky and T. F. Gallagher, *J. Biol. Chem.*, **184**, 393 (1950).

REAGENTS

[3] E. P. Oliveto, H. L. Herzog and E. B. Hershberg, *J. Am. Chem. Soc.*, **75**, 1505 (1953).

[4] H. Reich and T. Reichstein, *Helv. Chim. Acta*, **26**, 562 (1943); G. H. Ott and T. Reichstein, *ibid.*, **26**, 1799 (1943).

p-Bromobenzyl chloroformate, see *p*-Bromocarbobenzoxy chloride.

14. *p*-Bromocarbobenzoxy chloride, *p*-BrC$_6$H$_4$-CH$_2$OCOCl. Mol. wt. 249.50. A stable solid, this reagent gives derivatives of amino acids and peptides that are higher melting and better crystalline than the carbobenzoxy derivatives.[1]

[1] D. M. Channing, P. B. Turner and G. T. Young, *Nature*, **167**, 487 (1951).

15. *p*-Bromophenacyl bromide, *p*-BrC$_6$H$_4$CO-CH$_2$Br. Mol. wt. 277.96, m.p. 110°. Preparation.[1] Used for characterization of acids.[2]

[1] *Org. Synth., Coll. Vol.*, **1**, 127 (1941).

[2] F. Wild, "Characterization of Organic Compounds," 146, 147, Cambridge (1947).

16. N-Bromosuccinimide. Mol. wt. 178.00, m.p. 173°. See review.[1] Supplier: Arapahoe Chemicals, Inc. Use in aqueous dioxan as source of HOBr: Chapter 10.6. Whereas pure NBS effects side-chain bromination of aromatic hydrocarbons, aged material effects nuclear bromination.[2] The impurity can be removed by pumping out at 0.5 mm. for 8 hrs. over phosphorus pentoxide. Procedures for allylic bromination as used in commercial synthesis of cortisone.[3] Selective oxidation of steroid alcohols.[4]

Caution: Explosions have been reported in reactions of NBS.[5]

[1] T. D. Waugh, "N-Bromosuccinimide, Its Reactions and Uses," Arapahoe Chemicals, Inc., Boulder, Colo. (1951).

[2] N. B. Chapman and J. F. A. Williams, *J. Chem. Soc.*, 5044 (1952).

[3] L. Velluz, *Substances Naturelles de Synthèse*, **7**, 31 (1953).

[4] L. F. Fieser and S. Rajagopalan, *J. Am. Chem. Soc.*, **71**, 3935, 3938 (1949); **72**, 5530 (1950); **73**, 118 (1951).

[5] R. H. Martin, *Nature*, **168**, 32 (1951).

17. Butadiene. Mol. wt. 54.09°, b.p. −4.4°. Available in cylinders.

18. Butanone ethyleneketal,

$$CH_2O \diagdown \diagup CH_3$$
$$C$$
$$CH_2O \diagup \diagdown C_2H_5$$

Mol. wt. 116.16, b.p. 117°. Preparation and use in exchange ketal formation (dioxolonation).[1] The yields are sometimes higher and the selectivity greater than in direct reaction with ethylene glycol.

[1] H. J. Dauben, B. Löken and H. J. Ringold, *J. Am. Chem. Soc.*, **76**, 1359 (1954); G. Rosenkranz, M. Velasco and F. Sondheimer, *ibid.*, **76**, 5024 (1954).

19. *t*-Butyl chloride. Mol. wt. 92.57, b.p. 51°, sp. gr. 0.85. Shake vigorously in a separatory funnel a mixture of 50 ml. of *t*-butyl alcohol and 250 ml. of concd. hydrochloric acid. After agitating very thoroughly for 10 min. the conversion should be complete and the lower acid layer should be perfectly clear. Separate the *t*-butyl chloride layer, dry the liquid over calcium chloride, and purify by distillation. Yield, 45–50 g.

20. *t*-Butyl chloroacetate, ClCH$_2$CO$_2$C(CH$_3$)$_3$. Mol. wt. 150.61, b.p. 56°/16 mm. Preparation.[1] Useful in glycidic ester condensation because of avoidance of self-condensation.[2]

[1] *Org. Synth.*, **34**, 28 (1954).

[2] W. S. Johnson, and others, *J. Am. Chem. Soc.*, **75**, 4995 (1953).

21. *i*-Butyl chloroformate (chlorocarbonate), ClCO$_2$CH$_2$CH(CH$_3$)$_2$. Mol. wt. 136.58, b.p. 129°, sp. gr. 1.05; and *s*-butyl chloroformate, b.p. 116°. Used for making mixed anhydrides that serve as intermediates in peptide synthesis.[1,2,3] An N-protected amino acid, such as the carbobenzoxy (CBO) or phthalyl derivative, is brought into solution in toluene or tetrahydrofuran by addition of enough triethylamine to form the salt, and a butyl chloroformate is added at 0° (equation a). A solution of an amino acid ester (or peptide ester) to be acylated is added in an inert solvent and the mixture allowed to come to room temperature. Evolution of carbon dioxide begins immediately (b).

REAGENTS

(a) CBO—NHCHRCO₂N̄H(C₂H₅)₃

(a) $CBO-NHCHRCO_2\overset{-}{N}\overset{+}{H}(C_2H_5)_3$
$+ ClCO_2CH_2CH(CH_3)_2 \rightarrow$
$CBO-NHCHRCO \cdot O \cdot CO_2CH_2CH(CH_3)$
$+ (C_2H_5)_3\overset{+}{N}\overset{-}{H}Cl$

(b) $CBO-NHCHRCO \cdot O \cdot CO_2CH_2CH(CH_3)_2$
$+ H_2NCHR'CO_2CH_3 \rightarrow$
$CBO-NHCHRCONHCHR'CO_2CH_3$
$+ CO_2 + (CH_3)_2CHCH_2OH$

The butyl chloroformates [4] are preferred [1,2,3] to lower esters for preparation of peptides of moderate or high molecular weight; ethyl chloroformate is preferred for synthesis of dipeptides.[3]

[1] R. A. Boissonnas, and others, *Helv. Chim. Acta*, **34**, 874 (1951); **35**, 2229, 2237 (1952).
[2] J. R. Vaughan, Jr., and others, *J. Am. Chem. Soc.*, **73**, 3547 (1951); **74**, 676, 6137 (1952); **75**, 5556 (1953); **76**, 2474 (1954).
[3] T. Wieland and H. Bernhard, *Ann.*, **572**, 190 (1951).
[4] Eastman supplies *i*-butyl chloroformate. Preparation of *s*-isomer: J. R. Vaughan, Jr., and R. L. Osato, *J. Am. Chem. Soc.*, **74**, 676 (1952).

22. *t*-Butyl hydroperoxide, $(CH_3)_3C \cdot O \cdot OH$. Mol. wt. 90.12, m.p. 4°, b.p. 12.5°/20 mm. Supplier: Lucidol Division, Wallace and Tiernan, Inc. Preparation.[1] Decomposes smoothly at 95–100°. Hydroxylates double bonds, even of α,β-unsaturated ketones.[2] The reaction is catalyzed by a small amount of osmium tetroxide and affords *cis* glycols. The reagent can be prepared *in situ* from H_2O_2 and $(CH_3)_3COH$.

[1] N. A. Milas and D. M. Surgenor, *J. Am. Chem. Soc.*, **68**, 205 (1946).
[2] N. A. Milas, and others, *ibid.*, **58**, 1302 (1936); **59**, 2345 (1937); **61**, 1844 (1939).

23. *t*-Butyl hypochlorite, $(CH_3)_3COCl$. Mol. wt. 108.57, b.p. 78°/760 mm., sp. gr. 0.91. Preparation.[1] For oxidation of alcohols in the presence of pyridine in carbon tetrachloride or ether: cyclohexanol → cyclohexanone; *n*-butyl alcohol → *n*-butyl butyrate.[2] Used as C-chlorinating [3] and N-chlorinating agent.[4]

[1] *Org. Synth.*, **32**, 20 (1952).
[2] C. A. Grob and HJ. Schmid, *Helv. Chim. Acta*, **36**, 1763 (1953).

308

[3] D. Ginsburg, *J. Am. Chem. Soc.*, **73**, 2723 (1951); *ibid.*, **75**, 5489 (1953).
[4] H. Zimmer and L. F. Audrieth, *ibid.*, **76**, 3856 (1954).

1. Capryl alcohol (octanol-2). Useful for control of foaming of alkaline solutions.

2. Carbobenzoxy chloride, $C_6H_5CH_2OCOCl$ (liquid). Mol. wt. 170.59. Reagent of Bergmann [1] for protection of amino groups in peptide synthesis. Preparation.[2] See *p*-Nitro- and *p*-Bromocarbobenzoxy chloride. Discussion of relative merits of various α-amino protecting groups and methods of cleavage.[3]

[1] M. Bergmann and L. Zervas, *Ber.*, **65**, 1192 (1932).
[2] A. C. Farthing, *J. Chem. Soc.*, 3213 (1950).
[3] R. A. Boissonnas and G. Preitner, *Helv. Chim. Acta*, **36**, 875 (1953).

3. Caro's acid (sulfomonoperacid), H_2SO_5.[1] Prepared as required by stirring 10 g. of finely powdered potassium persulfate (mol. wt. 270.33) into 7 ml. of ice-cold concd. sulfuric acid and when the mixture is homogeneous adding 40–50 g. of ice.[2] *Uses:* (a) Oxidation of aryl amines to nitroso compounds.[1,3] (b) Oxidation of ketones to lactones (1) [2,4] or esters (3).[5] When an aromatic ring is present (2), cleavage occurs adjacent to it.[6]

Oxidative cleavage of ketones has been carried out in ligroin at 50–65° with Caro's acid prepared as described,[4] in a solution containing more sulfuric acid, less water, and no organic solvent,[2] by refluxing the ketone with

REAGENTS

a mixture of potassium persulfate (4 g.) and concd. sulfuric acid (1 ml.) in 90% acetic acid (150 ml.),[7] and with Baeyer and Villiger's dry reagent,[2] prepared by grinding 10 g. of potassium persulfate thoroughly in a mortar with 6 ml. of concd. sulfuric acid, adding 30 g. of potassium sulfate, and grinding the mixture to a dry powder. It is added to a cold solution of the ketone in glacial acetic acid and the reaction is allowed to proceed at room temperature for 7–10 days.

A similar reagent which can be employed for the oxidative cleavage of ketones is prepared by cautiously mixing acetic anhydride (65 g.), concd. sulfuric acid (30 g.), and perhydrol (25 g.).[5] Benzophenone (20 g.) added to this solution is converted, after standing for several days at 0°, into phenyl benzoate in nearly quantitative yield.

[1] H. Caro, *Z. angew. Chem.*, **11**, 845 (1898).
[2] A. Baeyer and V. Villiger, *Ber.*, **32**, 3625 (1899); **33**, 858 (1900).
[3] E. Bamberger and R. Hübner, *Ber.*, **36**, 3803 (1903); E. Borel and H. Deuel, *Helv. Chim. Acta*, **36**, 805 (1953): 3-nitro-4-aminotoluene → 3-nitro-4-nitrosotoluene in 92% yield.
[4] L. Ruzicka and M. Stoll, *Helv. Chim. Acta*, **11**, 1159 (1928).
[5] R. Marker and co-workers, *J. Am. Chem. Soc.*, **62**, 525, 650, 2543, 2621 (1940).
[6] G. Schroeter, German Patent 562,827 (1928) [*Chem. Zentr.*, **1**, 127 (1933)].
[7] A. Rollett and K. Bratke, *Monatsh*, **43**, 685 (1922).

4. Chloroacetic anhydride.

Mol. wt. 170.99, m.p. 46°. Preferred to chloroacetyl chloride for N-acetylation of amino acids in alkaline solution.[1]

[1] S. M. Birnbaum, L. Levintow, R. B. Kingsley and J. P. Greenstein, *J. Biol. Chem.*, **194**, 455 (1952).

5. Chloroacetyl chloride.

Mol. wt. 112.95, b.p. 105°, sp. gr. 1.50. Preparation from chloroacetic acid and benzoyl chloride (76% yield).[1] Preparation of N-chloroacetates of amino acids by refluxing with a suspension of acid in ethyl acetate.[2]

[1] H. C. Brown, *J. Am. Chem. Soc.*, **60**, 1325 (1938).
[2] E. Ronwin, *J. Org. Chem.*, **18**, 127 (1953).

6. N-Chlorosuccinimide.

Mol. wt. 133.54, m.p. 148°. Use as an oxidizing agent.[1]

[1] M. F. Hebbelynck and R. H. Martin, *Experientia*, **5**, 69 (1949); *Bull. soc. chim. Belg.*, **60**, 54 (1951); C. A. Grob and HJ. Schmid, *Helv. Chim. Acta*, **36**, 1763 (1953).

7. Chlorosulfonic acid, $ClSO_2OH$.

Mol. wt. 116.54, b.p. 151°, sp. gr. 1.79. Purified by distillation. For preparation of sulfate esters, commonly in pyridine solution.[1] Other solvents are sulfur dioxide[2] and dichloroethane.[3]

[1] C. Neuberg and L. Liebermann, *Biochem. Z.*, **121**, 326 (1921); R. S. Tipson, "Sulfonic Esters of Carbohydrates," *Adv. Carbohyd. Chem.*, **8**, 107 (1953).
[2] K. H. Meyer, R. P. Piroué and M. E. Odier, *Helv. Chim. Acta*, **35**, 574 (1952).
[3] I. B. Cushing, and others, *J. Am. Chem. Soc.*, **76**, 4590 (1954).

8. Choline, $(CH_3)_3N^+(OH^-)CH_2CH_2OH$.

Mol. wt. 121.18. The commercial 50% aqueous solution can be used like Triton B as catalyst for cyanoethylation.[1]

[1] S. Pietra, *Boll. Fac. Chim. Ind. Bologna*, **11**, 78 (1953).

9. Chromic anhydride, CrO_3.

Mol. wt. 100.01; 1.5 oxygen equivalent per mole of anhydride. The oxidizing power of the reagent increases with decreasing water content of the solvent medium. Procedures are as follows. (a) An *aqueous solution of chromic acid* is added to an acetic acid solution of the substance to be oxidized; example: β-methylnaphthalene → 2-methyl-1,4-naphthoquinone (Chapter 38.2). (b) An *acetone solution* of an alcohol to be oxidized is treated at −35° with an aqueous solution acidified with sulfuric acid containing the theoretical amount of chromic acid; the mixture separates into a green lower layer of chromium salts and an upper layer consisting of an acetone solution of the oxidation product.[1] The method has the merit that secondary alcohols containing double and triple bonds can be oxidized to the corresponding ketones without attack of the centers of unsaturation. (c) A *pyridine-chromic anhydride complex* used in pyridine solution is useful for oxidation of substances containing acid-sensitive groups[2]; the literature directions should be followed carefully. (d) Oxidation is conducted by stirring a solution of an alcohol in *anhydrous acetic acid with suspended chromic anhydride* at a controlled, low temperature.[3] Examples: 1-phenylcyclohexanol-1 → ϵ-phenyl-*n*-caproic acid[4]; cholestanol → cholestanone.[5] (e) Chromic anhydride is added in portions with cooling to a solution of $ArCH_3$ in an ice-cold *mixture of acetic acid (5 ml.), acetic anhydride (5–10 ml.), and concd. sulfuric acid (1 ml.).*[6] The initially formed aldehyde is protected by conversion to the diacetate, from which it is recovered by acid hydrolysis:

$$ArCH_3 \rightarrow ArCH(OCOCH_3)_2 \rightarrow ArCHO$$

Yields are in the range 30–50%. (f) 3,4-Dinitrotoluene is oxidized to 3,4-dinitrobenzoic acid by addition of chromic anhydride in portions to a stirred solution of the nitro compound *in concd. sulfuric acid* with cooling to 45–50°.[7]

[1] K. Bowden, I. M. Heilbron, E. R. H. Jones and B. C. L. Weedon, *J. Chem. Soc.*, 39 (1946); P. Bladon, and others, *ibid.*, 2402 (1951).
[2] G. I. Poos, G. E. Arth, R. E. Beyler and L. H. Sarett, *J. Am. Chem. Soc.*, **75**, 422 (1953).
[3] L. F. Fieser, *J. Am. Chem. Soc.*, **70**, 3237 (1948).
[4] L. F. Fieser and J. Szmuszkovicz, *ibid.*, **70**, 3352 (1948); K. Nakanishi and L. F. Fieser, *ibid.*, **74**, 3910 (1952).
[5] L. F. Fieser, *ibid.*, **75**, 4391 (1953).
[6] J. Thiele and E. Winter, *Ann.*, **311**, 353 (1900).
[7] E. Borel and H. Deuel, *Helv. Chim. Acta*, **36**, 806 (1953).

10. Chromous acetate, chromous chloride. Preparation: acetate,[1] chloride.[2] For reduction of α-haloketones to the parent ketones,[3] debromination of dibromides,[3] reduction of oxides,[4] reduction of imide chlorides to imines ($RCCl=NH \rightarrow RCH=NH$).[5]

[1] J. B. Conant and H. B. Cutter, *J. Am. Chem. Soc.*, **48**, 1016 (1926).
[2] *Inorg. Synth.*, **3**, 148 (1950).
[3] P. L. Julian, W. Cole, A. Magnani and E. W. Meyer, *J. Am. Chem. Soc.*, **67**, 1728 (1945).
[4] W. Cole and P. L. Julian, *J. Org. Chem.*, **19**, 131 (1954).
[5] J. v. Braun and W. Rudolph, *Ber.*, **67**, 269, 1735 (1934).

11. Chromyl chloride, CrO_2Cl_2. Mol. wt. 154.92, b.p. 116°, sp. gr. 1.92. Preparation.[1] For oxidation of $ArCH_3$ to $ArCHO$ (the Étard reaction)[2]; the reaction is catalyzed by a trace of olefin.[3] Reacts with olefins to form chlorohydrins (35–50% yield).[4]

[1] H. D. Law and F. M. Perkin, *J. Chem. Soc.*, **91**, 191 (1907); *Inorg. Synth.*, **2**, 205 (1946).
[2] L. N. Ferguson, *Chem. Rev.*, **38**, 237 (1946).
[3] A. Tillotson and B. Houston, *J. Am. Chem. Soc.*, **73**, 221 (1951).
[4] S. J. Cristol and K. R. Eilar, *ibid.*, **72**, 4353 (1950).

12. Claisen's alkali.[1] Dissolve 35 g. of potassium hydroxide in 25 ml. of water, cool, add 100 ml. of methanol, cool. For extraction from petroleum ether or ether of phenols insoluble in aqueous alkali.

[1] L. Claisen, *Ann.*, **418**, 96 (1919).

13. Cobaltous chloride, $CoCl_2$. Mol. wt. 129.85. Prepared from the hexahydrate by dehydration in a stream of hydrogen chloride and dried in vacuum at 100–150°.[1] A catalytic amount of this halide influences the course of Grignard reactions through intermediate formation of $RCoCl$, which promotes coupling: $RMgBr + CoCl_2 \rightarrow RCoCl$; $2RCoCl \rightarrow R \cdot R$. Examples: (a) $C_6H_5MgBr + C_6H_5Br \xrightarrow{CoCl_2} C_6H_5 \cdot C_6H_5$ (86%).[2] (b) $p\text{-}CH_3OC_6H_4CHBrC_2H_5 + C_6H_5MgBr \xrightarrow{CoCl_2} p\text{-}CH_3OC_6H_4CH(C_2H_5)CH(C_2H_5)\text{-}C_6H_4OCH_3\text{-}p'$ (41%).[1] (c) $C_6H_5MgBr + C_6H_5C\equiv CBr \xrightarrow{CoCl_2} C_6H_5C\equiv CC_6H_5$ (75%).[2]

[1] M. S. Kharasch, and others, *J. Am. Chem. Soc.*, **63**, 2316 (1941), and later papers. Reviewed by D. H. Hey, *Ann. Reports, Chem. Soc.*, **41**, 195 (1944); **45**, 160 (1948).
[2] H. K. Black, D. H. S. Horn and B. C. L. Weedon, *J. Chem. Soc.*, 1704 (1954).

14. s-Collidine (2,4,6-trimethylpyridine). Mol. wt. 121.18, b.p. 171°. Generally superior to pyridine for dehydrohalogenation. Redistil before use. Addition of 4% of 3,5-lutidine is advantageous.[1]

[1] H. H. Inhoffen, and others, *Ann.*, **585**, 132 (1954).

REAGENTS

15. Copper chromite catalyst. Preparation.[1] Use as catalyst[2] for decarboxylation: Chapter 30.

[1] H. Adkins, E. E. Burgoyne and H. J. Schneider, *J. Am. Chem. Soc.*, **72**, 2626 (1950).

[2] C. R. Kinney and D. P. Langlois, *ibid.*, **53**, 2189 (1931); T. Reichstein, and others, *Helv. Chim. Acta*, **15**, 1067 (1932).

16. Cupric acetate, $Cu(OCOCH_3)_2 \cdot H_2O$. Mol. wt. 199.64. The reagent oxidizes α-ketols to α-diketones in high yield in 50–70% aqueous acetic acid solution.[1] In another process cupric acetate is used in catalytic amount and regenerated internally by ammonium nitrate.[2] Since the reaction is conducted in acetic acid solution, ammonium nitrite is decomposed as formed: $NH_4NO_2 \rightarrow N_2 + 2H_2O$.

[1] P. Ruggli and P. Zeller, *Helv. Chim. Acta*, **28**, 741 (1945); H. Bloch, and others, *ibid.*, **28**, 1410 (1945); N. R. Campbell, and others, *J. Chem. Soc.*, 2743 (1950); A. T. Blomquist, and others, *J. Am. Chem. Soc.*, **74**, 3643 (1952).

[2] M. Weiss and M. Appel, *ibid.*, **70**, 3666 (1948).

17. Cupric nitrate–acetic anhydride. For nitration, probably via the intermediate acetyl nitrate.[1] Useful for nitration of azulenes, which are decomposed by nitric acid.[2]

[1] G. Bacharach, *J. Am. Chem. Soc.*, **49**, 1522 (1927).

[2] A. G. Anderson, J. A. Nelson and J. J. Tazuma, *ibid.*, **75**, 4980 (1953).

18. Cupric sulfate, $CuSO_4 \cdot 5H_2O$. Mol. wt. 249.69. The reagent, dissolved in pyridine–water, oxidizes α-ketols to α-diketones; the spent solution can be reoxidized with air.[1] An α-ketol that is soluble in aqueous alkali can be oxidized to the α-diketone or further oxidation product by addition of copper sulfate to a solution of the substance in alkali.[2]

[1] *Org. Synth., Coll. Vol.*, **1**, 87 (1941).

[2] L. F. Fieser and M. Fieser, *J. Am. Chem. Soc.*, **70**, 3215 (1948).

19. Cuprous ammonium chloride. The combination of cuprous chloride and ammonium chloride in a slightly acidic aqueous solution catalyzes oxidative (air) coupling of ethynyl compounds to diacetylenes: $RC\equiv CH \rightarrow RC\equiv C \cdot C\equiv CR$.[1] The groups NH_2, OH, CO_2H, and CO_2R do not interfere.

[1] K. Bowden, and others, *J. Chem. Soc.*, 1579 (1947); J. D. Rose and B. C. L. Weedon, *ibid.*, 782 (1949); H. K. Black and B. C. L. Weedon, *ibid.*, 1785 (1953); J. P. Riley, *ibid.*, 2193 (1953).

20. Cyanamide, NH_2CN. Mol. wt. 42.04, m.p. 46°. Preparation.[1]

[1] *Inorg. Synth.*, **3**, 39 (1950); *Org. Synth.*, **34**, 67 (1954).

21. Cyanic acid, $HN\equiv C=O$ (gas). Mol. wt. 43.03. Used for conversion of primary, secondary, or tertiary alcohols to allophanates:

$$ROH + 2HCNO \rightarrow ROCONHCONH_2$$

Reviews of early literature.[1] Recent papers;[2,3,4] see particularly Zobrist and Schinz.[4] The usual method utilizes cyanic acid generated by thermal depolymerization of cyanuric acid, a solid trimer available commercially (Eastman) or prepared[4] by hydrolysis of the less expensive cyanuric chloride (Eastman) with 1:1 concd. sulfuric acid-water. Depolymerization can be done at 360–400° in a slow stream of carbon dioxide and the gas absorbed directly in a liquid alcohol. Zobrist and Schinz, who give a detailed description of a generator, absorb cyanic acid in ether to a concentration of 30–35% and use 0.8 ml. of this solution for reaction with 0.1 g. of substance of molecular weight about 150. Simple alcohols react rapidly, and usually an overnight reaction period is adequate; in the case of α-phenylethanol several days are required.[2] If insufficient cyanic acid is used, the urethan, NH_2CO_2R, becomes the major product. Excess reagent polymerizes to cyanuric acid and cyamelide which, in the preparative procedure of Zobrist and Schinz, are eliminated by virtue of their insolubility in benzene. Methanol is usually a good solvent for crystallization, and no ester interchange occurs.

Except for derivatives of lower alcohols, allophanates are usually high-melting, well crystalline derivatives suitable for characterization and isolation and can be made even from alcohols highly sensitive to acids. The alcohol can be regenerated by warming the allophanate with methanolic alkali.[4]

[1] A. Béhal, *Bull. soc. chim.*, **25**, 345 (1919); J. Bougault and J. Leboucq, *ibid.*,, **47**, 594 (1930); Document 2858, Am. Doc. Inst., 1719 N St., Washington 6, D.C. (microfilm or photocopy).
[2] M. A. Spielman, J. D. Barnes and W. J. Close, *J. Am. Chem. Soc.*, **72**, 2520 (1950); H. W. Blohm and E. I. Becker, *ibid.*, **72**, 5342 (1950).
[3] E. S. Lane, *J. Chem. Soc.*, 2764 (1951), prepared allophanates of mono ethers of glycols by passing hydrogen chloride into a mixture of the alcohol, dioxane, and sodium cyanate (added in portions).
[4] F. Zobrist and H. Schinz, *Helv. Chim. Acta*, **35**, 2380 (1952).

22. Cyanogen bromide. Mol. wt. 105.93, m.p. 52°, b.p. 61°. The reagent is of use in degradation of nitrogen-containing ring compounds by the method of v. Braun.[1] Although the substance is toxic and can become extremely unpleasant when improperly handled, it can be prepared without difficulty if proper care is taken. The molten material should be manipulated in a hood and it is best to wear a gas mask when working with large quantities. Improved methods of preparation are described by Hartman and Dreger[2] and by Slotta.[3]

[1] J. v. Braun, *Ber.*, **40**, 3914 (1907); **42**, 2219 (1909); **44**, 1252 (1911); H. A. Hageman, "The von Braun Reaction," *Org. Reactions*, **7**, 198 (1953).
[2] *Org. Synth., Coll. Vol.*, **2**, 150 (1943).
[3] K. H. Slotta, *Ber.*, **67**, 1028 (1934).

23. Cyclopentadiene. Mol. wt. 66.10, b.p. 41°, sp. gr. 0.80. Generated by heating dicyclopentadiene (b.p. 170°, sp. gr. 0.98) at the boiling point.[1]

[1] E. C. Wagner and W. C. Hunt, *J. Chem. Ed.*, **28**, 309 (1951); *Org. Synth.*, **32**, 41 (1952).

24. Cyclopentanol. Mol. wt. 86.13, b.p. 134–135°/630 mm. Supplier: Arapahoe Chemicals, Inc.

25. Cyclopentanone. Mol. wt. 84.11, b.p. 130.7°, sp. gr. 0.95. Suppliers: Eastman, Arapahoe.

1. Dehydration catalyst.[1] Made from a mixture of alumina (90 g.), diatomaceous earth (60 g.), and cork powder (20 g.), moistened with water and heated to red heat. Cyclopentanol → cyclopentene (80% yield).

[1] A. Stoll, A. Lindenmann and E. Jucker, *Helv. Chim. Acta*, **36**, 268 (1953).

2. Diacyl peroxides, $RCOO \cdot OCOR$. Preparation[1]: (a) $RCOCl + Na_2O_2$; (b) $RCOCl + H_2O_2 + NaOH$. Use for alkylation of quinones.[2]

[1] L. F. Fieser, M. T. Leffler, and others, *J. Am. Chem. Soc.*, **70**, 3178 (1948).
[2] Idem, *ibid.*, **70**, 3174–3215 (1948).

3. 1,2-Dianilinoethane. Mol. wt. 212.29, m.p. 67.5°. Preparation and use as a specific reagent for aldehydes[1]:

$$
\begin{array}{l}
CH_2NHC_6H_5 \\
| \\
CH_2NHC_6H_5
\end{array}
+ OCHR \rightarrow
\begin{array}{c}
C_6H_5 \\
CH_2{-}N \\
| \quad\quad\ CHR \\
CH_2{-}N \\
C_6H_5
\end{array}
$$

[1] H.-W. Wanzlick and W. Löchel, *Ber.*, **86**, 1463 (1953).

3,3′-Dianisole bis-4,4′-(3,5-diphenyl)-tetrazolium chloride. See Blue tetrazolium.

4. Diazomethane.[1,2] Mol. wt. 42.04. One intermediate, N-methyl-N-nitroso-N′-nitroguanidine,[3] $CH_3N(NO)C(=NH)NHNO_2$, is available from Aldrich Chemical Co. A mixture of 100 ml. ether and 30 ml. 40% potassium hydroxide solution in a distilling flask is cooled to 0°, 10 g. of the crystalline reagent (m.p. 118°) is added in portions with shaking in 2–3 min., and the yellow diazomethane solution is distilled from the mixture. Other intermediates are nitrosomethylurethan, nitrosomethylurea, hydrazine plus chloroform. Alternative intermediate: p-tolylsulfonylmethylnitrosamide,[4] $p\text{-}CH_3C_6H_4SO_2N(NO)CH_3$; a readily accessible crystalline solid that is stable at 25° and not irritant to skin. Supplier: Aldrich.

Example of use of diazomethane for ring

enlargement: cyclohexanone → cyclohepta-none.[5,6]

Determination. The amount of reagent in an ethereal solution can be determined by diluting an aliquot portion of the solution and adding it slowly to a cold, measured quantity of a 0.2 N solution of benzoic acid in absolute ether, the benzoic acid solution used being more than sufficient to react with all of the diazomethane (colorless at the end). Water is added and the excess benzoic acid is titrated with 0.1 N sodium hydroxide solution.

[1] B. Eistert and F. W. Spangler, "Syntheses with Diazomethane," *Newer Methods of Preparative Organic Chemistry*, p. 513, Interscience (1948).
[2] F. G. Arndt, "Diazomethane for Determination of Active Hydrogen," *Org. Anal.*, **1**, 197 (1953).
[3] A. F. McKay and G. F. Wright, *J. Am. Chem. Soc.*, **69**, 3028 (1947); **70**, 1974 (1948).
[4] Th. J. de Boer and H. J. Backer, *Rec. trav. chim.*, **73**, 229 (1954); *Org. Synth.*, **34**, 96 (1954).
[5] E. P. Kohler, M. Tishler, H. Potter and H. T. Thompson, *J. Am. Chem. Soc.*, **61**, 1059 (1939).
[6] *Org. Synth.*, **34**, 24 (1954).

5. Diazonium fluoroborates, ArN_2BF_4. Prepared by diazotization of aromatic amines in the presence of fluoroboric acid. On decomposition diazonium fluoroborates yield the aryl fluorides (Schiemann reaction).[1] When treated with ethanol and zinc they yield the corresponding ArH (deamination reaction).[2]

[1] A. Roe, *Org. Reactions*, **5**, 193 (1949).
[2] A. Roe and J. R. Graham, *J. Am. Chem. Soc.*, **74**, 6297 (1952).

6. Dibenzylchlorophosphonate,[1]

$$(C_6H_5CH_2O)_2POCl \text{ (oil)}.$$

Mol. wt. 296.68. Prepared by chlorination of dibenzyl phosphite [2] with anhydrous N-chlorosuccinimide.[3] The reagent has found valuable use for phosphorylation of nucleosides.[4] It reacts with a free primary or secondary hydroxyl group to form a dibenzyl phosphate:

$$RCH_2OH + ClPO(OCH_2C_6H_5)_2 \rightarrow$$
$$RCH_2OPO(OCH_2C_6H_5)_2$$

Hydrogenation or treatment with potassium thiocyanate in boiling acetonitrile removes both benzyl groups to form a phosphate ester, $RCH_2OPO(OH)_2$; lithium chloride reacts to remove a single benzyl group and afford $RCH_2OPO(OH)OCH_2C_6H_5$.[5]

[1] Previously known as dibenzyl chlorophosphate. New nomenclature: *J. Chem. Soc.*, 5122 (1952).
[2] Preparation: O. M. Friedman, D. L. Klass and A. M. Seligman, *J. Am. Chem. Soc.*, **76**, 916 (1954).
[3] G. W. Kenner, A. R. Todd and F. J. Weymouth, *J. Chem. Soc.*, 3675 (1952); R. H. Hall and H. G. Khorana, *J. Am. Chem. Soc.*, **76**, 5056 (1954).
[4] A. R. Todd, The Pedler Lecture, *J. Chem. Soc.*, 647 (1946); G. W. Kenner, *Fortsch. Chemie Org. Naturstoffe*, **8**, 96 (1951).
[5] V. M. Clark and A. R. Todd, *J. Chem. Soc.*, 2030 (1950); S. M. H. Christie, D. T. Elmore, G. W. Kenner, A. R. Todd and F. J. Weymouth, *ibid.*, 2947 (1953).

7. Di-*t*-butyl malonate,

$$(CH_3)_3COCOCH_2CO_2C(CH_3)_3.$$

Mol. wt. 216.27, b.p. 112–115°/31 mm., m.p. −6°. Preparation.[1] Used in synthesis of ketones,[1] because the butyl groups of an acyl derivative can be eliminated pyrolytically: $RCOC(R')(CO_2t\text{-}Bu)_2 \rightarrow RCOCH_2R' + 2(CH_3)_2C=CH_2 + 2CO_2$. The reaction is done in refluxing toluene or acetic acid with *p*-toluenesulfonic acid as catalyst.

[1] G. S. Fonken and W. S. Johnson, *J. Am. Chem. Soc.*, **74**, 831 (1952).

8. 2,6-Di-*t*-butylpyridine, $C_{13}H_{21}N$. Mol. wt. 191.31. pK_a 3.58.[1] Combines with hydrogen chloride but not with methyl iodide or boron fluoride.

[1] H. C. Brown and B. Kanner, *J. Am. Chem. Soc.*, **75**, 3865 (1953).

9. Di-*t*-butyl succinate,

$$(CH_3)_3COCOCH_2CH_2CO_2C(CH_3)_3.$$

Mol. wt. 230.30, b.p. 106°/7 mm. Preparation.[1] Preferable to less hindered esters in Stobbe condensation because of avoidance of self-condensation.[2]

[1] *Org. Synth.*, **34**, 28 (1954).
[2] W. S. Johnson and G. H. Daub, *Org. Reactions*, **6**, 1 (1951).

REAGENTS

10. Dicyclohexylcarbodiimide (DCC),

$$C_6H_{11}N{=}C{=}NC_6H_{11}.$$

Mol. wt. 206.33, b.p. 155°/11 mm. Prepared by oxidation of N,N′-dicyclohexylthiourea, $C_6H_{11}NHCSNHC_6H_{11}$, with mercuric oxide.[1] Reacts rapidly and nearly quantitatively at 25° in ether solution with mono and di esters of phosphoric acid to yield the corresponding symmetrical di or tetra esters of pyrophosphoric acid, with immediate precipitation of dicyclohexylurea:[2]

$$2ROPO(OH)_2 + DCC \rightarrow$$
$$ROPO(OH)OPO(OH)OR$$
$$+ C_6H_{11}NHCONHC_6H_{11}$$

[1] E. Schmidt, F. Hitzler and E. Lahde, *Ber.*, **71**, 1938 (1938).
[2] H. G. Khorana and A. R. Todd, *J. Chem. Soc.*, 2257 (1953); H. G. Khorana, *J. Am. Chem. Soc.*, **76**, 3517 (1954); C. A. Dekker and H. G. Khorana, *ibid.*, **76**, 3522 (1954).

11. Diels-Alder reagents. Survey of common dienophiles.[1]

[1] L. Velluz, *Substances Naturelles de Synthèse*, **5**, 141–152 (1953).

12. Diethylchlorophosphonate, $(C_2H_5O)_2PCl$.

Mol. wt. 156.55, b.p. 57°/30 mm. Preparation.[1] Synthesis of peptides by the reactions:[2]

$$(C_2H_5O)_2PCl + H_2NCHRCO_2C_2H_5 \rightarrow$$
$$(C_2H_5O)_2PNHCHRCO_2C_2H_5$$

$$C_6H_5CH_2OCONHCHR'CO_2H$$

$$\xrightarrow{(C_2H_5O)_2PNHCHRCO_2C_2H_5}$$

$$C_6H_5CH_2OCONHCHR'CONHCHRCO_2C_2H_5$$
$$+ (C_2H_5O)_2POH$$

[1] H. G. Cook, and others, *J. Chem. Soc.*, 2921 (1949).
[2] G. W. Anderson, J. Blodinger, R. W. Young and A. D. Welcher, *J. Am. Chem. Soc.*, **74**, 5304 (1952).

13. Diethylene glycol,

$$HOCH_2CH_2OCH_2CH_2OH.$$

Mol. wt. 106.12, b.p. 235–255°. Crude phenanthrene is purified by azeotropic distillation of a solution in this solvent.[1] Ethyl-

ene glycol serves in the same way for purification of anthracene.

[1] *Org. Synth.*, **34**, 31 (1954).

14. Dihydropyran.

$$\begin{array}{ccc} CH_2{\cdot}O{\cdot}CH & & CH_2{\cdot}O{\cdot}CHOR \\ | \quad \quad \| & \xrightarrow[H^+]{ROH} & | \quad \quad | \\ CH_2CH_2CH & & CH_2CH_2CH_2 \end{array}$$

Mol. wt. 84.11, b.p. 85°. Preparation.[1] Used for protection of functional group of primary and secondary alcohols and phenols, with which it reacts under acid catalysis as shown.[2] The ethers are stable to base, acetic anhydride in pyridine, RMgX, and $LiAlH_4$, but are cleaved easily by acids (refluxing with acetic acid gives the corresponding acetate).[3] Protection of carboxyl group;[4] protection of sulfhydryl group.[5]

[1] *Org. Synth.*, **23**, 25 (1943).
[2] R. Paul, *Bull. Soc. Chim.*, [5], **1**, 973 (1934); G. F. Woods and D. N. Kramer, *J. Am. Chem. Soc.*, **69**, 2246 (1947); W. E. Parham and E. L. Anderson, *ibid.*, **70**, 4187 (1948); A. C. Ott, M. F. Murray and R. L. Pederson, *ibid.*, **74**, 1239 (1952); R. G. Jones and M. J. Mann, *ibid.*, **75**, 4048 (1953).
[3] W. G. Dauben and H. L. Bradlow, *ibid.*, **74**, 559 (1952).
[4] R. E. Bowman and W. D. Fordham, *J. Chem. Soc.*, 3945 (1952).
[5] W. E. Parham and D. M. DeLaitsch, *J. Am. Chem. Soc.*, **76**, 4962 (1954).

15. Diketene.

Mol. wt. 84.07, b.p. 67°/90 mm., m.p. −8°. Supplier: Aldrich Chem. Co. Preparation from ketene.[1] Structure.[2] Reacts with alcohols to form the acetoacetates:[3]

$$\begin{array}{ccc} CH_2{=}C{-}CH_2 + HOR \rightarrow CH_3COCH_2CO_2R \\ | \quad | \\ O{-}CO \end{array}$$

Reacts with aromatic amines to form the acetoacetanilides, $CH_3COCH_2CONHAr$.[4]

[1] *Org. Synth.*, **21**, 64 (1941).
[2] J. R. Johnson and V. J. Shiner, Jr., *J. Am. Chem. Soc.*, **75**, 1350 (1953).
[3] W. Kimel and A. C. Cope, *ibid.*, **65**, 1992 (1943).
[4] C. E. Kaslow and N. B. Sommer, *ibid.*, **68**, 644 (1946).

16. Dimethoxyethane, $CH_3OCH_2CH_2OCH_3$ (miscible with water). Mol. wt. 90.12, b.p. 85°, sp. gr. 0.86. Supplier: Arapahoe Chemi-

cals, Inc. Best solvent for the reaction of alkali metals with aromatic hydrocarbons,[1] and for making dispersions of potassium hydroxide (Michael condensation, cyanoethylation, addition of acetylene to ketones).

[1] N. D. Scott, J. F. Walker and V. L. Hansley, *J. Am. Chem. Soc.*, **58**, 2442 (1936); A. L. Wilds and N. A. Nelson, *ibid.*, **75**, 5360, note 22 (1953).

17. Dimethylaniline. Mol. wt. 121.18, b.p. 193°, sp. gr. 0.96, pK_b 9.62. Monomethylaniline, the usual contaminant, can be eliminated by addition of a small quantity of acetic anhydride and distillation. The secondary amine is converted into the less volatile acetyl compound and the acetic acid formed is retained as a salt. A rise in temperature on addition of the anhydride indicates the presence of the secondary (or even primary) amine; with the pure tertiary amine there is a lowering in temperature. After acetylation the tertiary amine can be extracted with dilute mineral acid.

Used with acetyl chloride for acetylation of 5α-hydroxysteroids; a 5β-hydroxyl group is unaffected.[1]

[1] Pl. A. Plattner, Th. Petrzilka and W. Lang, *Helv. Chim. Acta*, **27**, 513 (1944); P. Bladon, and others, *J. Chem. Soc.*, 4883 (1952).

18. 2,3-Dimethylbutadiene-1,3. Mol. wt. 82.14, b.p. 70°. Preparation from pinacol by slow distillation in the presence of a small amount of hydrobromic acid and by rapid distillation of anhydrous pinacol over alumina at 450–470°.[1] A suitable furnace is illustrated on p. 56 of both Fieser and Fieser's *Organic Chemistry* and *Textbook of Organic Chemistry*, and working directions for its construction are given below.[2]

[1] *Org. Synth.*, **22**, 39 (1942).
[2] The furnace is constructed by wrapping a 3-ft. length of $1\frac{1}{2}$-inch iron pipe with asbestos paper and winding on about 48 ft. of No. 18 B. and S. gauge nichrome resistance wire. The whole is enclosed in a length of steam-pipe insulation and mounted in a wooden frame. The temperature is recorded with a thermometer or thermocouple inserted alongside the alumina-packed tube. When used in conjunction with a

Variac, the winding specified will provide for a temperature of 470° with a Variac setting of about 90 volts. The furnace can be made more generally serviceable by adding another winding of resistance wire (40 ft., No. 28 B. and S. gauge) to provide for low heat.

19. 5,5-Dimethylcyclohexane-1,3-dione (dimedon). Mol. wt. 140.18, m.p. 149°. Supplier: Eastman. Preparation.[1] For identification and isolation of aldehydes.[2]

[1] *Org. Synth., Coll. Vol.*, **2**, 200 (1943).
[2] E. C. Horning and M. G. Horning, *J. Org. Chem.*, **11**, 95 (1946).

20. Dimethylformamide, $HCON(CH_3)_2$. Mol. wt. 73.10, b.p. 153°. See Solvents. Formylation of N,N-dimethylaniline;[1] of thiophene derivatives.[2] Reacts with an acid chloride or anhydride to form the N,N-dimethylamide; excess reagent is used as solvent.[3] A useful solvent for carbohydrates because mutarotation is slow in this medium.[4]

[1] *Org. Synth.*, **33**, 27 (1953).
[2] E. Campaigne and W. L. Archer, *J. Am. Chem. Soc.*, **75**, 989 (1953).
[3] G. M. Coppinger, *ibid.*, **76**, 1372 (1954).
[4] R. Kuhn and F. Haber, *Ber.*, **86**, 722 (1953).

21. N,N-Dimethylglycinehydrazide hydrochloride, $(CH_3)_2NCH_2CONHNH_2 \cdot HCl$ (Reagent D). Mol. wt. 153.62, m.p. 181°. Preparation and use as Girard reagent; it is more easily purified than Reagents T and P.[1]

[1] M. Viscontini and J. Meier, *Helv. Chim. Acta*, **33**, 1773 (1950).

22. Dimethyl sulfate–sodium. For permethylation of a sugar, partially methylated material is dissolved in absolute ether, sodium wire is added followed by dimethyl sulfate diluted with ether.[1] The reaction is complete in about one hour. The Haworth procedure (dimethyl sulfate and aqueous alkali) requires repeated addition of reagents to effect complete methylation.

[1] H. Bredereck, and others, *Ber.*, **87**, 35, 38 (1954).

23. 2,4-Dinitrobenzaldehyde. Mol. wt. 196.12, m.p. 70°. Preparation.[1] Conversion of amines to Schiff bases for characterization.[2]

[1] *Org. Synth., Coll. Vol.*, **2**, 223 (1943).
[2] F. Wild, "Characterization of Organic Compounds," p. 229, Cambridge (1947).

REAGENTS

24. 2,4-Dinitrobenzenesulfenyl chloride,

$$(NO_2)_2C_6H_3SCl.$$

Mol. wt. 234.62, m.p. 96°. Preparation.[1] Review of uses.[2] Addition to olefins.[3] Reaction with amines.[4] Friedel-Crafts substitution of aromatic compounds.[5]

[1] N. Kharasch, and others, *J. Am. Chem. Soc.*, **69**, 1612 (1947); **71**, 2724 (1949).
[2] N. Kharasch, S. J. Potempa and H. L. Wehrmeister, *Chem. Rev.*, **39**, 269 (1946).
[3] N. Kharasch, and others, *J. Am. Chem. Soc.*, **71**, 2724 (1949); D. Cram, *ibid.*, **71**, 3887 (1949).
[4] J. H. Billman, and others, *ibid.*, **63**, 1920 (1941).
[5] C. M. Buess and N. Kharasch, *ibid.*, **72**, 3529 (1950).

25. 3,4-Dinitrobenzoic acid.

Mol. wt. 212.12, m.p. 166°. Synthesis: p-$CH_3C_6H_4NH_2$ → p-$CH_3C_6H_4NHCOCH_3$ → $CH_3C_6H_3(NO_2)$-$NHCOCH_3$ → $CH_3C_6H_3(NO_2)NH_2$ → $CH_3C_6H_3(NO_2)NO$ → $CH_3C_6H_3(NO_2)_2$ → $HO_2CC_6H_3(NO_2)_2$.[1] Is reduced by sugars and by ascorbic acid to a dye and can be used for microdetermination of sugar components of polysaccharide hydrolyzates after separation by paper chromatography.

[1] E. Borel and H. Deuel, *Helv. Chim. Acta*, **36**, 801 (1953).

26. 3,5-Dinitrobenzoyl chloride.

Mol. wt. 230.57, m.p. 68°.

27. 2,4-Dinitrofluorobenzene,

$(NO_2)_2C_6H_3F$. Mol. wt. 186.10, b.p. 137°/2 mm. Supplier: Eastern Chemical Corp. Preparation.[1] For condensation with free amino groups of amino acids and polypeptides.[2] Use in modified Wohl degradation: an aldose oxime reacts with the reagent in sodium bicarbonate solution with formation of the next lower aldose, 2,4-dinitrophenol, and hydrogen cyanide.[3]

[1] H. G. Cook and B. C. Saunders, *Biochem. J.*, **41**, 558 (1947).
[2] F. Sanger, *Biochem. J.*, **39**, 507 (1945); **40**, 261 (1946); **45**, 563 (1949); R. R. Porter and F. Sanger, *ibid.*, **42**, 287 (1948).
[3] F. Weygand and R. Löwenfeld, *Ber.*, **83**, 559 (1950).

28. Dinitrogen tetroxide,

N_2O_4. Mol. wt. 92.02. Available in cylinders. Nitration of olefins to vic.-dinitroalkanes, nitro-nitrites, or nitro-nitrates.[1] A preparation rich in N_2O_4 made by slow distillation of a mixture of nitric acid, sulfuric acid, and arsenous oxide is recommended for oxidation of hydroquinones.[2] Ponzio reaction:

$$C_6H_5CH{=}NOH \xrightarrow{N_2O_4} C_6H_5CH(NO_2)_2.[3]$$

[1] N. Levy, C. W. Scaife and co-workers, *J. Chem. Soc.*, 1093, 1096, 1100 (1946); 52 (1948); 2627 (1949). C. E. Anagnostopoulos and L. F. Fieser, *J. Am. Chem. Soc.*, **76**, 532 (1954).
[2] A. G. Brook, *J. Chem. Soc.*, 5040 (1952).
[3] G. Ponzio, *J. prakt. Chem.*, **73**, 494 (1906); L. F. Fieser and W. von E. Doering, *J. Am. Chem. Soc.*, **68**, 2252 (1946).

29. 2,4-Dinitrophenylhydrazine.

Mol. wt. 198.14. Solution for reaction with a carbonyl compound (Chapter 14.2): (a) dissolve 1 millimole of reagent and 6–8 micro drops of concd. hydrochloric acid in 10 ml. of 95% ethanol; (b) dissolve 1 millimole of reagent in 30 ml. of 95% ethanol, add the test compound and then 6–8 drops of concd. hydrochloric acid. (c[1]) Dissolve 5 g. of reagent in 60 ml. of 85% phosphoric acid by warming, dilute with 39.5 ml. of 95% ethanol, and clarify by filtration. The resulting 0.25 M solution is stable indefinitely. Add the calculated volume of solution to a solution of the carbonyl compound in ethanol. Although less destructive to sensitive compounds than solutions containing a mineral acid, the reagent sometimes results in elimination of a tertiary hydroxyl group.[2]

[1] G. D. Johnson, *J. Am. Chem. Soc.*, **73**, 5888 (1951).
[2] H. Reich, K. F. Crane and S. J. Sanfilippo, *J. Org. Chem.*, **18**, 822 (1953).

30. Dioxane–sulfur trioxide,

$OC_4H_8O \cdot SO_3$. Mol. wt. 168.17. Preparation: Sulfur trioxide is distilled from an all-glass apparatus containing 60% fuming sulfuric acid or Sulfan B (General Electric Co.; γ-form stabilized with an inhibitor to prevent polymerization) into a tared flask containing ethylene dichloride.[1,2] On addition of an equimolar quantity of purified dioxane with rapid stirring and efficient cooling the reagent separates as fine granules. This complex is much more reactive than sulfur trioxide–pyridine; it is hydrolyzed by cold water. Use for sulfonation of olefins;[3] for example, styrene, sulfonated in ethylene dichloride followed by hydrolysis and neutralization, gives chiefly either $C_6H_5CH(OH)CH_2SO_3Na$ (below 5°) or $C_6H_5CH=CHSO_3Na$ (at 54.4°).[1] α-Sulfonation of aldehydes and ketones.[4]

[1] F. G. Bordwell and C. S. Rondestvedt, Jr., *J. Am. Chem. Soc.*, **70**, 2429 (1948).
[2] *Inorg. Synth.*, **2**, 174 (1946).
[3] C. M. Suter and W. E. Truce, *J. Am. Chem. Soc.*, **66**, 1105 (1944); R. Sperling, *J. Chem. Soc.*, 1925 (1949); *Org. Synth.*, **34**, 85 (1954).
[4] W. E. Truce and C. C. Alfieri, *J. Am. Chem. Soc.*, **72**, 2740 (1950).

31. Diphenyldiazomethane, $(C_6H_5)_2CN_2$. Mol. wt. 194.23. Preparation.[1] Reacts with carboxylic acids to form the benzhydryl esters; the protective group is removed by hydrogenolysis.[2]

[1] *Org. Synth.*, **24**, 53 (1944).
[2] E. Hardegger, Z. El Heweihi and F. G. Robinet, *Helv. Chim. Acta*, **31**, 439 (1948).

32. N,N′-Diphenylformamidine,

$$C_6H_5NHCH=NC_6H_5.$$

Mol. wt. 196.25, m.p. 141°. Supplier: Eastman. Preparation.[1] Reacts with acetylacetone at 140° thus:[2] $C_6H_5NHCH=NC_6H_5 + H_2C(COCH_3)_2 \rightarrow C_6H_5NHCH=C(COCH_3)_2 + C_6H_5NH_2$. Resorcinol, probably reacting as cyclohexenedione, condenses with the reagent at 180° to give the double Schiff base of 2,4-dihydroxyisophthalaldehyde;[3] the free aldehyde is obtainable in 21–24% overall yield.[1]

[1] R. Kuhn and H. A. Staab, *Ber.*, **87**, 272 (1954).
[2] F. B. Dains, *ibid.*, **35**, 2504 (1902).
[3] J. B. Shoesmith and J. Haldane, *J. Chem. Soc.*, 2704 (1923).

33. α,α-Diphenylhydrazine, $(C_6H_5)_2NNH_2$. Mol. wt. 184.24, m.p. 34.5°. Preparation.[1] Reacts selectively with the aldehydic group of osones to give crystalline osonehydrazones.[2]

[1] R. Stahel, *Ann.*, **258**, 243 (1890).
[2] G. Henseke and W. Liebenow, *Ber.*, **87**, 1068 (1954).

34. Diphenyl phosphoroisothiocyanatidate,

$$(C_6H_5O)_2P(=O)NCS.$$

Mol. wt. 291.26, b.p. 210°/0.1 mm., sp. gr. 1.29. Prepared by reaction of diphenyl phosphorochloridate with potassium thiocyanate in acetonitrile solution,[1] from which potassium chloride promptly precipitates:

$$(C_6H_5O)_2P(=O)Cl + KNCS \rightarrow$$
$$KCl + (C_6H_5O)_2P(=O)NCS$$

The reagent reacts with the triethylamine salt of an N-acylated peptide to form a mixed anhydride that decomposes to an acyl thiohydantoin bearing a substituent group identifying the amino acid at the carboxyl end of the peptide chain.

[1] G. W. Kenner, H. G. Khorana and R. J. Stedman, *J. Chem. Soc.*, 673 (1953).

35. Diphenylphosphoryl chloride, $(C_6H_5O)_2POCl$. Mol. wt. 268.63. Preparation and use as phosphorylating agent.[1]

[1] E. Baer, *Biochem. Preparations*, **1**, 50 (1951).

1. Ethanedithiol, $HSCH_2CH_2SH$. Mol. wt. 94.20, b.p. 95°, sp. gr. 1.14. Supplier: Aldrich Chemical Co. Preparation from ethylene bromide: (a) and thiourea (55–62% yield),[1] (b) and potassium thiolacetate (56% yield).[2] Summary of acidic agents for condensation of the reagent with ketones and suggestion of an additional agent: boron fluoride etherate, alone or in acetic acid solution.[3]

[1] *Org. Synth.*, **30**, 35 (1950).
[2] L. N. Owen and P. N. Smith, *J. Chem. Soc.*, 2973 (1951).
[3] L. F. Fieser, *J. Am. Chem. Soc.*, **76**, 1945 (1954).

2. Ethoxyacetylene, $HC\equiv COC_2H_5$. Mol. wt. 86.09, b.p. 50°/749 mm. Preparation.[1] Useful for the synthetic sequence:[2] $R_2CO \rightarrow R_2C(OH)C\equiv COC_2H_5 \rightarrow R_2C=CHCHO \rightarrow R_2C=CHCO_2H$

[1] *Org. Synth.*, **34**, 46 (1954).
[2] I. Heilbron, E. R. H. Jones, M. Julia and B. C. L. Weedon, *J. Chem. Soc.*, 1823 (1949); D. A. van Dorp and J. F. Arens, *Nature*, **160**, 189 (1947); L. H. Sarett, and others, *J. Am. Chem. Soc.*, **74**, 4974 (1952).

REAGENTS

3. Ethyl chloroformate (cathyl chloride), $ClCO_2C_2H_5$. Mol. wt. 108.53, b.p. 95°, sp. gr. 1.14. Preparation of urethans; selective cathylation [1] of equatorial secondary hydroxyl groups of steroids; synthesis of peptides, see *i*-Butyl chloroformate.

> [1] L. F. Fieser, J. E. Herz, M. W. Klohs, M. A. Romero and T. Utne, *J. Am. Chem. Soc.*, **74,** 3309 (1952).

4. Ethyl diazoacetate, $N_2CHCO_2C_2H_5$. Mol. wt. 114.10, b.p. 42°/10 mm., sp. gr. 1.09. Preparation.[1]

> [1] *Org. Synth.*, **24,** 56 (1944); C. Grundmann and G. Ottmann, *Ann.*, **582,** 173 (1953).

5. Ethylenediamine, $H_2NCH_2CH_2NH_2$. Mol. wt. 60.10, b.p. 117°, m.p. 8.5°, sp. gr. 0.90. Iodination of phenols and arylamines (KI_3 solution) is advantageously carried out in the presence of an HI-acceptor. Ethylamine [1] and ethylenediamine [2] are recommended.

> [1] J. C. Clayton and B. A. Hems, *J. Chem. Soc.*, 840 (1950).
> [2] K. T. Potts, *ibid.*, 3711 (1953).

6. Ethylene glycol, $HOCH_2CH_2OH$. Mol. wt. 62.07, b.p. 197.5°, sp. gr. 1.11.

7. Ethylenimine,

$$HN \begin{array}{c} CH_2 \\ | \\ | \\ CH_2 \end{array}$$

Mol. wt. 43.07, b.p. 55–56.5°, sp. gr. 0.83. Prepared by interaction of ethanolamine and sulfuric acid, and treatment of the resulting 2-aminoethyl hydrogen sulfate with alkali.[1] Review.[2] Relatively toxic.[3] Alkylates primary or secondary amines ($AlCl_3$):[4]

$$\begin{array}{c} CH_2 \\ | \\ | \\ CH_2 \end{array} NH + HNR_2 \rightarrow H_2NCH_2CH_2NR_2$$
$$(77-89\%)$$

Used in synthesis of S-acetylpantethein.[5] The intermediate acid, RCO_2H, is treated as the triethylamine salt in dimethylforma- mide solution with ethyl chloroformate to produce a mixed anhydride; this is allowed to react with ethylenimine and the ring is then opened with thiolacetic acid:

$$RCO_2H \rightarrow RCO \cdot O \cdot CO_2 \cdot C_2H_5 \xrightarrow{(CH_3)_2NH}$$

$$RCON \begin{array}{c} CH_2 \\ | \\ | \\ CH_2 \end{array} \xrightarrow{HSCOCH_3}$$

$$RCONHCH_2CH_2SCOCH_3$$
$$(R = HOCH_2C(CH_3)_2CHOHCONHCH_2CH_2-)$$

Ethylenimine reacts with aldehydes and ketones to form 2-oxazolidines.[6] Other reactions.[7] Supplier: Monomer-Polymer.

> [1] W. A. Reeves, G. L. Drake, Jr. and C. L. Hoffpauir, *J. Am. Chem. Soc.*, **73,** 3522 (1951), review earlier procedures and give an improved procedure for effecting cyclization in 83% yield.
> [2] J. S. Fruton in Elderfield's "Heterocyclic Compounds," I, 61 (1950).
> [3] J. P. Danehy and D. J. Pflaum, *Ind. Eng. Chem.*, **30,** 778 (1950).
> [4] G. H. Coleman and J. E. Callen, *J. Am. Chem. Soc.*, **68,** 2006 (1946).
> [5] R. Schwyzer, *Helv. Chim. Acta*, **35,** 1903 (1952).
> [6] J. B. Doughty, C. L. Lazzell and A. R. Collett, *J. Am. Chem. Soc.*, **72,** 2866 (1950).
> [7] H. Bestian, *Ann.*, **566,** 210 (1950).

8. Ethylene oxide. Mol. wt. 44.05, b.p. 10.7°, sp. gr. 0.89. Available in small cylinders. The gas is passed through a short tower filled with soda lime and then either passed directly into the reaction mixture or condensed to a liquid in a spiral condenser packed with salt and ice.

9. Ethyl formate, $HCO_2C_2H_5$. Mol. wt. 74.08, b.p. 54.2°, sp. gr. 0.92. When required for use in the Grignard synthesis of a dialkyl carbinol,[1] the commercial ester should be dried over potassium carbonate, then over phosphorus pentoxide, and distilled.

> [1] For an example see G. H. Coleman and D. Craig, *Org. Synth.*, Coll. Vol., **2,** 179 (1943).

10. Ethyl orthocarbonate, $C(OC_2H_5)_4$. Mol. wt. 192.25, b.p. 159°, sp. gr. 0.92. Preparation.[1]

> [1] *Org. Synth.*, **32,** 68 (1952).

REAGENTS

11. Ethyl orthoformate, $HC(OC_2H_5)_3$. Mol. wt. 148.20, b.p. 146°, sp. gr. 0.94. Preparation.[1] (a) For synthesis of aldehydes: $RMgBr \rightarrow RCHO$;[2] $ArMgBr \rightarrow ArCHO$.[3] (b) Reacts with both aldehydes and ketones to form a diethyl acetal:[4]

$$R_2CO + HC(OC_2H_5)_3 \rightarrow R_2C(OC_2H_5)_2 + HCO_2C_2H_5 \text{ (b.p. 54°)}$$

The reaction is usually carried out in absolute ethanol in the presence of a catalytic amount of ferric chloride, ammonium chloride, or ammonium nitrate either at room temperature (6–8 hrs.) or at the boiling point (30 min.). Examples: acrolein diethyl acetal,[5] phenylpropargyl aldehyde diethyl acetal.[6] (c) Acetals are stable to base but not to acid, and when $R_2C(OR')_2$ is heated with $R''OH$ in the presence of a mineral acid an equilibrium between the original acetal and $R_2C(OR'')_2$ is set up; the equilibrium is displaced by distillation of the lower alcohol.[7] Thus the diethyl acetal of an α-keto ester, prepared from $RCOCO_2C_2H_5$, $HC(OC_2H_5)_3$, C_2H_5OH, and dry hydrogen chloride at room temperature, when heated with ethylene glycol and a trace of sulfuric acid yields the ethylene ketal of the keto ester.[8] (d) When a diethyl acetal is distilled or heated in a high-boiling solvent, a molecule of ethanol is eliminated with formation of the enol ether: $RCH_2C(R)(OC_2H_5)_2 \rightarrow RCH=C(R)—OC_2H_5 + C_2H_5OH$. This route has been used for preparation of enol ethers of 3-ketosteroids[9] and of cyclohexane-1,3-diones.[10]

[1] *Org. Synth., Coll. Vol.,* **1**, 258 (1941).
[2] *Ibid., Coll. Vol.,* **2**, 323 (1943).
[3] *Org. Synth.,* **28**, 83 (1948).
[4] L. Claisen, *Ber.,* **29**, 1005 (1896); **31**, 1020 (1898); **40**, 3903 (1907).
[5] *Org. Synth.,* **32**, 5 (1952).
[6] *Ibid.,* **25**, 92 (1945).
[7] M. Delépine, *Ann. chim.,* [7] **23**, 482 (1901).
[8] E. Vogel and H. Schinz, *Helv. Chim. Acta,* **33**, 116 (1950).
[9] A. Serini and H. Köster, *Ber.,* **71**, 1766 (1938); H. H. Inhoffen, and others, *ibid.,* **84**, 361 (1951).
[10] E. G. Meek, J. H. Turnbull and W. Wilson, *J. Chem. Soc.,* 811 (1953).

1. Fehling's solution: Chapter 21.1.

Fenton's reagent. See Hydrogen peroxide (h).

2. Ferric chloride, $FeCl_3 \cdot 6H_2O$. Mol. wt. 270.32. Oxidation of aminonaphthols to naphthoquinones or quinonimines: Chapters 38.1, 42; literature.[1]

[1] M. Gates, *J. Am. Chem. Soc.,* **72**, 228 (1950).

3. Ferrous hydroxide, $Fe(OH)_2$. Mol. wt. 89.87. For reduction of aromatic nitro compounds, particularly nitrocarboxylic acids and nitrobenzaldehydes.[1]

[1] L. Claisen, and others, *Ber.,* **12**, 353, 1946 (1879); E. Bamberger and Ed. Demuth, *ibid.,* **34**, 1330 (1901).

4. Fischer reagent. For determination of water in inert organic solvents.[1] A solution of iodine, sulfur dioxide, and pyridine in methanol. The reaction with water is: $I_2 + SO_2 + H_2O \rightarrow 2HI + SO_3$; pyridine combines with both products. A similar reagent utilizing bromine instead of iodine has been developed.[2]

[1] Karl Fischer, *Angew. Chem.,* **48**, 394 (1935).
[2] R. Belcher and T. S. West, *J. Chem. Soc.,* 1772 (1953).

5. Fluorosulfonic acid, FSO_2OH. Use as cyclodehydrating agent.[1]

[1] W. Baker, G. E. Coates and F. Glockling, *J. Chem. Soc.,* 1376 (1951).

6. Formaldehyde. Mol. wt. 30.03, b.p. −21°, sp. gr. 0.81. Commercial formalin is an aqueous solution containing 30–40% formaldehyde and some methanol. Where so much excess water is undesirable but a little can be tolerated, use can be made of methylal (mol. wt. 76.09, b.p. 42°, sp. gr. 0.87), which is readily hydrolyzed in an acidic medium. Dry gaseous formaldehyde (Grignard reaction) is generated by heating the solid polymer paraformaldehyde and leading the gas into the reaction mixture.

Formaldoxime. See Acetaldoxime.

7. Formamide, $HCONH_2$. Mol. wt. 45.04, b.p. 193°, sp. gr. 1.14. Reacts with α-hy-

REAGENTS

droxy, α-halo, and α-amino ketones to form imidazoles: [1]

$$\text{RCOCHXR}' \xrightarrow{\text{HCONH}}
\begin{array}{c}
\text{RC}\!=\!=\!\text{CR}' \\
| \qquad\qquad | \\
\text{N} \qquad\quad \text{NH} \\
\diagdown\ \diagup \\
\text{CH}
\end{array}$$

$(X = OH, Br, NH_2)$

Also converts oxazoles into imidazoles. When a halogen compound is heated with formamide at 150° for several hours, the corresponding formylamine (a) or formate (b) is formed.[2]

(a) $RX + 2HCONH_2 \rightarrow$
$$RNH \cdot CHO + CO + NH_4X$$

(b) $RX + 2HCONH_2 \rightarrow$
$$ROCHO + HCN + NH_4X$$

[1] H. Bredereck and G. Theilig, *Ber.*, **86**, 88 (1953); G. Theilig, *ibid.*, **86**, 96 (1953).
[2] H. Bredereck, R. Gompper and G. Theilig, *ibid.*, **87**, 537 (1954).

8. Formic acid. Mol. wt. 46.03, b.p. 100.5, sp. gr. 1.22, pK_a 3.77. A reactive acylating agent for alcohols and amines. Cholic acid yields the triformyl derivative on being heated with 87% formic acid (sp. gr. 1.2, 2 ml. per gram) at 50–55° for 5 hrs.[1] An example of formylation of an amino acid is as follows: a mixture of 40 g. of DL-cystine and 600 ml. of 87% formic acid is stirred at 60° and treated with 200 ml. of acetic anhydride, added at such a rate as to maintain a temperature of 60°.[2] Formylation of the 11 α-hydroxyl group of 11-epicorticosterone was accomplished in pyridine at 0° by dropwise addition of a mixture of 1 ml. of 99% formic acid and 0.4 ml. of acetic anhydride.[3] Hydroxylation of a double bond with hydrogen peroxide proceeds much faster in formic acid than in acetic acid solution.[4] Use as reducing agent $(Ar_3COH \rightarrow Ar_3CH)$.[5]

[1] F. Cortese and L. Bauman, *J. Am. Chem. Soc.*, **57**, 1393 (1935).
[2] V. du Vigneaud, R. Dorfmann and H. S. Loring, *J. Biol. Chem.*, **98**, 577 (1932).
[3] F. Reber, A. Lardon and T. Reichstein, *Helv. Chim. Acta*, **37**, 45 (1954).
[4] D. Swern, G. N. Billen, T. W. Findley and J. T. Scanlan, *J. Am. Chem. Soc.*, **67**, 1786 (1945).

[5] H. Kauffmann and P. Pannwitz, *Ber.*, **45**, 766 (1912); A. Kovache, *Ann. chim.* [9], **10**, 184 (1918).

1. Girard's reagent P (P = pyridine),

$$Py^+(Cl^-)CH_2CONHNH_2.$$

Mol. wt. 187.63. Supplier: Arapahoe Chemicals, Inc.

2. Girard's reagent T,

$$(CH_3)_3N^+(Cl^-)CH_2CONHNH_2.$$

Mol. wt. 153.64. Suppliers: Eastern Chemical Corp., Arapahoe Chemicals, Inc. Example of use: Chapter 14.9.

3. Glyoxal bisulfite,

$$OCHCHO \cdot 2NaHSO_3 \cdot H_2O.$$

Preparation.[1]

[1] *Org. Synth.*, **24**, 61 (1944).

4. Gold chloride crystals, $HAuCl_4 \cdot 3H_2O$. Mol. wt. 394.08. Oxidation of α-tocopherol to α-tocopherylquinone.[1]

[1] P. Karrer and A. Geiger, *Helv. Chim. Acta*, **23**, 455 (1940).

1. Hexamethylenetetramine, $(CH_2)_6N_4$. Mol. wt. 140.19. (a) Sommelet reaction.[1] The reagent reacts with a benzyl-type halide to form a salt, $ArCH_2 \cdot C_6H_{12}N_4^+Cl^-$, which is hydrolyzed by hot aqueous hydrochloric acid to the aldehyde, ArCHO, formaldehyde, methylamine, and ammonia. Examples: α-naphthaldehyde,[2] syringic aldehyde,[3] 3-thenaldehyde,[4] dialdehydes.[5]

(b) Duff reaction.[6] The reagent condenses with a phenol in the ortho position to give a Schiff base, which on hydrolysis yields the *o*-hydroxy aldehyde:

$$o\text{-HOC}_6H_4CH\!=\!NCH_2C_6H_4OH\text{-}o \rightarrow$$
$$o\text{-HOC}_6H_4CHO + H_2NCH_2C_6H_4OH\text{-}o$$

Use in synthesis of aurantiogliocladin (2,3-dimethoxy-5,6-dimethyl-1,4-benzoquinone).[7]

(c) Delépine reaction.[8] The hexamethylene salt of a benzyl-type or phenacyl-type [9] halide on hydrolysis with alcoholic hydrochloric acid in the cold yields a primary amine, $ArCH_2NH_2$ or $ArCOCH_2NH_2$.

[1] M. Sommelet, *Compt. rend.*, **157**, 852 (1913).
[2] *Org. Synth.*, **30**, 67 (1950).

REAGENTS

[3] *Ibid.*, **31**, 92 (1951).
[4] *Ibid.*, **33**, 93 (1953).
[5] J. H. Wood, C. C. Tung, M. A. Perry and R. E. Gibson, *J. Am. Chem. Soc.*, **72**, 2992 (1950).
[6] J. C. Duff, *J. Chem. Soc.*, 547 (1941).
[7] W. Baker, J. F. W. McOmie and D. Miles, *ibid.*, 820 (1953).
[8] M. Delépine, *Compt. rend.*, **120**, 501 (1895).
[9] L. M. Long and H. D. Troutman, *J. Am. Chem. Soc.*, **71**, 2473 (1949).

2. Heyn's catalyst, a 10% platinum catalyst carried on purified charcoal. Preparation.[1] Catalyzes oxidation of primary alcohols by oxygen or air to carboxylic acids.[2]

[1] K. Heyns, *Ann.*, **558**, 177 (1947).
[2] K. Heyns, and others, *Ann.*, **558**, 177, 187, 192 (1947); *Ber.*, **86**, 110, 833 (1953); **87**, 13 (1954).

3. Hippuric acid, $C_6H_5CONHCH_2CO_2H$. Mol. wt. 179.17, m.p. 188°. Condenses with aldehydes in the presence of acetic anhydride and sodium acetate to form azlactones of use in synthesis.[1] Previously limited to condensation with aromatic aldehydes, the reaction has been applied to aliphatic aldehydes by use of tetrahydrofuran as solvent and substitution of lead acetate for sodium acetate.[2]

[1] H. E. Carter, *Org. Reactions*, **3**, 198 (1946).
[2] E. Baltazzi and R. Robinson, *Chem. Ind.*, 191 (1954).

4. Hyamine 1622,

$$p\text{-}C_8H_{17}C_6H_4OCH_2CH_2OCH_2CH_2N^+(CH_3)_2^-$$
$$CH_2C_6H_5Cl.^-$$

This Rohm and Haas Co. germicide and deodorant is marketed as a 10% aqueous solution, which is diluted 1:100 with water for use as a laboratory deodorant spray (nontoxic but irritating if breathed because of surface-activity). A stronger solution, even 0.1%, may be required for a mercaptan odor, a 5% solution for washing up spilled mercaptan.

5. Hydrazine. Mol. wt. 32.05, b.p. 113.5°, sp. gr. 1.01. Review.[1] Preparation of anhydrous reagent.[2] In the presence of Raney nickel catalyst it reduces aryl nitro compounds to amines at steam bath temperature; carbonyl groups present are not affected.[3]

Huang-Minlon procedure for Wolff-Kishner reduction.[4] Preparation of numerous carboxylic hydrazides by the reaction $RCO_2R' + H_2NNH_2$.[5]

[1] C. C. Clark, "Hydrazine," Mathieson Chem. Corp. (1953).
[2] *Org. Synth.*, **24**, 53 (1944).
[3] D. Balcom and A. Furst, *J. Am. Chem. Soc.*, **75**, 4334 (1953).
[4] Huang-Minlon, *ibid.*, **68**, 2487 (1946).
[5] H. L. Yale, and others, *ibid.*, **75**, 1933 (1953).

6. Hydrazoic acid, HN_3. Mol. wt. 43.03. Addition of an aqueous solution of sodium azide to acetic acid results in liberation of hydrazoic acid. Example: α-naphthoquinone $\rightarrow$ 2-amino-1,4-naphthoquinone.[1] In concd. sulfuric acid solution hydrazoic acid reacts with benzo- and anthraquinones with rupture of the carbon skeleton of the quinone ring.[2]

[1] L. F. Fieser and J. L. Hartwell, *J. Am. Chem. Soc.*, **57**, 1482 (1935).
[2] G. Caronna and S. Palazzo, *Gazz. chim. ital.*, **83**, 315, 533 (1953).

7. Hydrogen bromide, anhydrous. Preparation.[1]

[1] *Org. Synth., Coll. Vol.*, **2**, 338 (1943).

8. Hydrogen cyanide. Mol. wt. 27.03. Although hydrogen cyanide is an active poison, the reagent can be prepared in quantities up to 0.5 kg. without undue danger if a good hood is available and proper care is taken.[1,2]

Anhydrous hydrogen cyanide is used in synthesis of hydroxy aldehydes according to Gattermann:

$$HC{\equiv}N + HCl \longrightarrow ClCH{=}NH$$
$$HO{\cdot}C_6H_5 + ClCH{=}NH \xrightarrow[-HCl]{ZnCl_2}$$
$$p\text{-}HO{\cdot}C_6H_4{\cdot}CH{=}NH$$
$$\xrightarrow{H_2O} p\text{-}HOC_6H_4{\cdot}CH{=}O + NH_3$$

The phenol is treated in anhydrous ether solution with anhydrous hydrogen cyanide, zinc chloride, and dry hydrogen chloride; the imide separates as hydrochloride and is hydrolyzed by aqueous acid. Phenol ethers, as well as some phenols, react with difficulty unless zinc chloride is replaced by the more active aluminum chloride.

REAGENTS

Adams[3] modified the Gattermann synthesis to avoid use of anhydrous hydrogen cyanide. Hydrogen chloride is passed into a mixture of the phenol and zinc cyanide in ether. The reagent and catalyst are produced in the reaction flask at the time required.

[1] *Org. Synth., Coll. Vol.*, **1**, 314 (1941).
[2] K. H. Slotta, *Ber.*, **67**, 1028 (1934).
[3] R. Adams, and others, *J. Am. Chem. Soc.*, **45**, 2373 (1923); **46**, 1518 (1924).

9. Hydrogen fluoride. B.p. 19.4°. Liquid hydrogen fluoride containing only 0.1–0.2% water is available commercially in steel cylinders. The liquid reagent has a powerful solvent action for many organic compounds, particularly for oxygen-containing substances and for aromatic compounds. It is an effective dehydrating and condensing agent, often exhibiting an action comparable to that of concd. sulfuric acid, and it is less prone than the latter acid to give rise to secondary reactions such as enolization and aromatic substitution. Liquid hydrogen fluoride functions similarly to aluminum chloride or boron fluoride as catalyst for alkylations and acylations, and it sometimes serves as promoter for polymerization reactions. One important synthetic use of the reagent is in the preparation of ketones of the α-hydrindone, α-tetralone, and anthrone types by cyclization of the appropriate acids.[1] Other significant applications arise from the fact that the orientation in both intramolecular cyclizations and intermolecular acylations is sometimes different from that in the Friedel-Crafts procedure.[2]

Hydrogen fluoride is highly corrosive to tissue and should be handled with care and not breathed. When spilled on the skin it produces severe burns which only become apparent some 5–8 hrs. later. Parts known or suspected to have been in contact with the reagent should be treated immediately, first by thorough washing with water and then by application of a paste of magnesia, water, and glycerol. When these precautions are kept in mind, hydrogen fluoride can be handled safely.

Reactions that proceed satisfactorily at room temperature can be carried out in a platinum crucible or, with larger amounts, in an open copper flask or polyethylene vessel. The cylinder is stored in a cold place (5°) until required, when it is removed and fitted with a copper delivery tube. The vessel containing the organic reactants is tared on a balance in the hood, the tank is inverted and the required weight of hydrogen fluoride is run in (use goggles and rubber gloves). The material usually dissolves at once or on brief stirring with a metal spatula, and the reaction may be complete in 10–20 min., or at least before the bulk of the reagent has evaporated. The excess reagent can be evaporated by gentle heating over a steam bath or in a current of air, or the solution poured into water and a little ice in a beaker and the product quickly collected by suction filtration or by ether or benzene extraction, followed immediately by washing with soda solution. For use at higher temperatures (100°), a pressure vessel can be constructed from a welded steel cylinder fitted with a stainless steel condenser tube carrying a glass water jacket and connected through the condenser to a stainless steel gauge and a steel receiver into which the excess reagent can be distilled at the end of the reaction.[3]

[1] K. Wiechert and J. E. Jones, "Use of Hydrogen Fluoride in Organic Reactions," *Newer Methods of Preparative Organic Chemistry*, p. 315, Interscience (1948).
[2] See review by J. H. Simons, *Ind. Eng. Chem.*, **32**, 178 (1940).
[3] L. F. Fieser and E. B. Hershberg, *J. Am. Chem. Soc.*, **61**, 1272 (1939); **62**, 49 (1940).

10. Hydrogen peroxide. Mol. wt. 34.02. (a) *In acetic*[1] *or formic acid*[2] *solution* for *trans* hydroxylation of a double bond or for oxidation of phenanthrenequinones to diphenic acids.[3] (b) *In weakly alkaline solution* (aqueous-alcoholic sodium carbonate) for conversion of an α,β-unsaturated ketone to an oxide[4] (example: Chapter 38.5). (c) *In alkaline solution* for replacement of an aldehydic group of a phenol by hydroxyl (Dakin reaction); pyridine can be added if the phenol is sparingly soluble.[5] (d) Anhydrous hydrogen peroxide *in t-butanol with osmium tetroxide* as catalyst oxidizes olefins to glycols in 30–60% yield.[6] The same reagent oxidizes a steroid 17,20-ene to the 17α-ol-20-one.[7] (e) Hydrogen peroxide *in ether catalyzed by osmium tetroxide cis*-hydroxylates the double bond of α,β-unsaturated ketones.[8] Hydroxylation catalyzed by pertungstic acid, however, gives *trans* glycols.[9] (f) A mixture of *30% hydrogen peroxide and nitric acid* (sp. gr. 1.26) oxidizes aromatic nitroso compounds to nitro compounds.[10] (g) Hydrogen peroxide *catalyzed by peroxyvanadic* acid effects the transformations:[11] cyclohexene → cyclohexenone (43% yield); tetralin → α-tetralone (65% yield). (h) *Fenton's reagent:* $H_2O_2 + Fe^{++}$.[12] A small amount of ferrous sulfate catalyzes decomposition to OH and OOH radicals. The combination oxidizes α-hydroxy acids,[13] hydroxylates nitrobenzene,[14] and dehydrogenates 3,4-dihydroquinoxalines.[15] (i) Hydrogen peroxide (30%) *in fuming sulfuric acid* oxidizes aminopyridines to nitropyridines.[16] (j) The peroxide *in acetone* oxidizes thioethers to sulfoxides ($RSCH_3 \rightarrow RSOCH_3$); in 50% acetic acid oxidation proceeds to the sulfone.[17] (k) 30% Hydrogen peroxide (34 ml.) *and selenium dioxide* (1.3 g.) in *t*-butanol (34 ml.) oxidizes cyclopentadiene to *cis* and *trans* cyclopentanediol-1,3 at 0° in 51% yield.[18] Other solvents: dioxan, acetone. (l) *90% Hydrogen peroxide* made by the Buffalo Electrochemical Co. is very pure and requires no stabilizer. The rate of decomposition, 1% per year at 30°, is much less than for usual 30% solutions.[19] B.p. 140° dec., f.p. −11°, d = 1.393 $^{18°}$.

[1] T. P. Hilditch, *J. Chem. Soc.*, 1828 (1926).

[2] D. Swern, G. N. Billen, T. W. Findley and J. T. Scanlan, *J. Am. Chem. Soc.*, **67**, 1786 (1945); L. F. Fieser and S. Rajagopalan, *ibid.*, **71**, 3938 (1949); *Org. Synth.*, **28**, 35 (1948).

[3] R. P. Linstead and A. L. Walpole, *J. Chem. Soc.*, 842 (1939).

[4] E. P. Kohler, N. K. Richtmeyer and W. F. Hester, *J. Am. Chem. Soc.*, **53**, 205 (1931); Pl. A. Plattner, and others, *Helv. Chim. Acta*, **31**, 1822 (1948).

[5] G. Barger, *J. Chem. Soc.*, **113**, 218 (1918); *Org. Synth.*, *Coll. Vol.*, **1**, 149 (1941); *ibid.*, **26**, 90 (1946).

[6] N. A. Milas and S. Sussman, *J. Am. Chem. Soc.*, **58**, 1302 (1936).

[7] K. Miescher and J. Schmidlin, *Helv. Chim. Acta*, **33**, 1840 (1950).

[8] A. Butenandt and H. Wolz, *Ber.*, **71**, 1483 (1938).

[9] M. Mugdan and D. P. Young, *J. Chem. Soc.*, 2988 (1949).

[10] R. Kuhn and W. van Klaveren, *Ber.*, **71**, 779 (1938).

[11] W. Triebs, G. Franke, G. Leichsenring and H. Röder, *Ber.*, **86**, 616 (1953).

[12] H. S. H. Fenton, *J. Chem. Soc.*, **65**, 899 (1894).

[13] O. Ruff, *Ber.*, **31**, 1573 (1898).

[14] H. Loebl, G. Stein and J. Weiss, *J. Chem. Soc.*, 2074 (1949).

[15] K. Pfister, A. P. Sullivan, Jr., J. Weijlard and M. Tishler, *J. Am. Chem. Soc.*, **73**, 4955 (1951).

[16] A. Kirpal and W. Böhm, *Ber.*, **64**, 767 (1931); **65**, 680 (1932); R. W. Wiley and J. L. Hartman, *J. Am. Chem. Soc.*, **73**, 494 (1951); E. V. Brown, *ibid.*, **76**, 3167 (1954).

[17] M. Gazdar and S. Smiles, *J. Chem. Soc.*, **93**, 1833 (1908); S. Hünig and O. Boes, *Ann.*, **579**, 23 (1953).

[18] A. Stoll, A. Lindenmann and E. Jucker, *Helv. Chim. Acta*, **36**, 268 (1953).

[19] E. S. Shanley and F. P. Greenspan, *Ind. Eng. Chem.*, **39**, 1536 (1947); W. C. Schumb, *ibid.*, **41**, 992 (1947).

11a. Hypochlorite solution. Prepared from chlorine and alkali[1] or from calcium hypochlorite.[2]

[1] *Org. Synth.*, *Coll. Vol.*, **1**, 309 (1941).

[2] *Ibid.*, **2**, 429, Note 2 (1943).

11b. Hypochlorous acid in ether. Chlorine is passed into sodium bicarbonate solution, the solution is extracted with ether, and the ethereal solution is dried quickly at a low temperature and used for oxidation of a secondary amine to a chloroamine.[1]

[1] Fiat Report No. 996.

1. Indicators (pH). Table of over 100 indicators, with notes and references.[1]

[1] L. Velluz, *Substances Naturelles de Synthèse*, **7**, Part III (1953).

REAGENTS

2. Iodine monobromide.
Mol. wt. 206.83, m.p. 42°, b.p. 116°. A mild brominating agent employed for effecting aromatic substitutions. A solution suitable for use is prepared by the interaction of bromine and iodine in acetic acid at 50°.[1]

> [1] W. Militzer, *J. Am. Chem. Soc.*, **60**, 256 (1938).

3. Iodine monochloride.
Mol. wt. 162.38, m.p. 27°, b.p. 97°. Prepared by passing chlorine into iodine,[1] the reagent is used for iodination in acetic acid of *p*-nitroaniline,[1] salicylic acid,[2] anthranilic acid,[3] α-cyclohexyl-β-(*m*-hydroxyphenyl)-propionic acids.[4]

> [1] *Org. Synth., Coll. Vol.*, **2**, 196 (1943).
> [2] *Ibid.*, **2**, 344 (1943).
> [3] J. F. McKenna and F. J. Sowa, *J. Am. Chem. Soc.*, **59**, 470 (1937).
> [4] D. Papa, H. F. Ginsberg, I. Lederman and V. DeCamp, *ibid.*, **75**, 1107 (1953).

4. Iodine–pyridine.
Methyl ketones of the types $ArCOCH_3$ and $R_2CHCOCH_3$ react with iodine in pyridine solution to give the pyridinium iodides in yields sometimes as high as 95%.[1] The salts are cleaved by alkali to the corresponding acids:

$$C_6H_5COCH_3 \rightarrow C_6H_5COCH_2Py^+I^-$$
$$\rightarrow C_6H_5CO_2H$$

2-Methylchromon, a vinylogous methyl ketone, is similarly substituted (88%).[2]

> [1] L. C. King, *J. Am. Chem. Soc.*, **66**, 894, 1612 (1944).
> [2] J. Schmutz, R. Hirt and H. Lauener, *Helv. Chim. Acta*, **35**, 1168 (1952).

5. Iodine–silver acetate–aqueous acetic acid.
For *cis* hydroxylation of double bonds.[1] Compare the acetolysis of *meso*-stilbene dibromide, Chapter 32.

> [1] See D. Ginsburg, *J. Am. Chem. Soc.*, **75**, 5746 (1953); L. B. Barkley, and others, *ibid.*, **76**, 5014 (1954).

6. Iodine–silver sulfate–sulfuric acid.[1]
This combination effects direct iodination of aromatic compounds, e.g., $C_6H_5Cl \rightarrow p\text{-}IC_6H_4Cl$

(60%); $C_6H_5CHO \rightarrow m\text{-}IC_6H_4CHO$ (45% crude); $C_6H_5NO_2 \rightarrow m\text{-}IC_6H_4NO_2$ (55%); naphthalene $\rightarrow \alpha\text{-}C_{10}H_7I$ (34%).

> [1] I. R. L. Barker and W. A. Waters, *J. Chem. Soc.*, 150 (1952).

7. Iodobenzene dichloride (phenyliodo dichloride), $C_6H_5ICl_2$.
Mol. wt. 274.92, m.p. 115–120°, dec. Adds to double bonds to give *cis* dichlorides.[1]

> [1] D. H. R. Barton and E. Miller, *J. Am. Chem. Soc.*, **72**, 370 (1950).

8. Iodosilver benzoate, $Ag(C_6H_5CO_2)_2I$.
Mol. wt. 355.91. Reacts with alkenes in benzene to form *trans* glycol dibenzoates.[1]

> [1] C. Prévost, *Compt. rend.*, **196**, 1129 (1933); **197**, 1661 (1933); E. B. Hershberg, *Helv. Chim. Acta*, **17**, 351 (1934); M. Sletzinger and C. R. Dawson, *J. Org. Chem.*, **14**, 670 (1949); C. Niemann and C. D. Wagner, *ibid.*, **7**, 227 (1942); H. Wittcott and S. E. Miller, *J. Am. Chem. Soc.*, **69**, 3138 (1947); G. E. McCasland and E. C. Horswill, *ibid.*, **76**, 1654 (1954).

9. Iodosobenzene, C_6H_5IO.
Mol. wt. 220.01. Preparation.[1] Oxidation of sulfides to sulfoxides (aqueous solution or suspension, reagent converted to iodobenzene).[2]

> [1] C. Willgerodt, *Ber.*, **25**, 3494 (1892); *Org. Synth.*, **22**, 70 (1942).
> [2] A. H. Ford-Moore, *J. Chem. Soc.*, 2126 (1949).

10. Iodosobenzene diacetate (phenyliodoso acetate), $C_6H_5I(OCOCH_3)_2$.
Mol. wt. 322.10, m.p. 158°. Preparation of salts of iodosobenzene with acetic acid and other acids.[1,2] Improved preparation.[3] Resembles lead tetraacetate in cleavage of glycols, allylic acetoxylation, dehydrogenation, and effecting addition of two acetoxyl groups to a double bond.[2] Oxidizes aromatic amines to the corresponding azo compounds.[4]

> [1] C. Willgerodt, *Ber.*, **25**, 3494 (1892); N. V. Sidgwick and E. D. P. Barkworth, *J. Chem. Soc.*, 807 (1931).
> [2] R. Criegee and H. Beucker, *Ann.*, **541**, 218 (1939).
> [3] K. H. Pausacker, *J. Chem. Soc.*, 107 (1953).
> [4] K. H. Pausacker, *ibid.*, 1989 (1953); G. B. Barlin, K. H. Pausacker and N. V. Riggs, *ibid.*, 3122 (1954).

REAGENTS

11. *o*-**Iodosobenzoic acid,** *o*-HO$_2$CC$_6$H$_4$IO. Mol. wt. 264.02. Oxidizes mercaptans to disulfides.[1]

> [1] L. Hellerman, F. P. Chinard and P. A. Ramsdell, *J. Am. Chem. Soc.*, **63**, 2551 (1941).

12. **N-Iodosuccinimide.** Mol. wt. 224.98, m.p. 201°. Supplier: Arapahoe Chemicals. Preparation and use for iodination of ketones and aldehydes.[1]

> [1] C. Djerassi and C. T. Lenk, *J. Am. Chem. Soc.*, **75**, 3493 (1953).

13. **Ion-exchange resins.** Survey of uses in preparative organic chemistry.[1] Most commonly used resins for acid catalysis: Amberlites IR 100 and 120, Dowex 50; for base catalysis: Amberlite IR-4B and IR 400. Separations by ion exchange.[2]

> [1] F. Helfferich, *Angew. Chem.*, **66**, 241 (1954).
> [2] L. Velluz, *Substances Naturelles de Synthèse*, **6**, 114–143 (1953).

14. **Isopropenyl acetate,** CH$_3$COOC(CH$_3$)=CH$_2$. Mol. wt. 100.11, b.p. 96°/750 mm., sp. gr. 0.93. Suppliers: Tennessee Eastman; Monomer-Polymer. This reagent when heated in the presence of *p*-toluenesulfonic acid decomposes into acetone and ketene and thus serves as a convenient source of the latter reagent, particularly for preparation of enol acetates.[1]

> [1] H. J. Hagemeyer and D. C. Hull, *Ind. Eng. Chem.*, **41**, 2920 (1949).

1. **Ketene,** CH$_2$=C=O. Mol. wt. 42.04, b.p. —56°. Useful for acetylation of amino acids, proteins, and other sensitive compounds. It is made by pyrolysis of acetone over pumice at 650°[1] or in a generator consisting of a boiling flask with a heated filament suspended in the vapor space and a condenser for return of acetone.[2] The ketene can be condensed in a cooling trap (CO$_2$) or passed directly into the reaction mixture through a delivery tube provided with a sintered glass plate. Another method is pyrolysis of acetic anhydride at 505° in an apparatus permitting rapid separation of ketene.[3] Since amines react with ketene more rapidly than water does, an amino acid can be acetylated by passing ketene into an alkaline solution of the substance at room temperature.[4] In the case of an optically active acid, the solution must be kept alkaline throughout the reaction or racemization may occur.[5] Sensitive, water-insoluble substances often can be acetylated by adding excess liquid ketene to a cold solution or suspension of the material in an organic solvent (e.g., acetone).[6] For production of ketene in a reaction mixture, see Isopropenyl acetate.

> [1] *Org. Synth., Coll. Vol.*, **1**, 330 (1941).
> [2] C. H. Li, *Science*, **90**, 143 (1939).
> [3] J. W. Williams and C. D. Hurd, *J. Org. Chem.*, **5**, 122 (1940).
> [4] G. J. Fisher, A. F. MacLean and A. W. Schnizer, *ibid.*, **18**, 1055 (1953).
> [5] M. Bergmann and F. Stern, *Ber.*, **63**, 437 (1930).
> [6] R. W. Jackson and W. M. Cahill, *J. Biol. Chem.*, **126**, 37 (1938).

1. **Lead dioxide,** PbO$_2$. Mol. wt. 239.21. Highly reactive dioxide[1] is made by rubbing 50 g. of lead tetraacetate with 460 ml. of water in centrifuge tubes until it is changed to brown oxide. After centrifugation the material is washed with water until the wash liquor is neutral to litmus and then collected by filtration and washed four times with acetone and four times with ether. Yield 23 g. 2,6-Dihydroxynaphthalene is oxidized to the quinone with a suspension of the reagent in boiling benzene; *o*-benzoquinone can be prepared by oxidation of catechol in ether in the presence of anhydrous sodium sulfate. Oxidation of naphthalene-2,6-dibenzenesulfonamide to the quinonediimine.[2]

> [1] R. Kuhn and I. Hammer, *Ber.*, **83**, 413 (1950).
> [2] R. Adams and R. A. Wankel, *J. Am. Chem. Soc.*, **73**, 2219 (1951).

2. **Lead tetraacetate.**[1] Mol. wt. 443.39. Supplier: Arapahoe Chemicals (small crystals moistened with acetic acid; scrape some of the paste onto a suction funnel, wash it with acetic acid, suck the cake thoroughly, let dry at room temperature in a hood in the dark). Destruction of excess reagent: use ethylene glycol. Preparation:[2] a mixture of 600 ml.

of acetic acid and 400 ml. of acetic anhydride in a wide-mouthed or three-necked flask is heated to 55° with mechanical stirring, and 700 g. (1.02 moles) of dry red lead powder is added in portions of 15–20 g. A fresh addition is made only after the color due to the preceding portion has largely disappeared, and the temperature is kept between 55° and 80°. At the end of the reaction the thick and somewhat dark solution is cooled and the crystalline lead tetraacetate which separates is collected and washed with acetic acid. The crude product without being dried is dissolved in hot acetic acid and the solution is clarified with Norit, filtered, and cooled. The colorless crystalline product is dried in a vacuum desiccator over potassium hydroxide and stored in the desiccator; yield 320–350 g.

[1] R. Criegee, C. O. Edens, Jr. and B. Graham, "Oxidations with Lead Tetraacetate and Periodic Acid," *Newer Methods of Preparative Organic Chemistry*, p. 1, Interscience (1948).
[2] This is essentially the procedure of O. Dimroth and R. Schweizer, *Ber.*, **56**, 1375 (1923), as modified by R. Hellmuth, Dissertation, Würzburg (1930).

3. Lead tetrabenzoate, $Pb(OCOC_6H_5)_4$. Mol. wt. 691.65. Preparation.[1] Oxidizing agent similar to lead tetraacetate.

[1] R. Criegee, *Ann.*, **481**, 263 (1930); N. Elming and N. S. K. Clauson-Kaas, *Acta chim. Scand.*, **6**, 535 (1952).

4. Lindlar catalyst. A palladium–calcium carbonate catalyst, partially inactivated by treatment with lead acetate, for selective and partial reduction of triple bonds to ethylenes (*cis* addition).[1]

[1] H. Lindlar, *Helv. Chim. Acta*, **35**, 446 (1952).

5. Lithium aluminum hydride, $LiAlH_4$. Mol. wt. 37.95. Supplier: Metal Hydrides, Inc. Reviews.[1] Solvents: ether, dibutyl ether, tetrahydrofuran. The solvent must be tested for the presence of peroxide just before use and freed of peroxide if any is present. A sample of tetrahydrofuran that had been distilled from lithium aluminum hydride and let stand for 2 yrs. over calcium hydride took fire when filtered and treated with lithium aluminum hydride; subsequent tests revealed the presence of considerable peroxide.

[1] v. U. Solms, *Chimia*, **5**, 25 (1951); W. G. Brown, *Org. Reactions*, **6**, 469 (1951).

6. Lithium amide, $LiNH_2$. Mol. wt. 22.96. Preparation and use in aldol-type condensations of esters with carbonyl compounds.[1]

[1] C. R. Hauser and W. H. Puterbaugh, *J. Am. Chem. Soc.*, **75**, 1068 (1953).

7. Lithium chloride. Mol. wt. 42.40. Used in formamide solution for dehydrohalogenation of 4-halo-3-ketosteroids in 60–80% yield.[1]

[1] R. P. Holysz, *J. Am. Chem. Soc.*, **75**, 4432 (1953).

8. Lithium diethyl amide, $LiN(C_2H_5)_2$. Use in the Tiffeneau rearrangement of oxides.[1]

[1] A. C. Cope and B. D. Tiffany, *J. Am. Chem. Soc.*, **73**, 4158 (1951).

9. Lithium–ethanol–liquid ammonia. This combination[1] is a modification of the Birch reduction:[2] $Na–C_2H_5OH–NH_3$; lithium is more reactive than sodium. It is used to reduce phenol ethers to dihydro enol ethers convertible by acid hydrolysis to α,β-unsaturated ketones; for reduction of ketones to alcohols;[3] for reduction of α,β-unsaturated ketones (in the absence of alcohol only the double bond is reduced);[4] for reduction of α,β-unsaturated acids.[5]

[1] A. L. Wilds and N. A. Nelson, *J. Am. Chem. Soc.*, **75**, 5360 (1953).
[2] A. J. Birch, *Quarterly Reviews*, **4**, 69 (1950); see also G. W. Watt, *Chem. Rev.*, **46**, 317 (1950).
[3] F. Sondheimer, O. Mancera, G. Rosenkranz and C. Djerassi, *J. Am. Chem. Soc.*, **75**, 1282 (1953).
[4] E. Schoenewaldt, and others, *ibid.*, **74**, 2696 (1952); F. Sondheimer, and others, *ibid.*, **74**, 2696 (1952); D. H. R. Barton and B. R. Thomas, *J. Chem. Soc.*, 1842 (1953).
[5] G. E. Arth, and others, *J. Am. Chem. Soc.*, **76**, 1715 (1954).

10. Lithium–N-methylaniline. The combination of lithium (or sodium) with an amine, usually N-methylaniline, effects reduction in ether solution of conjugated dienes to olefins:[1]

$$RCH{=}CHCH{=}CHR' + 2Li + 2R_2NH \rightarrow$$
$$RCH_2CH{=}CHCH_2R' + 2R_2NLi$$

REAGENTS

Examples: butadiene → butene-2; naphthalene → 1,4-dihydronaphthalene; naphthalene → Δ^9-octalin (Li and $C_2H_5NH_2$, 52% yield).[2]

[1] K. Ziegler, and others, *Ann.*, **511**, 64 (1934); **528**, 101 (1937); **567**, 1 (1950).
[2] R. A. Benkeser, and others, *J. Am. Chem. Soc.*, **76**, 631 (1954).

11. 2,6-Lutidine-3,5-dicarboxylic hydrazide, $(CH_3)_2C_5HN(CONHNH_2)_2$. Mol. wt. 223.23. Preparation and use for precipitation of progesterone as the 1:1 derivative in over 95% yield; progesterone is recoverable by displacement with benzaldehyde.[1]

[1] L. Velluz and G. Rousseau, *Bull. Soc. Chim.*, **13**, 288 (1946).

1. Magnesium. Atomic wt. 24.32. See Chapter 46. Use in Claisen condensation of acid chlorides with ethyl acetoacetate in synthesis of β-keto esters.[1]

[1] M. Viscontini and N. Merckling, *Helv. Chim. Acta*, **35**, 2280 (1952).

2. Magnesium bromide etherate. Preparation: a mixture of 0.3 g. magnesium dust, 60 ml. of absolute ether, and 30 ml. of benzene is treated with 2.16 g. of mercuric bromide, refluxed for 2 hrs., filtered and the solution used immediately.[1] Used for effecting Tiffeneau rearrangement of oxides.

[1] W. E. Bachmann, J. P. Horwitz and R. J. Warzynski, *J. Am. Chem. Soc.*, **75**, 3268 (1953).

3. Magnesium oxide, MgO. Mol. wt. 40.32. Use as hydrogen chloride acceptor in catalytic dehydrochlorination.[1]

[1] N. Whittaker, *J. Chem. Soc.*, 1565 (1951); 1646 (1953); B. Lythgoe and L. S. Rayner, *ibid.*, 2323 (1951).

4a. Manganese dioxide, active. Mol. wt. 86.93. A selective reagent for oxidation of allylic alcohols.[1] Commercial material is not satisfactory; the reagent should be freshly prepared either from potassium permanganate and sodium sulfite[2] or from potassium permanganate and manganese sulfate.[3]

[1] S. Ball, T. W. Goodwin and R. A. Morton, *Biochem. J.*, **42**, 516 (1948).

[2] M. Viscontini, C. Ebnöther and P. Karrer, *Helv Chim. Acta*, **34**, 1834 (1951).
[3] J. Attenburrow, and others, *J. Chem. Soc.*, 1094 (1952).

4b. Manganese dioxide, ordinary. Mol. wt. 86.93. For oxidation of primary alcohols[1] or amines[2] to the corresponding aldehyde; o-toluidine → toluquinone (steam distillation of acidified mixture).[3]

[1] A. N. Wilson and S. A. Harris, *J. Am. Chem. Soc.*, **73**, 4693 (1951).
[2] D. Heyl, *ibid.*, **70**, 3434 (1948).
[3] T. H. Clark, *Am. Chem. J.*, **14**, 565 (1892).

5. β-Mercaptoethanol, $HOCH_2CH_2SH$. Mol. wt. 78.13, b.p. 155°. For condensing agents for preparation of ethylenehemithioketals, see Ethanedithiol.

6. Mercuric acetate, $Hg(OCOCH_3)_2$. Mol. wt. 318.70. Dehydrogenation of ergosterol to dehydroergosterol[1] (in chloroform–acetic acid at 25° under nitrogen for 24 hrs.). Preparation of ergosterol-D.[2] Hydration of acetylenes.[3] Allylic acetoxylation.[4]

[1] A. Windaus and O. Linsert, *Ann.*, **465**, 148 (1928); W. V. Ruyle, M. Tishler, and others, *J. Am. Chem. Soc.*, **75**, 2604 (1953).
[2] G. Saucy, P. Geistlich, R. Helbling and H. Heusser, *Helv. Chim. Acta*, **37**, 250 (1954).
[3] M. M. Fraser and R. A. Raphael, *J. Chem. Soc.*, 226 (1952).
[4] W. Treibs and H. Bast, *Ann.*, **561**, 165 (1949); W. Treibs, G. Lucius, H. Kögler and H. Breslauer, *ibid.*, **581**, 59 (1953).

7. Mercuric oxide (yellow). Mol. wt. 216.61. (a) Oxidation in nonaqueous solvents, e.g.:[1]

$$(C_6H_5)_2C=NNH_2 \xrightarrow{\text{HgO}} (C_6H_5)_2C\underset{N}{\overset{N}{\diagdown\parallel}}$$

Diphenyldiazomethane

Anhydrous sodium sulfate can be added to absorb the water formed and the oxidation accelerated by addition of a little saturated aqueous potassium hydroxide solution.[2] (b) In combination with iodine, for iodination of thiophene.[3]

[1] H. Staudinger, E. Anthes and F. Pfenninger, *Ber.*, **49**, 1932 (1916).
[2] *Org. Synth., Coll. Vol.*, **2**, 496 (1943).
[3] *Ibid.*, 357 (1943).

REAGENTS

8. Mercuric sulfate. Catalyst[1] for hydration of acetylenes; mercuric oxide is also used.

> [1] J. D. Billimoria, *J. Chem. Soc.*, 2626 (1953).

9. Mercury toluene-*p*-sulfonamide,

$$(C_7H_7SO_2NH)_2Hg.$$

Mol. wt. 541.02. Preparation and use for hydration of an acetylenic linkage.[1]

> [1] M. W. Goldberg, R. Aeschbacher and E. Hardegger, *Helv. Chim. Acta*, **26**, 680 (1943).

10. Metaphosphoric acid,

$$\begin{array}{c} O-PO(OH)-O \\ | \qquad\qquad | \\ PO(OH)-O-PO(OH) \end{array}$$

Preparation by heating orthophosphoric acid until a clear liquid is formed.[1] Use as phosphorylating agent.[2]

> [1] M. Viscontini, G. Bonetti and P. Karrer, *Helv. Chim. Acta*, **32**, 1478 (1949).
> [2] M. Viscontini, C. Ebnöther and P. Karrer, *ibid.*, **34**, 1834, 2198 (1951).

11. Methanephosphonyl dichloride, CH_3POCl_2. Mol. wt. 132.92, m.p. 32°. Preparation.[1] Reacts with 1,2-, 1,3-, and 1,4-glycols to form cyclic esters (cleaved by acid hydrolysis):[2]

$$\begin{array}{c} RCHOH \\ | \\ (CH_2)_n \\ | \\ RCHOH \end{array} \rightarrow \begin{array}{c} RCH-O \\ | \qquad\qquad O \\ (CH_2)_n \qquad \diagdown P \diagup \\ | \qquad\qquad \diagup \diagdown \\ RCH-O \qquad CH_3 \end{array}$$

$$n = 0, 1, 2$$

> [1] A. M. Kinnear and E. A. Perren, *J. Chem. Soc.*, 3437 (1952).
> [2] A. F. McKay, and others, *J. Am. Chem. Soc.*, **74**, 5540 (1952); **76**, 3546 (1954).

12. Methanesulfonic anhydride, $(CH_3SO_2)_2O$. Mol. wt. 174.20, m.p. 70°, b.p. 138°/10 mm. Prepared by heating the acid with thionyl chloride[1] or with phosphorus pentoxide.[2] Sometimes affords a mesyl derivative where mesyl chloride fails;[3] used in Friedel-Crafts synthesis of sulfones and as catalyst for esterification (like trifluoroacetic anhydride).

> [1] L. N. Owen and S. P. Whitelaw, *J. Chem. Soc.*, 3723 (1953).

> [2] L. Field and P. H. Settlage, *J. Am. Chem. Soc.*, **76**, 1222 (1954).
> [3] R. P. Linstead, L. N. Owen and R. F. Webb, *J. Chem. Soc.*, 1225 (1953).

13. Methanesulfonyl chloride (mesyl chloride), CH_3SO_2Cl. Mol. wt. 114.56, b.p. 70°/20 mm., sp. gr. 1.47. Supplier: Eastman. Preparation.[1] Preparation of mesyl derivatives of sugars,[2] phenols,[3] sterols,[4] α-amino acids.[5]

> [1] C. R. Noller and P. J. Hearst, *J. Am. Chem. Soc.*, **70**, 3955 (1948); *Org. Synth.*, **30**, 58 (1950).
> [2] B. Helferich and F. v. Stryk, *Ber.*, **74**, 1794 (1941), and earlier papers.
> [3] B. Helferich and P. Papalambrou, *Ann.*, **551**, 235 (1942).
> [4] R. Jeanlos, D. A. Prins and J. von Euw, *Helv. Chim. Acta*, **30**, 374 (1947); A. Fürst and F. Koller, *ibid.*, **30**, 1454 (1947).
> [5] B. Helferich and R. Mittag, *Ber.*, **71**, 1480 (1938).

14. 3% Methanolic hydrogen chloride. Add 5 ml. of acetyl chloride to 100 ml. of methanol.

15. Methoxyacetylene, $CH_3OC\equiv CH$. Mol. wt. 56.06, b.p. 23°. Converts a carboxylic acid into its anhydride at or below room temperature:[1]

$$2RCO_2H + CH_3OC\equiv CH \rightarrow$$
$$(RCO)_2O + CH_3OCOCH_3$$

> [1] G. Eglinton, E. R. H. Jones, B. L. Shaw and M. C. Whiting, *J. Chem. Soc.*, 1860 (1954).

16. Methylene chloride, CH_2Cl_2. B.p. 40.8, sp. gr. 1.34. Useful solvent for Friedel-Crafts acylations. In this solvent chrysene yields only the 2-acetyl derivative (75% yield), whereas in carbon bisulfide or nitrobenzene it affords 2-, 4-, and 5-acetylchrysene.[1]

> [1] W. Carruthers, *J. Chem. Soc.*, 3486 (1953).

17. N-Methylformanilide, $C_6H_5N(CH_3)CHO$. Mol. wt. 135.16, b.p. 131°/22 mm. Preparation.[1] Formylation of: anthracene,[2] β-naphthol ethyl ether,[2] N,N-dimethylaniline,[3] thiophene.[4]

> [1] *Org. Synth.*, **20**, 66 (1940).
> [2] *Ibid.*, 11 (1940).
> [3] A. Vilsmeier and A. Haack, *Ber.*, **60**, 119 (1927).
> [4] *Org. Synth.*, **31**, 108 (1951).

18. Methyl iodide. Mol. wt. 141.94. (a) For esterification of a carboxylic acid: dissolve

REAGENTS

0.1 mole of acid in methanol, add 15.5 g. of methyl iodide and 14 g. of potassium carbonate and stir overnight.[1] (b) Decker[2] method for monomethylation of primary amines:

$$RNH_2 \xrightarrow{C_6H_5CHO} RN{=}CHC_6H_5 \xrightarrow{CH_3I}$$

$$[RN^+(CH_3){=}CHC_6H_5]I^- \xrightarrow{H_2O}$$

$$[RN^+(CH_3){=}CHC_6H_5]OH^- \rightarrow$$

$$RNHCH_3 \cdot HI + C_6H_5CHO$$

[1] Communication from L. H. Sarett.
[2] H. Decker and P. Becker, *Ann.*, **395**, 362 (1913).

19. Methyl iodide–silver oxide, Purdie's reagent for methylation of sugars.[1] A solution of the sugar in methanol is shaken at 25° with methyl iodide and silver oxide and four further additions are made at 12-hr. intervals with occasional filtration from silver salts.[2]

[1] T. Purdie and J. C. Irvine, *J. Chem. Soc.*, 1021 (1903).
[2] A. S. Anderson, G. R. Barker, J. M. Gulland and M. V. Lock, *ibid.*, 369 (1952).

20. Methyllithium, CH_3Li. Prepared from lithium and methyl iodide. Reduces α-ketols to vic.-glycols.[1]

[1] W. J. Hickinbottom, A. A. Hyatt and M. B. Sparke, *J. Chem. Soc.*, 2533 (1954).

21. Methylmagnesium iodide. For cleavage of phenol ethers.[1]

[1] A. L. Wilds and W. B. McCormack, *J. Am. Chem. Soc.*, **70**, 4127 (1948).

22. Methyl vinyl ether, $CH_3OCH{=}CH_2$. Mol. wt. 58.08, b.p. 80°. Supplier: Monomer-Polymer, Inc. Use in synthesis of lepidine,[1] of dialdehydes.[2]

[1] K. N. Campbell and I. J. Schaffner, *J. Am. Chem. Soc.*, **67**, 86 (1945).
[2] *Org. Synth.*, **34**, 29, 71 (1954).

23. Monoperphthalic acid, $C_6H_4(CO_2H)CO_3H$. Mol. wt. 182.13. Prepared from sodium perborate (92 g.), phthalic anhydride (66 g., from benzene-ligroin), and water (280 ml.);

stir for 2 hrs. at 0°, acidify with 120 ml. of iced 30% sulfuric acid, extract with ethyl acetate or ether.[1] The titer changes but little on storage at 5°. With ether as solvent the course of an oxidation is indicated by separation of phthalic acid. Reacts with an olefinic compound in aqueous solution to give the *trans* glycol directly.[2]

[1] M. A. Stahmann and M. Bergmann, *J. Org. Chem.*, **11**, 589 (1946).
[2] Th. Posternak and H. Friedli, *Helv. Chim. Acta*, **36**, 251 (1953).

24. Monophenylphosphoryl dichloride,

$$C_6H_5OPOCl_2.$$

Mol. wt. 210.99, b.p. 103–106°/9 mm. Preparation.[1] Used in synthesis of α-lecithins[2] and α-cephalins:[3]

$$RCH_2OH + C_6H_5OPOCl_2 \xrightarrow{Py}$$

$$\underset{\underset{O}{\|}}{RCH_2OPCl} \overset{OC_6H_5}{|} \xrightarrow{HOCH_2R'} \underset{\underset{O}{\|}}{RCH_2OPOCH_2R'} \overset{OC_6H_5}{|}$$

$$\xrightarrow{H_2} RCH_2OPOCH_2R' \overset{OH}{|}$$

[1] P. Brigl and H. Müller, *Ber.*, **72**, 2121 (1939); E. Baer and H. C. Stancer, *J. Am. Chem. Soc.*, **75**, 4510 (1953).
[2] E. Baer and M. Kates, *ibid.*, **72**, 942 (1950).
[3] E. Baer, J. Maurukas and M. Russell, *ibid.*, **74**, 152 (1952).

1. Naphthalene-β-sulfonic acid,

$$C_{10}H_7SO_3H \cdot H_2O.$$

Mol. wt. 226.24. Catalyst for dehydration; a mixture of an alcohol with a trace of the acid is slowly distilled.[1]

[1] E. P. Kohler, M. Tishler, H. Potter and H. T. Thompson, *J. Am. Chem. Soc.*, **61**, 1057 (1939); L. N. Owen and G. S. Saharia, *J. Chem. Soc.*, 2582 (1953).

2. α-Naphthylisocyanate, α-$C_{10}H_7N{=}C{=}O$. Mol. wt. 169.18. Characterization of hydroxy compounds by conversion to the α-naphthylurethans: α-$C_{10}H_7NHCO_2R$ (Chapter 41; Group IV, note 5).

REAGENTS

3. Nicotinic acid hydrazide,

$$C_5H_4NCONHNH_2.$$

Mol. wt. 137.14, m.p. 161°. Preparation and use for selective precipitation of Δ^4-androstene-3,6-dione as the sparingly soluble di derivative.[1] Steroid monoketones and progesterone are not precipitated. Androstenedione is recoverable by acid hydrolysis in 90% yield.

[1] L. Velluz and A. Petit, *Bull. Soc. Chim.*, **12**, 951 (1945).

4. Nitric acid, 70–90% HNO_3.

Mol. wt. 63.02, sp. gr. 1.49. Oxidation of benzoin to benzil in acetic acid solution: Chapter 31.2; of 3-nitro-4-nitrosotoluene to 3,4-dinitrotoluene at 25° in 96.5% yield.[1]

[1] E. Borel and H. Deuel, *Helv. Chim. Acta*, **36**, 806 (1953).

5. *p*-Nitrocarbobenzoxy chloride,

$$p\text{-}NO_2C_6H_4CH_2OCOCl.$$

Mol. wt. 215.59, m.p. 34°. Has the advantage over carbobenzoxy chloride of being a solid and hence more easily purified.[1] The nitro group permits detection by spectroscopy.

[1] F. H. Carpenter and D. H. Gish, *J. Am. Chem. Soc.*, **74**, 3818 (1952); **75**, 950 (1953).

6. Nitrogen pentoxide, N_2O_5.

Mol. wt. 108.02, m.p. 30°, b.p. 47°. Preparation of reagent suitable for use in synthesis of nitrate esters: $ROH + N_2O_5 \rightarrow RONO_2 + HONO_2.$[1] The reaction is carried out with a solution of nitrogen pentoxide in chloroform and sodium fluoride is added to precipitate the nitric acid formed as a complex, $NaF \cdot HONO_2$. Used for complete nitration of starches,[1] for preparation of nitrate esters of aldonic acids.[2]

[1] G. V. Caesar and M. Goldfrank, *J. Am. Chem. Soc.*, **68**, 372 (1946).
[2] M. L. Wolfrom and A. Rosenthal, *ibid.*, **75**, 3662 (1953).

7. Nitromethane.

Mol. wt. 61.04, b.p. 101°, sp. gr. 1.31. Example of addition to a carbonyl group.[1]

[1] *Org. Synth.*, **34**, 19 (1954).

8a. *p*-Nitroso-N,N-dimethylaniline,

$$(CH_3)_2NC_6H_4NO.$$

Mol. wt. 150.18, m.p. 86°. The Kröhnke reaction[1] involves reaction of a halogen compound with pyridine to form a pyridinium salt, which is condensed with *p*-nitrosodimethylaniline to form a nitrone; this on acid hydrolysis yields a carbonyl compound:

$$R_2CHCl \rightarrow [R_2CHN^+C_5H_5]Cl^- \rightarrow$$
$$R_2C{=}N^+(O^-)C_6H_4N(CH_3)_2 \rightarrow R_2CO$$

[1] F. Kröhnke, *Ber.*, **71**, 2583 (1938).

8b. *p*-Nitroso-N,N-dimethylaniline hydrochloride.

Mol. wt. 186.65. Preparation and use in synthesis of aldehydes.[1]

[1] *Org. Synth., Coll. Vol.*, **1**, 214 (1941); **2**, 223 (1943).

9. Nitrosyl chloride, NOCl (gas).

Mol. wt. 65.47. Supplier: Solvay Process Co. Preparation.[1] Generation *in situ* by addition of hydrochloric acid to a mixture of the reactant and amyl nitrite dissolved in ethanol or acetic acid.[2] *Uses:* (a) Nitrosyl chloride adds to both liquid and solid alkenes to give crystalline nitroso chloride derivatives of use in characterization and identification.[3] If two comparably substituted double bonds are present, as in *dl*-limonene, addition occurs preferentially to the endocyclic rather than the exocyclic double bond:

$$
\begin{array}{ccc}
& & Cl \\
CH_2C(CH_3){=}CH & & CH_2C(CH_3)CHNO \\
| \quad\quad\quad\quad | & \xrightarrow{NOCl} & | \quad\quad\quad\quad | \\
CH_2CH{-}{-}{-}{-}CH_2 & & CH_2CH{-}{-}{-}CH_2 \\
| & & | \\
CH_3C{=}CH_2 & & CH_3C{=}CH_2 \\
\textit{dl}\text{-Limonene} & & \text{Nitroso chloride}
\end{array}
$$

In this and other instances the chlorine atom appears at the more highly substituted carbon atom. The addition products of tetrasubstituted and of some trisubstituted alkenes are blue. A useful transformation of a nitroso chloride is reaction with a base to give the oxime of an α,β-unsaturated ketone, for example:[4]

REAGENTS

$$CH_2C(CH_3)=CH \quad\quad \overset{Cl}{\underset{|}{CH_2C(CH_3)CHNO}}$$

$$
\begin{array}{ccc}
CH_2C(CH_3){=}CH & & \overset{Cl}{CH_2C(CH_3)CHNO} \\
| & & | \\
CH_2C(CH_3){-}CH_2 & \longrightarrow & CH_2C(CH_3)CH_2 \quad \xrightarrow{\;OH^-\;} \\
| & & | \\
CH_2CH_3 & & CH_2CH_3
\end{array}
$$

$$
\begin{array}{c}
CH{=}C(CH_3)C{=}NOH \\
|\qquad\qquad | \\
CH_2{-}C(CH_3)CH_2 \\
| \\
CH_2CH_3
\end{array}
$$

(b) Nitrosyl chloride deaminates an amide to the acid without disturbance of ester groups.[5] Thus an aldoamide pentaacetate, treated with the reagent in chloroform solution, affords the corresponding aldonic acid pentaacetate:

$$CH_2(OCOCH_3)(CHOCOCH_3)_4CONH_2 \xrightarrow{\;NOCl\;}$$
$$CH_2(OCOCH_3)(CHOCOCH_3)_4CO_2H$$

(c) For N-nitrosation of amines ($R_2NH \rightarrow R_2NNO$) by reaction with nitrosyl chloride in either pyridine [6] or acetic acid.[7] (d) For preparation of alkyl nitrites: $ROH \xrightarrow{\;NOCl\;} RONO$; the method is reported to be superior to reaction of the alcohol with sodium nitrite and sulfuric acid.[8] (d) Reacts with cyclohexane under illumination to form cyclohexanone oxime in 71% yield.[9]

[1] M. L. Wolfrom, M. Konigsberg and D. I. Weisblat, *J. Am. Chem. Soc.*, **61**, 574 (1939); *Inorg. Synth.*, **1**, 55 (1939).
[2] O. Wallach, "Terpene und Campher," 2nd ed., pp. 69–75, Leipzig (1914).
[3] W. A. Tilden and W. A. Shenstone, *J. Chem. Soc.*, **31**, 554 (1877).
[4] R. Pummerer and F. Graser, *Ann.*, **583**, 207 (1953).
[5] M. L. Wolfrom and H. B. Wood, *J. Am. Chem. Soc.*, **73**, 730 (1951).
[6] M. S. Newman and A. Kutner, *ibid.*, **73**, 4199 (1951).
[7] R. Huisgen and J. Reinertshofer, *Ann.*, **575**, 174 (1952).
[8] N. Kornblum and E. P. Oliveto, *J. Am. Chem. Soc.*, **69**, 465 (1947).
[9] M. A. Naylor and A. W. Anderson, *J. Org. Chem.*, **18**, 115 (1953).

10. Nitrous acid–acetic acid. Oxidation of 5,8-dihydro-1,4-naphthohydroquinone to 5,8-dihydro-1,4-naphthoquinone in 91–97% yield by addition of excess sodium nitrite to a hot solution of the hydroquinone in acetic acid.[1]

[1] L. F. Fieser, *J. Am. Chem. Soc.*, **70**, 3165 (1948).

1. Osmium tetroxide. Mol. wt. 254.20. For *cis* hydroxylation of olefins.[1] Reacts in ether or dioxan at room temperature (2–4 days) with separation of the osmic ester, which is converted to the glycol with aqueous-alcoholic sodium sulfite,[2] sodium sulfite and zinc dust,[3] alkaline formaldehyde,[4] or ascorbic acid.[4] The addition is catalyzed by pyridine.[5]

[1] R. Criegee, *Ann.*, **522**, 75 (1936).
[2] A. Butenandt, J. Schmidt-Thomé and H. Paul, *Ber.*, **72**, 1112 (1939).
[3] A. Serini and W. Logemann, *Ber.*, **71**, 1362 (1938); A. Serini, W. Logemann and W. Hildebrand, *ibid.*, **72**, 391 (1939).
[4] H. Reich, M. Sutter and T. Reichstein, *Helv. Chim. Acta*, **23**, 170 (1940).
[5] R. Criegee, B. Marchand, and H. Wannowius, *Ann.*, **550**, 99 (1942).

2. Oxalic acid. Mol. wt. 90.04, m.p. 187°, pK_a 1.46, 4.40. Condensing agent: synthesis of vitamin K_1 hydroquinone.[1] Cleavage of semicarbazones.[2] Dehydration of alcohols.[3] Formation of olefins from amines.[4] Isomerization of a β,γ- to an α,β-unsaturated ketone in ethanol.[5]

[1] L. F. Fieser, *J. Am. Chem. Soc.*, **61**, 3467 (1939).
[2] Y. R. Naves, *Helv. Chim. Acta*, **26**, 1034 (1947).
[3] R. B. Carlin and D. A. Constantine, *J. Am. Chem. Soc.*, **69**, 50 (1947); R. E. Miller and F. F. Nord, *J. Org. Chem.*, **15**, 89 (1950).
[4] H. M. E. Cardwell, *J. Chem. Soc.*, 1056 (1950).
[5] L. F. Fieser, *J. Am. Chem. Soc.*, **75**, 5421 (1953).

3. Oxalyl chloride, $(COCl)_2$. Mol. wt. 126.93, b.p. 62°, sp. gr. 1.50. (a) For conversion of an acid to the acid chloride.[1] With a sensitive acid, pyridine is added as catalyst and the reaction conducted below 15°;[2] sometimes, however, pyridine is harmful.[3] Recommended for conversion of half-esters of the succinic, glutaric, and phthalic acid series to the ester-acid chlorides, where thionyl chloride leads to rearrangements.[4]

(b) Under the influence of light or an organic peroxide, oxalyl chloride reacts with paraffins[5] and olefins[6] to introduce the —COCl group. Examples: cyclohexane → $C_6H_{11}COCl$;[5] $ArCH=CH_2$ → $ArCH=CHCOCl$.[7] Aromatic hydrocarbons of adequate reactivity undergo substitution without catalysis, e.g., anthracene → 9-anthroic acid chloride (67% yield).[8]

[1] R. Adams and L. H. Ulich, *J. Am. Chem. Soc.*, **42**, 599 (1920).
[2] A. L. Wilds and C. H. Shunk, *ibid.*, **70**, 2427 (1948).
[3] F. Reber, A. Lardon and T. Reichstein, *Helv. Chim. Acta*, **37**, 45 (1954).
[4] J. E. H. Hancock and R. P. Linstead, *J. Chem. Soc.*, 3490 (1953).
[5] M. S. Kharasch and H. C. Brown, *J. Am. Chem. Soc.*, **64**, 329 (1942).
[6] M. S. Kharasch, S. S. Kane, and H. C. Brown, *ibid.*, **64**, 333 (1942).
[7] F. Bergmann, and others, *ibid.*, **70**, 1612 (1948).
[8] H. G. Latham, Jr., E. L. May and E. Mosettig, *ibid.*, **70**, 1079 (1948).

4. Oxides of Nitrogen, N_2O_3, NO_2, etc. Preparation of the gas from arsenous oxide and nitric acid and use in the following oxidation:[1]

$$CH_2(COOC_2H_5)_2 \rightarrow CO(COOC_2H_5)_2$$
Ethyl oxomalonate

[1] *Org. Synth., Coll. Vol.*, **1**, 266 (1941).

5. Ozone. Description of generator and procedure.[1]

[1] *Org. Synth.*, **26**, 63 (1946).

1. Palladium catalysts. Palladium on carbon and on barium sulfate.[1] See Lindlar catalyst. Catalyst can be activated for hydrogenolysis ($C_6H_5COCH_3 \rightarrow C_6H_5CH_2CH_3$; $ArCHOH— \rightarrow ArCH_2—$) by addition of perchloric acid[2] or washing with dilute sulfuric acid.[3]

[1] *Org. Synth.*, **26**, 77 (1946).
[2] K. W. Rosenmund and E. Karg, *Ber.*, **75**, 1850 (1942).
[3] K. Kindler, E. Schärfe and P. Henrich, *Ann.*, **565**, 51 (1949).

2. Peracetic acid, crude. Material available from Buffalo Electro-Chemical Co. has the composition: 40% peracetic acid, 5% hydrogen peroxide, 39% acetic acid, 1% sulfuric acid, 13% water. It has been found suitable as a substitute for perbenzoic acid or monoperphthalic acid for effecting the transformation:[1]

$$R_2C=C(OAc)CH_3 \rightarrow R_2C(OH)COCH_3.$$

Oxidation of β-naphthol to *o*-carboxycinnamic acid.[2]

[1] E. P. Oliveto and E. B. Hershberg, *J. Am. Chem. Soc.*, **76**, 5167 (1954).
[2] *Org. Synth.*, **34**, 8 (1954).

3. Perbenzoic acid, $C_6H_5CO_3H$. Mol. wt. 138.12. Suggestions regarding the standard preparatory procedure:[1] recrystallize commercial benzoyl peroxide by dissolving it in the least cold chloroform and adding methanol; cool the solution of sodium methoxide in dry ice–acetone and add it all at once. *Uses:* preparation of oxides; oxidation of cyclic ketones to lactones and noncyclic ketones to esters. Reacts with an olefinic compound in aqueous solution to give the *trans* glycol directly.[2] Oxidation of β-naphthol methyl ether to methyl *o*-carboxycinnamate.[3]

[1] *Org. Synth., Coll. Vol.*, **1**, 431 (1941).
[2] Th. Posternak and H. Friedli, *Helv. Chim. Acta*, **36**, 251 (1953).
[3] H. Fernholz, *Ber.*, **84**, 110 (1951).

4. Perchloric acid. Catalyst for: Thiele reaction (addition of Ac_2O to a quinone),[1] hydrogenation,[2] hydrogenolysis (see Palladium catalysts), acylation,[3] hydrogen peroxide oxidation of α-diketones,[4] enol acetylation[5] (CCl_4 preferred solvent), reaction of an ethylenic compound with N-bromoacetamide in aqueous acetone for conversion to a bromohydrin.[6]

[1] H. Burton and P. F. G. Praill, *J. Chem. Soc.*, 755 (1952).
[2] E. B. Hershberg, and others, *J. Am. Chem. Soc.*, **73**, 1144 (1951).
[3] J. B. Ziegler and A. C. Shabica, *J. Am. Chem. Soc.*, **74**, 4891 (1952); A. Stoll and E. Seebeck, *Helv. Chim. Acta*, **35**, 1942 (1952); S. Pataki, K. Meyer and T. Reichstein, *ibid.*, **36**, 1295 (1953).
[4] J. E. Leffler, *J. Org. Chem.*, **16**, 1785 (1951).
[5] D. H. R. Barton, and others, *J. Chem. Soc.*, 747, 903 (1954).

REAGENTS

[6] J. Fried and E. F. Sabo, *J. Am. Chem. Soc.*, **75**, 2273 (1953); L. B. Barkley, and others, *ibid.*, **76**, 5017 (1954).

5. Periodic acid, $HIO_4 \cdot 2H_2O$ (water soluble). Mol. wt. 227.95, pK_a 1.6. For glycol cleavage [1,2] and hydrolysis of some oxides.[3]

[1] E. L. Jackson, *Org. Reactions*, **2**, 341 (1944).
[2] R. Criegee, C. O. Edens, Jr. and B. Graham, "Oxidations with Lead Tetraacetate and Periodic Acid," *Newer Methods of Preparative Organic Chemistry*, p. 1, Interscience (1948).
[3] L. F. Fieser and S. Rajagopalan, *J. Am. Chem. Soc.*, **71**, 3938 (1949).

6. Phenetole, $C_6H_5OC_2H_5$. Mol. wt. 122.16, b.p. 172°, sp. gr. 0.97. In saponification of difficultly split esters with potassium hydroxide in ethylene glycol,[1] addition of a small amount of phenetole increases the solvent power of the medium and provides a blanket of vapor that excludes oxygen.[2]

[1] C. E. Redemann and H. J. Lucas, *Anal. Chem.*, **9**, 521 (1937).
[2] W. E. Shaefer and W. J. Balling, *ibid.*, **23**, 1126 (1951).

7. *o*-Phenylenediamine, o-$H_2NC_6H_4NH_2$. Mol. wt. 108.14, m.p. 103°. Preparation.[1] Purification and use for characterization of an α-diketone: Chapter 31.2. Characterization of α-keto acids.[2]

[1] *Org. Synth., Coll. Vol.*, **2**, 501 (1943).
[2] D. C. Morrison, *J. Am. Chem. Soc.*, **76**, 4483 (1954).

8. Phenylhydrazine. Mol. wt. 108.14, sp. gr. 1.10. Test solution (Chapter 14.1): 1 ml. reagent and 3 ml. acetic acid diluted to 10 ml. with water; 1 ml. of solution contains 1 millimole of phenylhydrazine acetate. Use in the Gabriel synthesis for cleavage of the phthaloyl protective group.[1] Use as a reducing agent.[2]

[1] I. Schumann and R. A. Boissonnas, *Helv. Chim. Acta*, **35**, 2235 (1952).
[2] H. Bredereck and H. von Schuh, *Ber.*, **81**, 215 (1948).

9. Phenylisocyanate, C_6H_5NCO. Mol. wt. 119.11, b.p. 166°, sp. gr. 1.10. Purification and use as dehydrating agent (catalyzed by ethyl-

magnesium bromide or ferric acetonylacetate); it yields diphenylurea.[1]

[1] W. Oroshnik, G. Karmas and A. D. Mebane, *J. Am. Chem. Soc.*, **74**, 295 (1952).

10. Phenyllithium. See Chapter 46.

11. Phosphoric acid, anhydrous. Mol. wt. 98.00. Phosphorus pentoxide (25 g.) is dissolved in 33 g. of 85% orthophosphoric acid;[1] the reagent is more satisfactory than phosphoryl chloride ($POCl_3$) for phosphorylation of alcohols.[1,2]

[1] R. E. Ferrel, H. S. Olcott and H. Fraenkel-Conrat, *J. Am. Chem. Soc.*, **70**, 2101 (1948).
[2] A. N. Wilson and S. A. Harris, *ibid.*, **73**, 4693 (1951).

12. Phosphoric acid (90%)–formic acid (98%). A 1:3 combination of the acids cyclizes allyl, vinyl, and divinyl ketones to substituted cyclopentenones in 60–75% yield.[1] Used in a convenient synthesis of azulenes.[2]

[1] E. A. Braude and J. A. Coles, *J. Chem. Soc.*, 1430 (1952).
[2] E. A. Braude and W. F. Forbes, *ibid.*, 2208 (1953); A. M. Islam and R. A. Raphael, *ibid.*, 2247 (1953).

13. Phosphorus diiodide, P_2I_4. Mol. wt. 569.59, m.p. 124.5°. For dehydration of polyene glycols.[1] Preparation.[2]

[1] R. Kuhn and K. Wallenfels, *Ber.*, **71**, 1889 (1938); F. Bohlmann, *ibid.*, **85**, 386 (1952).
[2] F. E. E. Germann and R. N. Traxler, *J. Am. Chem. Soc.*, **49**, 307 (1927).

14. Phosphorus heptasulfide, P_4S_7. Mol. wt. 348.36. Supplier: Oldbury Electrochemical Co. Use in synthesis of 3-methylthiophene.[1]

[1] *Org. Synth.*, **34**, 73 (1954).

15. Phosphorus trichloride. Mol. wt. 137.35, b.p. 76°, sp. gr. 1.57. Use in peptide synthesis:[1]

$$2C_2H_5OCOCH(R)NH_2 +$$
$$2HO_2CCH(R'')NHCOC_6H_5 + PCl_3 \rightarrow$$
$$2C_2H_5OCOCH(R)NHCOCH(R')NHCOC_6H_5$$
$$+ HPO_2 + 3HCl.$$

The components are mixed in benzene or benzene–dioxan and the solution let stand 24 hrs. at room temperature.

[1] O. Süs, *Ann.*, **572**, 96 (1951).

REAGENTS

16. Phosphoryl chloride, $POCl_3$. Mol. wt. 153.35, b.p. 107°, sp. gr. 1.67. Treatment of riboflavin with the reagent in moist pyridine yields cyclic riboflavin-4',5'-hydrogen phosphate, which on acid hydrolysis yields riboflavin-5'-phosphate.[1] Pantetheine on similar treatment yields the cyclic 2',4'-hydrogen phosphate.[2]

[1] H. S. Forrest and A. R. Todd, *J. Chem. Soc.*, 3295 (1950).
[2] J. Baddiley and E. M. Thain, *ibid.*, 903 (1953).

17. Phthalic anhydride. Mol. wt. 148.11, m.p. 131°. Used, with benzenesulfonic acid as catalyst, for dehydration of alcohols.[1]

[1] H. Waldmann and F. Petrů, *Ber.*, **83**, 287 (1950).

18. Phthaloyl chloride, $C_6H_4(COCl)_2$. Mol. wt. 203.03, b.p. 281°, sp. gr. 1.41. Supplier: Eastman. Preparation.[1] Used for preparation of acid chlorides.[2]

[1] *Org. Synth., Coll. Vol.*, **2**, 528 (1943).
[2] L. P. Kyrides, *J. Am. Chem. Soc.*, **59**, 206 (1937); W. A. Van Dorp and G. C. A. Van Dorp, *Rec. trav. chim.*, **25**, 96 (1906).

19. Picric acid. Mol. wt. 229.10, m.p. 122.5°. Naphthalene complex (Chapter 6.3); amine salt (Chapter 20.3c).

20. Piperidine. Mol. wt. 85.15, b.p. 106°, sp. gr. 0.86, pK_b 2.9.

21. Piperylene, $CH_3CH=CHCH=CH_2$. Mol. wt. 68.11, b.p. 44°. Can be prepared by dehydration (Al_2O_3) of the carbinol resulting from addition of methylmagnesium chloride to crotonaldehyde (84%).

22. Platinum catalyst. Preparation.[1] Apparatus for catalytic hydrogenation.[2] See also Heyn's catalyst.

[1] *Org. Synth., Coll. Vol.*, **1**, 463 (1941).
[2] *Ibid.*, 61 (1941).

23. Polyphosphoric acid. Supplier: Victor Chemical Works. The reagent, readily prepared from phosphoric acid and phosphorus pentoxide, is generally useful for cyclodehydrations and is often effective where liquid hydrogen fluoride fails.[1] Used also as catalyst in the Friedel-Crafts ketone synthesis,[2] in

preparation of phenyl esters;[3] for acylation of amines, hydrolysis of nitriles to amides, Beckmann rearrangement.[4] Some aromatic acids are converted to amines by reaction with hydroxylamine and polyphosphoric acid at 160°.[4]

[1] A. J. Birch, R. Jaeger and R. Robinson, *J. Chem. Soc.*, 582 (1945); R. C. Gilmore and W. J. Horton, *J. Am. Chem. Soc.*, **73**, 1411 (1951); R. C. Gilmore, *ibid.*, **73**, 5879 (1951); H. R. Snyder and F. X. Werber, *ibid.*, **72**, 2965 (1950); J. Koo, *ibid.*, **73**, 1889 (1953); C. D. Hurd and S. Hayao, *ibid.*, **76**, 5065 (1954); A. J. Birch and H. Smith, *J. Chem. Soc.*, 1882 (1951).
[2] P. D. Gardner, *J. Am. Chem. Soc.*, **76**, 4550 (1954).
[3] A. R. Bader and A. D. Kontowicz, *ibid.*, **75**, 5416 (1953).
[4] H. R. Snyder, and others, *J. Am. Chem. Soc.*, **75**, 2014 (1953); **76**, 3039 (1954); E. C. Horning, V. L. Stromberg and H. A. Lloyd, *ibid.*, **74**, 5153 (1952).

24. Potassium. Atomic wt. 39.10, m.p. 62.3°. Directions for handling.[1]

[1] W. S. Johnson and G. H. Daub, *Org. Reactions*, **6**, 42 (1951).

25. Potassium amide, KNH_2. Mol. wt. 55.13. Used in liquid ammonia for dehydrobromination of alkyl halides that tend to rearrange in the presence of acidic reagents,[1] and for rearrangement of benzyl ethers to carbinols:

$$C_6H_5CH_2OR \rightarrow C_6H_5CHOHR.[2]$$

[1] C. R. Hauser, P. S. Skell, R. D. Bright and W. B. Renfrow, *J. Am. Chem. Soc.*, **69**, 589 (1947).
[2] C. R. Hauser and S. W. Kantor, *ibid.*, **73**, 1437 (1951); A. J. Weinheimer, S. W. Kantor and C. R. Hauser, *J. Org. Chem.*, **18**, 801 (1953).

26. Potassium bisulfate, $KHSO_4$. Mol. wt. 136.17. For selective dehydration.

(a[1]) $\underset{\underset{OH}{|}}{C_4H_9CH_2C(CH_3)}C\equiv C(CH_2)_2OH \rightarrow$

$C_4H_9CH=C(CH_3)C\equiv C(CH_2)_2OH$

(b[2])

$\underset{\underset{CH_2CH_2}{|}}{CH_2C(CH_3)_2}\overset{\overset{OH}{|}}{C}-\underset{\underset{CHCH_3}{|}}{CH}=CHC\overset{\overset{CH_3}{|}}{\underset{\underset{OH}{|}}{C}}H_2OCH_3 \rightarrow$

$\underset{\underset{CH_2CH_2}{|}}{CH_2C(CH_3)_2}C=CHCH=\overset{\overset{CH_3}{|}}{C}CHO$
$\underset{CHCH_3}{|}$

REAGENTS

Catalyst for condensation of an allylic alcohol with a phenol.[3]

[1] C. L. Leese and R. A. Raphael, *J. Chem. Soc.*, 2725 (1950).

[2] H. H. Inhoffen, H. Siemer and K.-D. Möhle, *Ann.*, **585**, 126 (1954).

[3] R. Hirschmann, R. Miller and N. L. Wendler, *J. Am. Chem. Soc.*, **76**, 4592 (1954).

27. Potassium borohydride, KBH₄. Mol. wt. 97.96. Supplier: Metal Hydrides, Inc.

28. Potassium *t*-butoxide, (CH₃)₃COK. Mol. wt. 112.21. **Preparation.**[1] An effective reagent for glycidic ester condensation,[2] Dieckmann[3] and Stobbe[1] condensations. Useful for control of the direction of elimination of HX from alkyl halides; gives predominantly the 1-olefin where sodium ethoxide results largely in the 2-olefin.[4] A diaryl ketone is cleaved to ArH + Ar′CO₂H by refluxing an ether solution containing 1 mole of water and 3 moles of reagent.[5] Most satisfactory reagent for dehydrobromination of α-bromo carboxylic acids (in *t*-butyl alcohol) to Δ²-alkenoic acids.[6] Potassium hydroxide in methanol, ethanol, or propanol gave mixtures of Δ²- and Δ³-isomers.

[1] W. S. Johnson and G. H. Daub, *Org. Reactions*, **6**, 1 (1951).

[2] W. S. Johnson, J. S. Belew, L. J. Chinn and R. H. Hunt, *J. Am. Chem. Soc.*, **75**, 4995 (1953); *Org. Synth.*, **34**, 54 (1954).

[3] W. S. Johnson, and others, *J. Am. Chem. Soc.*, **75**, 2275 (1953).

[4] H. C. Brown and I. Moritani, *ibid.*, **75**, 4112 (1953).

[5] G. A. Swan, *J. Chem. Soc.*, 1408 (1948); A. W. Schrecker and J. L. Hartwell, *J. Am. Chem. Soc.*, **75**, 5924 (1953).

[6] J. Cason, N. L. Allinger and G. Sumrell, *J. Org. Chem.*, **18**, 850 (1953).

29. Potassium ferricyanide. Mol. wt. 329.26. A mild oxidizing agent that sometimes attacks a side chain (slowly) without affecting the aromatic ring:[1]

Oxidizes *o*-aminophenols to 3-aminophenoxazones.[2]

[1] R. Weissgerber and O. Kruber, *Ber.*, **52**, 352 (1919); L. Ruzicka and co-workers, *Helv. Chim. Acta*, **9**, 976 (1926); **14**, 238 (1931).

[2] A. Butenandt, U. Schiedt and E. Biekert, *Ann.*, **588**, 106 (1954).

30. Potassium hydrosulfide, KSH. Preparation in alcoholic solution and use for reaction with alkyl bromides to form alkylmercaptans.[1]

[1] H. Zinner, *Ber.*, **86**, 825 (1953).

31. Potassium hydroxide. Mol. wt. 56.10, m.p. 380°. The pellets contain about 85% KOH.

32. Potassium hydroxide–acetone. For dechlorination;[1] an acetone solution of the substance is treated either with pellets of potassium hydroxide or with a $2 N$ alcoholic solution of the base. Example (90% yield):

$$CCl_2=CClCCl_2CCl_2CCl=CCl_2 \rightarrow$$
$$CCl_2=CClCCl=CClCCl=CCl_2$$

[1] A. Roedig, G. Voss and E. Kuchinke, *Ann.*, **580**, 24 (1953).

33. Potassium nitrosodisulfonate, NO(SO₃K)₂. Mol. wt. 268.33. **Preparation.**[1] This reagent (Fremy's salt) has the remarkable ability of oxidizing phenols to *o*-quinones in high yield.[2]

[1] H.-J. Teuber and G. Jellink, *Ber.*, **85**, 95 (1952).

[2] H.-J. Teuber and W. Rau, *ibid.*, **86**, 1036 (1953); H.-J. Teuber and N. Götz, *ibid.*, **87**, 1236 (1954).

34. Potassium permanganate. Mol. wt. 158.05. Oxygen equivalents per mole: 1.5. (a) *Alkaline oxidation:* cyclohexanone → adipic acid (Chapter 16.2); mandelic acid → phenylglyoxylic acid (Chapter 36.3). (b) *Acid oxidation:* mandelic acid → benzoic acid (Chapter 36.1). (c) Permanganate oxidation of an alkene *in dry acetone* gives a cyclic manganate ester which on hydrolysis yields a *cis* glycol. Example:[1] A solution of 90 g. (0.226 mole) of Δ¹⁷-20-cyanopregnene-21-ol-3, 11-dione acetate in 2.9 l. of acetone is stirred at −5°, treated with 108 ml. piperidine and 86.3 g. (0.545 mole) potassium permanganate, stirred 30 min., and treated below 2° with 18 ml. of acetic acid in 225 ml. acetone. After 4 hrs. at 0–2°, 1.8 l. of chloroform is

REAGENTS

added (2–3°), followed by 270 ml. of concd. hydrochloric acid in 1350 ml. water and 126 g. of sodium bisulfite in 900 ml. water. Extraction with chloroform and crystallization gave pure pregnane-17α,21-diol-3,11,20-trione 21-acetate in 98.4% yield. (d) Permanganate *in pyridine* has been employed for the quantitative determination of the oxygen equivalent of unsaturated substances and in degradative studies.[2] (e) Permanganate *in carefully buffered solutions* (pH 7) oxidizes —C≡C— to —COCO—.[3] (f) Neutral oxidation *in a hot mixture of methylcyclohexane and water*.[4] (g) *In acetic acid solution, oxides as well as diols (or α-ketols) are obtained from olefins.*[5]

[1] Communicated by Max Tishler. For other examples, see H. S. Boyd-Barrett and R. Robinson, *J. Chem. Soc.*, 319 (1932); Hs. H. Günthard, S. D. Heinemann and V. Prelog, *Helv. Chim. Acta*, **36**, 1147 (1953).
[2] J. H. C. Smith and H. A. Spoehr, *J. Biol. Chem.*, **86**, 87 (1930); J. E. Bucher, *J. Am. Chem. Soc.*, **32**, 374 (1910).
[3] N. A. Khan and M. S. Newman, *J. Org. Chem.*, **17**, 1063 (1952).
[4] M. Fieser, and others, *J. Am. Chem. Soc.*, **75**, 4066 (1953).
[5] M. Ehrenstein and M. T. Decker, *J. Org. Chem.*, **5**, 544 (1940).

35. Potassium persulfate, $K_2S_2O_8$. Mol. wt. 270.33. See also Caro's acid. Used in oxidation of phenols to dihydric phenols (Elbs oxidation [1]), e.g., salicylaldehyde to gentisaldehyde:[2]

Gentisaldehyde

Potassium persulfate oxidizes arylamines in aqueous alkali, with addition of acetone if required, to o-hydroxy sulfate esters, isolated by extraction with butanol.[3] Thus

$$(CH_3)_2NC_6H_5 \rightarrow o\text{-}(CH_3)_2NC_6H_4OSO_3K.$$

[1] K. Elbs, *J. prakt. Chem.*, **48**, 179 (1893).
[2] O. Neubauer and L. Flatow, *Z. physiol. Chem.*, **52**, 380 (1907); R. U. Schock and D. L. Tabern, *J. Org. Chem.*, **16**, 1772 (1951); see also W. Baker and N. C. Brown, *J. Chem. Soc.*, 2303 (1948).
[3] E. Boyland, D. Manson and P. Sims, *J. Chem. Soc.*, 3623 (1953).

36. Potassium thiocyanate. Mol. wt. 97.18. Reacts with alkyl halides, dialkyl sulfates,[1] and tosylates [2] to form the thiocyano derivatives, which can be desulfurized with Raney nickel:[3]

$$RX(ROTs) \rightarrow RSCN \rightarrow RH.$$

Used for conversion of cyclohexene oxide to cyclohexene sulfide.

[1] P. Walden, *Ber.*, **40**, 3214 (1907).
[2] R. M. Hann, N. K. Richtmeyer, H. W. Diehl and C. S. Hudson, *J. Am. Chem. Soc.*, **72**, 561 (1950).
[3] H. R. Snyder, J. M. Stewart and J. B. Ziegler, *ibid.*, **69**, 2672 (1947); *Org. Synth.*, **32**, 39 (1952).

37. Potassium thiolacetate, CH_3COSK. Mol. wt. 114.21. Preparation.[1] Reacts with a tosylate to form a thiolacetate, which can be hydrolyzed to a thiol:

$$ROTs \rightarrow RSCOCH_3 \rightarrow RSH.[2]$$

[1] C. Ulrich, *Ann.*, **109**, 272 (1859).
[2] J. H. Chapman and L. N. Owen, *J. Chem. Soc.*, 579 (1950).

38. Propane-1,3-dithiol, $HSCH_2CH_2CH_2SH$. Mol. wt. 108.23, b.p. 152°. Preparation.[1] Better yields of thioketals are obtained with this reagent than with the frequently used ethanedithiol.[2] Supplier: Aldrich Chemical Co.

[1] W. Autenrieth and K. Wolff, *Ber.*, **32**, 1368 (1899).
[2] H. Hauptmann and M. M. Campos, *J. Am. Chem. Soc.*, **72**, 1405 (1950); S. Archer, and others, *ibid.*, **76**, 4915 (1954).

39. β-Propiolactone,

REAGENTS

Mol. wt. 72.06, b.p. 51°/10 mm., sp. gr. 1.15. Made by B. F. Goodrich Chemical Co. by reaction of ketene with formaldehyde. For many reactions and uses see papers cited.[1] Use in Michael condensation.[2]

[1] T. L. Gresham, J. E. Jansen, F. W. Shaver and others (Papers I and XIII), *J. Am. Chem. Soc.*, **70**, 999 (1948); *ibid.*, **74**, 1323 (1952).
[2] L. B. Barkley, and others, *ibid.*, **76**, 5014 (1954).

40. Pyridine. Mol. wt. 79.10, b.p. 115°, sp. gr. 0.98, pK_b 8.8. See Solvents.

41. Pyridine hydrochloride. Mol. wt. 115.56, m.p. 144°, b.p. 218°. Preparation: hydrogen chloride is passed into a weighed flask containing pyridine through a tube extending above the surface of the liquid until 1 equivalent is absorbed. The solid is crystallized from chloroform–ethyl acetate and washed with ether.[1] For cleavage of phenol ethers:[1]

$$C_6H_5OCH_3 + 5Py \cdot HCl \rightarrow C_6H_5OH + 4Py \cdot HCl + Py \cdot CH_3Cl$$

Example: anisole is heated with 3 parts of the reagent for 5–6 hrs. at 200°. *Methoxyl determination* by determination of amount of reagent consumed (titration).[2]

[1] V. Prey, *Ber.*, **75**, 445 (1942).
[2] *Ibid.*, **74**, 1219 (1941); **75**, 350 (1942).

42. Pyridine perbromide, $C_5H_5NBr_2$. Mol. wt. 238.93. Preparation: mix carbon tetrachloride solutions of equivalent amounts of pyridine and bromine, collect, wash and dry the red precipitate.[1] The reagent neutralizes hydrogen bromide as it is formed. It served for bromination of a sensitive acetal where other methods failed.[1]

[1] S. M. McElvain and L. R. Morris, *J. Am. Chem. Soc.*, **73**, 206 (1951).

43. Pyridine–sulfur trioxide, $C_5H_5N \cdot SO_3$. Mol. wt. 159.16, m.p. 175°. Preparation: (a) Pyridine (1 mole) is slowly dropped into a cooled and stirred mixture of crushed sulfur trioxide (1 mole) and carbon tetrachloride (4 parts) and the product is collected and washed with a little ice water to remove a trace of pyridinium sulfate. (b) Chlorosulfonic acid

(0.5 mole) is dropped into a cooled and stirred solution of pyridine (1 mole) in carbon tetrachloride; the product is washed with ice water to remove pyridine hydrochloride, the second reaction product. The reagent is stable to heat and to cold water; it reacts with warm water.[1]

Uses: as a sulfonating agent,[2] preparation of carbohydrate sulfate esters,[3] sterol sulfate esters,[4] phenol sulfate esters.[5] Comparison of the stability of sulfate esters of primary, secondary, and tertiary alcohols.[6]

[1] P. Baumgarten, *Ber.*, **59**, 1166 (1926).
[2] *Ibid.*, 1976 (1926).
[3] R. B. Duff, *J. Chem. Soc.*, 1597 (1949).
[4] A. E. Sobel, I. J. Drekter and S. Natelson, *J. Biol. Chem.*, **115**, 381 (1936); A. E. Sobel and P. E. Spoerri, *J. Am. Chem. Soc.*, **63**, 1259 (1941); **64**, 361 (1942).
[5] G. N. Burkhardt and A. Lapworth, *J. Chem. Soc.*, 684 (1926).
[6] L. F. Fieser, *J. Am. Chem. Soc.*, **70**, 3232 (1948).

44. Pyridinium bromide perbromide. Mol. wt. 319.87. Preparation and supplier: Chapter 10.5. Examples of use, Chapter 10.5, 23 (V), 31.6.

45. Pyrrolidine. Mol. wt. 71.12, b.p. 88°, sp. gr. 0.87. Condenses with ninhydrin[1] as proline does to give the same product, Proline Yellow (Chapter 24.0). Reacts with steroidal ketones in boiling benzene, sometimes with addition of a catalytic amount of *p*-toluenesulfonic acid, to form N-pyrrolidyl enamines:[2]

$$CH_2CH_2CH_2CH_2NH + O{=}CCH_2{-} \rightarrow$$
$$CH_2CH_2CH_2CH_2N{-}C{=}CH{-}$$

Polyketones react preferentially at the 3-position. The protective group is not attacked by lithium aluminum hydride and can be removed by brief boiling with ethanol or with an acetic acid–sodium acetate buffer in aqueous methanol. Use of pyrrolidine enamines in a synthesis of 2-alkyl and 2-acyl ketones.[3]

[1] W. Grassmann and K. v. Arnim, *Ann.*, **509**, 288 (1934).

REAGENTS

[2] F. W. Heyl and M. E. Herr, *J. Am. Chem. Soc.*, **75**, 1918 (1953); M. E. Herr and F. W. Heyl, *ibid.*, **75**, 5927 (1953).

[3] G. Stork, R. Terrell and J. Szmuszkovicz, *J. Am. Chem. Soc.*, **76**, 2029 (1954).

46. Pyruvic acid, GH_3COCO_2H. Mol. wt. 88.06, b.p. 165°, sp. gr. 1.27. For regeneration of ketones from their semicarbazones, phenyl-hydrazones, or oximes by exchange reaction.[1] Technical pyruvic acid is distilled at 5–10 mm. and stored as a 50% solution in water (does not discolor on standing). The ketone derivative is heated with aqueous pyruvic acid and sodium acetate in acetic acid and the hot solution is diluted slowly until the ketone has crystallized.

[1] E. B. Hershberg, *J. Org. Chem.*, **13**, 542 (1948).

1. Raney alloy (nickel–aluminum). For reduction of cinnamic acids in alkaline solution.[1]

[1] E. Schwenk, D. Papa, B. Whitman and H. F. Ginsberg, *J. Org. Chem.*, **9**, 175 (1944); *Org. Synth.*, **34**, 8 (1954).

2. Raney nickel. Suppliers of sponge nickel (about 50%): Davidson Chemical Corp.; Raney Catalyst Co. Preparation of most active form, W-6 RN;[1] preparation of less active forms.[2] The activity is enhanced by addition of small amounts of triethylamine chloroplatinate.[3] Hydrogenolysis of sulfur compounds.[4] Desulfurization of thiophene derivatives.[5] In desulfurization of ethylene-thioketals, Raney nickel sometimes effects reduction of the ketone liberated; a preventive measure is to deactivate the catalyst by refluxing with acetone.[6] Raney nickel suspended in aqueous alkali reduces —CO— to —CHOH— and ArCO— to ArCH$_2$—.[7] Raney nickel deactivated with piperidine and zinc acetate is suitable for semihydrogenation of the acetylenic linkage.[8] Reduction of 1-(nitromethyl)-cyclohexanol to the amine with W-4 catalyst.[9] In the presence of a hydrogen acceptor (cyclohexanone), Raney nickel catalyzes dehydrogenation of secondary alcohols (cholesterol → cholestenone in 80% yield); in the presence of a hydrogen donor (cyclohexanol, diethylcarbinol) it cat-

alyzes reduction of carbonyl groups and activated double or triple bonds (cholestanone → cholestanol, 50% yield; stilbene → dibenzyl, 60% yield).[10]

[1] H. Adkins and H. R. Billica, *J. Am. Chem. Soc.*, **70**, 695 (1948); *Org. Synth.*, **29**, 24 (1949).

[2] H. Adkins and A. A. Pavlic, *J. Am. Chem. Soc.*, **69**, 3039 (1947).

[3] D. R. Levering and E. Lieber, *ibid.*, **71**, 1515 (1949).

[4] R. Mozingo, D. E. Wolf, S. A. Harris and K. Folkers, *ibid.*, **65**, 1013 (1943).

[5] G. M. Badger, H. J. Rodda and W. H. F. Sasse, *Chem. Ind.*, 308 (1954).

[6] G. B. Spero, A. V. McIntosh, Jr., and R. H. Levin, *J. Am. Chem. Soc.*, **70**, 1907 (1948); G. Rosenkranz, St. Kaufmann and J. Romo, *ibid.*, **71**, 3689 (1949); L. B. Barkley, and others, *ibid.*, **76**, 5017 (1954).

[7] D. Papa, E. Schwenk and B. Whitman, *J. Org. Chem.*, **7**, 587 (1942).

[8] W. Oroshnik, G. Karmas and A. D. Mebane, *J. Am. Chem. Soc.*, **74**, 295 (1952).

[9] *Org. Synth.*, **34**, 19 (1954).

[10] E. C. Kleiderer and E. C. Kornfeld, *J. Org. Chem.*, **13**, 455 (1948).

3. Reinecke salt, $NH_4[Cr(NH_3)_2(SCN)_4] \cdot 2H_2O$. Mol. wt. 372.48. Preparation.[1] Forms sparingly soluble complexes with some amino acids.

[1] *Org. Synth., Coll. Vol.*, **2**, 555 (1943).

4. Resolving agents. Survey of methods, list of reagents, and procedures for preparation.[1]

[1] L. Velluz, *Substances Naturelles de Synthèse*, **9**, 119–174 (1954).

5. Ruthenium hydrogenation catalyst. Supplier: Baker and Co., Astor St., Newark, N.J. Very active at both high and low temperatures. Useful for avoiding hydrogenolysis.

6. Ruthenium tetroxide, RuO_4. Mol. wt. 165.70. Oxidizing agent similar to osmium tetroxide, but more reactive.[1] Suitable solvents: CCl_4 and $CHCl_3$. Not poisonous, but vapor is irritating.

[1] C. Djerassi and R. R. Engle, *J. Am. Chem. Soc.*, **75**, 3838 (1953).

1. Selenium dioxide and selenious acid.[1] Mol. wt. 110.96, 128.98. Suppliers: Fairmount Chemical Co. (SeO$_2$), Fisher Chemical Co. (H$_2$SeO$_3$, smells of nitric acid). An effective expedient for removal of traces of colloidal selenium from a reaction mixture is chromatography on a column of alumina provided with a layer of commercial precipitated silver.[2]

[1] N. Rabjohn, "Selenium Dioxide Oxidation," *Org. Reactions*, **5**, 331 (1949); G. R. Waitkins and C. W. Clark, *Chem. Rev.*, **36**, 235 (1945); W. A. Waters, in H. Gilman's "Organic Chemistry," IV, 1225 (1953).

[2] L. F. Fieser and G. Ourisson, *J. Am. Chem. Soc.*, **75**, 4404 (1953).

2. Semicarbazide hydrochloride. Mol. wt. 111.54. Stock solution (Chapter 14.3): 1.11 g. of hydrochloride in 5 ml. of water. To 0.5 ml. of solution add 1 millimole of carbonyl compound and enough methanol to give a clear solution, then add 10 micro drops of pyridine.

Silver benzoate–iodine complex. See Iodosilver benzoate.

3. Silver chlorate, $AgClO_3$. Mol. wt. 191.34, m.p. 230°, 10 g. dissolves in 100 g. $H_2O^{15°}$. Used in aqueous solution at room temperature in the presence of osmium tetroxide catalyst for oxidation of olefins to *cis* glycols; silver chloride precipitates.[1] Other chlorates give mixtures of the glycol and chlorohydrin.[2]

[1] G. Braun, *J. Am. Chem. Soc.*, **51**, 228 (1929).

[2] Th. Posternak and H. Friedli, *Helv. Chim. Acta*, **36**, 251 (1953).

4. Silver diphenyl phosphate, $(C_6H_5O)_2OPOAg$. Mol. wt. 357.05. Preparation.[1] Use as phosphorylating agent.[2]

[1] T. Posternak, *J. Biol. Chem.*, **180**, 1269 (1949).

[2] T. Posternak, *J. Am. Chem. Soc.*, **72**, 4824 (1950).

5. Silver nitrite, $AgNO_2$. Mol. wt. 153.89. Reacts with primary alkyl halides to form primary nitroparaffins.[1]

[1] V. Meyer and O. Stuber, *Ber.*, **5**, 203 (1872); N. Kornblum, B. Taub and H. E. Ungnade, *J. Am. Chem. Soc.*, **76**, 3209 (1954); C. W. Plummer and N. L. Drake, *ibid.*, **76**, 2720 (1954).

6. Silver oxide, Ag_2O. Mol. wt. 231.76. Preparation: of anhydrous material suitable for oxidation of catechol to *o*-benzoquinone;[1]

of material for oxidation of sugars;[2] of reagent for oxidation of aldehydes to carboxylic acids;[3] of material suitable for dehydrobromination.[4] Oxidation of vitamin K_1 hydroquinone (Chapter 38.4). Oxidation of diaryl ketone hydrazones to diaryldiazomethanes.[5] Used with pyridine for conversion of halohydrins to oxides.[6]

[1] R. Willstätter and A. Pfannenstiel, *Ber.*, **37**, 4744 (1904).

[2] K. G. A. Busch, and others, *J. Org. Chem.*, **1**, 1 (1936).

[3] *Org. Synth.*, **33**, 94 (1953).

[4] U. Steiner and H. Schinz, *Helv. Chim. Acta*, **34**, 1176 (1951).

[5] W. Schroeder and L. Katz, *J. Org. Chem.*, **19**, 718 (1954).

[6] J. Schmidlin and A. Wettstein, *Helv. Chim. Acta*, **36**, 1241 (1953).

7. Sodium. Atomic wt. 23.00. See article: "Useful Hints for Sodium Handling in the Laboratory."[1]

[1] A. S. Hawkes, E. F. Hill and M. Sittig, *J. Chem. Ed.*, **30**, 467 (1953).

8. Sodium aluminum chloride. Condensations and dehydrations requiring rather drastic conditions can be accomplished effectively with fusible mixtures of sodium chloride and aluminum chloride. A procedure employed for cyclodehydration of γ-keto acids,[1] for conducting the Scholl condensation of a *peri*-aroylnaphthalene to a benzanthrone,[2] for synthesis of naphthazarin by condensation of hydroquinone with maleic anhydride,[3] and for Fries rearrangement[4] consists in heating a mixture of 1 part of sodium chloride with 5 parts of aluminum chloride over a free flame until molten, allowing the melt to cool until it begins to solidify (about 100°), adding the substance or substances to be condensed, and heating the mixture in an oil bath with occasional stirring at the desired temperature (120–180°). A preformed reagent of the composition $NaCl \cdot AlCl_3$ can be employed for dehydration of amides.[5] One part of sodium chloride and 2.28 parts (1 equiv.) of aluminum chloride are heated in a flask at 230–250° for 1 hr. and the melt is poured into a beaker and stirred to a meal as it solidifies;

REAGENTS

the solid is kept in a well-stoppered bottle and powdered before use. An aromatic or aliphatic amide is heated cautiously with 0.03–0.20 mole of sodium aluminum chloride over a free flame until the evolution of hydrogen chloride nearly ceases and the nitrile is then distilled from the charred residue (60–90% yields).

¹ I. G. Farbenind., English Patent 303,375 (1930); French Patent 636,065 (1928); Swiss Patent 131,959 (1929); H. Gruene, U. S. Patent 1,759,111 (1930); L. F. Fieser, *J. Am. Chem. Soc.*, **53**, 3546 (1931); L. F. Fieser and M. Peters, *ibid.*, **54**, 3742, 4347 (1932); L. F. Fieser and M. Fieser, *ibid.*, **55**, 3342 (1933).
² L. F. Fieser and E. B. Hershberg, *J. Am. Chem. Soc.*, **60**, 1658 (1938).
³ K. Zahn and P. Ochwat, *Ann.*, **462**, 81 (1928).
⁴ D. B. Bruce, and others, *J. Chem. Soc.*, 2403 (1953).
⁵ J. F. Norris and A. J. Klemka, *J. Am. Chem. Soc.*, **62**, 1432 (1940).

9. Sodium amalgam. A 1.2% amalgam is semi-solid at room temperature and melts completely at 50°; amalgams of higher concentration are solids which can be pulverized. Preparation of 2% amalgam.[1]

Sodium (6.9 g., 0.3 mole) is placed in a 250-ml. round-bottomed three-necked flask fitted with nitrogen inlet and outlet tubes in the side openings and a dropping funnel in the center opening. The flask is flushed out with nitrogen and the funnel charged with 340 g. of mercury. About 10 ml. of mercury is added and the flask is warmed slightly with a free flame until the reaction starts. Once this point is reached little further heating is required, for the reaction can be kept in progress by slow addition of mercury until the total amount has been added. At the end, the still hot, molten amalgam is poured onto a piece of Transite board. While it is still warm and soft, the silvery amalgam is crushed in a mortar and transferred to a tightly stoppered bottle.

The method is equally applicable to the preparation of 3% amalgam. In this case the mixture begins to solidify when about half of the mercury has been added, and the mixture is then kept molten by external heating, with occasional shaking.

Reduction of oximes to primary amines.[2] Reductive detosylation.[3] Reduction of aldonolactones to aldoses.[4]

¹ Communication by Max Tishler.
² F. A. Hochstein and G. F. Wright, *J. Am. Chem. Soc.*, **71**, 2257 (1949).
³ K. Freudenberg and F. Brauns, *Ber.*, **55**, 3238 (1922); C. A. Grob and D. A. Prins, *Helv. Chim. Acta*, **28**, 840 (1945).
⁴ N. Sperber, H. E. Zaugg and W. M. Sandstrom, *J. Am. Chem. Soc.*, **69**, 915 (1947).

10. Sodium amide, $NaNH_2$. Mol. wt. 39.02, m.p. 210°. Preparation[1] (a sample that has turned yellow may become explosive and should be destroyed). Preparation in liquid ammonia solution.[2] Use in dehydrohalogenation,[3] for Claisen acylation and carbethoxylation.[4] Sodium in liquid ammonia is a mild but efficient dehydrobrominating agent.[5]

¹ *Org. Synth.*, **20**, 86 (1940).
² *Inorg. Synth.*, **2**, 128 (1946); *Org. Synth.*, **25**, 25 (1945); **30**, 72 (1950).
³ T. L. Jacobs, *Org. Reactions*, **5**, 1 (1949); *Org. Synth.*, **30**, 72 (1950).
⁴ C. R. Hauser, R. Levine and R. F. Kibler, *J. Am. Chem. Soc.*, **68**, 26 (1946); R. Levine and C. R. Hauser, *ibid.*, **66**, 1768 (1944).
⁵ T. H. Vaughn, R. R. Vogt and J. A. Nieuwland, *J. Am. Chem. Soc.*, **56**, 2120 (1934).

11. Sodium azide, NaN_3. Mol. wt. 65.02. Supplier: Dupont. Conversion of an acid chloride to an azide.[1] Reacts with oxides to form azido alcohols reducible to amino alcohols.[2]

¹ *Org. Synth.*, **33**, 53 (1953).
² C. A. VanderWerf, R. Y. Heisler and W. E. McEwen, *J. Am. Chem. Soc.*, **76**, 1231 (1954).

12. Sodium bismuthate, $NaBiO_3$. Mol. wt. 280.00. Supplier: Mallinckrodt. The reagent effects scission of *vic*-glycols in aqueous phosphoric acid solution; the progress of the reaction is indicated by disappearance of the color of the reagent and precipitation of bismuth phosphate.[1] The oxidation can also be done in acetic acid solution and the bismuth removed by precipitation with phosphoric acid. Unlike oxidation with lead tetraacetate, the reaction apparently proceeds at equal rates with *cis* and *trans* glycols.

REAGENTS

Sodium bismuthate is also a reagent for oxidation of acyloins and α-hydroxy acids:

$$R_2C(OH)CO_2H \rightarrow R_2CO + CO_2.$$

Use in synthesis of glutardialdehyde from dicyclopentadiene and from cyclopentanone.[2]

[1] W. Rigby, *J. Chem. Soc.*, 1907 (1950).
[2] A. Stoll, A. Lindenmann and E. Jucker, *Helv. Chim. Acta*, **36**, 268 (1953).

13. Sodium borohydride. Mol. wt. 37.85. Supplier: Metal Hydrides, Inc. Examples: Chapters 31.3; 31.5.

14. Sodium chlorate. Mol. wt. 106.46. Catalyzed by vanadium pentoxide, for oxidation of hydroquinone to quinone.[1]

[1] *Org. Synth., Coll. Vol.*, **2**, 553 (1943).

15. Sodium dichromate dihydrate,

$$Na_2Cr_2O_7 \cdot 2H_2O.$$

Mol. wt. 298.05. Oxygen equivalents per mole: 3. (a) Unlike chromic anhydride, the dichromate is soluble *in acetic acid without addition of water;* a 25% solution in hot acetic acid can be cooled to 10° with no separation of solid. Example: cyclohexanol → cyclohexanone (Chapter 16), initially at 15°. (b) With use as solvent of *1 part benzene–2 parts acetic acid*, oxidations can be conducted in homogeneous solution at 0°. When solutions at 10° of 15 g. dichromate in 25 ml. acetic acid and 15 g. cyclohexanol in 12.5 ml. benzene are mixed and the mixture chilled in ice, a crystalline chromate ester separates and then slowly dissolves and yields cyclohexanone. Anhydrous *oxidation at reflux temperature:* fluorene → fluorenone (Chapter 14.8). An alternative to the usual procedure of work-up by dilution with water and extraction with ether is addition of petroleum ether, which causes separation to an upper layer containing the reaction product and a lower layer containing acetic acid and chromium compounds.[2] (c) Dichromate oxidation *in aqueous solution:* hydroquinone → quinone.[3]

[1] L. F. Fieser, *J. Am. Chem. Soc.*, **75**, 4377 (1953).
[2] L. F. Fieser, *ibid.*, **75**, 4395 (1953).
[3] *Org. Synth., Coll. Vol.*, **1**, 482 (1941).

16. Sodium diethyl phosphate, $NaPO(OC_2H_5)_2$. Mol. wt. 160.09. Preparation in tetrahydrofuran solution from diethyl phosphite and sodium and use for synthesis of a diethyl phosphonate from an alcohol tosylate:[1]

$$NaPO(OC_2H_5)_2 + ROTs \rightarrow$$
$$RPO(OC_2H_5)_2 + NaOTs$$

The free phosphonic acid, $RPO(OH)_2$, can be obtained on acid hydrolysis.

[1] T. C. Myers, S. Preis and E. V. Jensen, *J. Am. Chem. Soc.*, **76**, 4172 (1954).

17a. Sodium ethoxide, alcohol-free.[1] About 25 ml. of purified xylene is poured into a 100-ml. round-bottomed long-necked flask, 11.5 g. of sodium is added, a cork is inserted loosely, and the flask is heated in a sand bath until the rim of boiling xylene rises to the top of the neck. The flask is removed, wrapped in towels, the stopper is inserted, and the flask is shaken five or six times in the direction of its length, giving a sharp whip to each stroke. A little air is admitted and the mixture allowed to cool. Too much shaking often causes the particles to coalesce. Finely divided, powdery metal of bright appearance results. Often the product is more properly described as bird shot sodium and is rather gray. If larger lumps are present the heating and shaking should be repeated.

When the flask has cooled the xylene is decanted and the sodium washed twice with absolute ether by decantation. The flask is filled with fresh absolute ether and the contents poured into a 1-liter round bottomed flask. Enough more ether is added to bring the volume to about 300 ml., a condenser provided with a tube packed with calcium chloride and soda lime is attached, and 29.2 ml. of absolute ethanol is added in 5–6 portions through the condenser. When all the ethanol has been added a Bunsen valve is attached at the top of the system and, when the reaction begins to subside, the mixture is refluxed for 6–7 hrs. to complete the reaction. The hydrogen evolved protects the metal from becoming oxidized (yellow color). After cooling, the flask is transferred to a large vacuum desiccator containing calcium chloride and the ether is removed at the pump. The sodium ethoxide is obtained as a white powder. Sodium methoxide may be prepared by the same procedure; the reagent is available commercially.

[1] J. W. Brühl, *Ber.*, **35**, 3516 (1902); **37**, 2067 (1904).

17b. Sodium ethoxide solution, 10%.[1] A 2-l. flask equipped with a dropping funnel and an efficient condenser protected with a calcium chloride tube is charged with 23 g. (1 mole) of freshly cut sodium (it is advantageous to pass a slow stream of dry nitrogen into the flask during the reaction). Then 830 ml. (660 g.) of absolute ethanol is allowed to run in intermittently, the rate of addition being such that rapid refluxing is maintained. After all the ethanol has been added, the mixture is heated on the steam bath until the sodium has reacted. The process takes 2–3 hrs. Sodium methoxide solution can be prepared in the same way.

[1] Communicated by Max Tishler.

18. Sodium hydride, NaH. Mol. wt. 24.01. Supplier: Metal Hydrides, Inc. This reagent is often more satisfactory than sodium ethoxide for effecting condensations: Claisen acylation,[1] Stobbe condensation,[2] condensation of alkyl halides with acylaminomalonates,[3] Dieckmann condensation.[4] The reaction can be carried out in dry benzene or toluene and its progress followed by liberation of hydrogen. If humidity is high, provide a dry nitrogen atmosphere. Directions for handling.[5]

Caution: Use the same precautions as in handling sodium (safety glasses!).

[1] F. W. Swamer and C. R. Hauser, *J. Am. Chem. Soc.*, **72**, 1352 (1950).
[2] G. H. Daub and W. S. Johnson, *ibid.*, **72**, 501 (1950).
[3] J. Shapira, R. Shapira and K. Dittmer, *ibid.*, **75**, 3655 (1953).
[4] N. Green and L. B. LaForge, *ibid.*, **70**, 2287 (1948); F. F. Blicke, and others, *ibid.*, **75**, 5418 (1953).

[5] W. S. Johnson and G. H. Daub, *Org. Reactions*, **6**, 46 (1951).

19. Sodium hydrosulfide, NaSH. Preparation of a water–methanol solution of almost pure reagent.[1] For reduction of nitro compounds to amines; particularly useful for partial reduction of dinitro compounds — sometimes also displacement:

$$Ar(NO_2)_2 \rightarrow Ar(NO_2)SNa.[2]$$

[1] H. H. Hodgson and E. R. Ward, *J. Chem. Soc.*, 242 (1948).
[2] H. H. Hodgson and E. R. Ward, *ibid.*, 1187 (1949).

20. Sodium hydrosulfite, $Na_2S_2O_4 \cdot 2H_2O$. Mol. wt. 210.15. Powerful reagent for reduction in alkaline solution; pH must not be lower than 7 and preferably higher. Reduction of anthrone (Chapter 29.3b), Orange II (Chapter 38.1), 2-methyl-1,4-naphthoquinone (Chapter 38.3), 2,4-dinitro-1-naphthol (Chapter 42.1).

21. Sodium hydroxide. Mol. wt. 40.00, m.p. 318°.

22. Sodium iodide (soluble in ethanol and in acetone). Mol. wt. 149.91. For dechlorination;[1] $R_2CClC(Cl)=NR \rightarrow R_2C=C=NR$. Debromination.[2] Steric requirements for debromination.[3] Reacts in acetone solution with esters of *p*-toluenesulfonic acid (tosylates) to form alkyl (aryl) iodides:

$$ROTs + NaI \rightarrow RI + NaOTs.[4]$$

Converts ditosylates (or dimesylates) of the type $RCH(OTs)CH_2OTs$ to the unsaturated products, $RCH=CH_2$.[5] The elimination is slow if both groups are secondary.[6]

[1] C. L. Stevens and J. C. French, *J. Am. Chem. Soc.*, **75**, 657 (1953).
[2] R. Schoenheimer, *J. Biol. Chem.*, **110**, 461 (1935).
[3] D. H. R. Barton and E. Miller, *J. Am. Chem. Soc.*, **72**, 1066 (1950).
[4] H. Finkelstein, *Ber.*, **43**, 1528 (1910); J. W. H. Oldham and J. K. Rutherford, *J. Am. Chem. Soc.*, **54**, 366 (1932); R. S. Tipson, M. A. Clapp and L. H. Cretcher, *J. Org. Chem.*, **12**, 133 (1947).
[5] P. Bladon and L. N. Owen, *J. Chem. Soc.*, 598 (1950); A. B. Foster and W. G. Overend, *ibid.*, 3452 (1951).
[6] R. P. Linstead, L. N. Owen and R. F. Webb, *ibid.*, 1211 (1953).

REAGENTS

23. Sodium polysulfide. Preparation from $Na_2S \cdot 9H_2O + S$ and use for the transformation $p\text{-}NO_2C_6H_4CH_3 \rightarrow p\text{-}NH_2C_6H_4CHO$.[1]

> [1] *Org. Synth.*, **31**, 6 (1951).

24. Sodium–potassium alloy (1:5, liquid). Preparation.[1] Metallation of benzene by reaction with an alkyllithium and potassium in *n*-pentane.[2]

$$RLi + K \rightarrow RK + Li;$$
$$RK + C_6H_6 \rightarrow RH + C_6H_5K.$$

> [1] H. Gilman and R. V. Young, *J. Org. Chem.*, **1**, 315 (1936).
> [2] D. Bryce-Smith and E. E. Turner, *J. Chem. Soc.*, 861 (1953).

25. Sodium thiosulfate, $Na_2S_2O_3 \cdot 5H_2O$. Mol. wt. 248.21. Reacts with a halide to form a Bunte salt (RS_2O_3Na), which is hydrolyzed by acid to the mercaptan (RSH)[1] or oxidized by iodine to the disulfide ($RS \cdot SR$).[2] The latter reaction has been used in a synthesis of pantethine.[3] Chlorination of a Bunte salt leads to the sulfonyl chloride in good yield.[4]

> [1] H. E. Westlake, Jr. and G. Dougherty, *J. Am. Chem. Soc.*, **63**, 658 (1941).
> [2] *Ibid.*, **64**, 149 (1942).
> [3] M. Viscontini, K. Adank, N. Merckling, K. Ehrhardt and P. Karrer, *Helv. Chim. Acta*, **36**, 835 (1953).
> [4] C. Ziegler and J. M. Sprague, *J. Org. Chem.*, **16**, 621 (1951).

26. Sodium trimethoxyborohydride,

$$NaBH(OCH_3)_3.$$

Mol. wt. 127.93. Preparation and use for reduction of aldehydes, ketones, acid anhydrides, and acid chlorides.[1] Esters and nitriles are reduced only slowly at elevated temperatures.

> [1] H. C. Brown and E. J. Mead, *J. Am. Chem. Soc.*, **75**, 6263 (1953).

27. Stannic chloride, $SnCl_4$. Mol. wt. 260.53, b.p. 114°. A mild catalyst for Friedel-Crafts reactions and cyclodehydrations.

28a. Stannous chloride. $SnCl_2 \cdot 2H_2O$. Mol. wt. 225.65. (a) The reagent is usually dissolved in concd. hydrochloric acid, 1 ml. per g. of chloride. Reduction of: triphenylcarbinol (Chapter 13.4d); nitrobenzene (Chapter 26.2); anthrone (Chapter 29.3a). (b) 2,4-Dinitrophenylhydrazones are cleaved by stannous chloride in acetone–hydrochloric acid and both saturated and α,β-unsaturated ketones are recovered in 84–98% yield.[1]

> [1] J. Demaecker and R. H. Martin, *Nature*, **173**, 266 (1954).

28b. Stannous chloride, anhydrous. Mol. wt. 189.61, m.p. 247°. Heat hydrated stannous chloride for 1 hr. in a bath at 195–200° and pulverize the cooled melt. Employed in ether solution saturated with hydrogen chloride for reduction of imidochlorides, $-C(Cl)=NH$ and $-C(Cl)=NC_6H_5$, to $-CH=NH$ and $-CH=NC_6H_5$.

29. Sulfamic acid, H_2NSO_2OH. Mol. wt. 97.10. Used to destroy excess nitrous acid in diazotizations.

30. Sulfoacetic acid (concd. sulfuric acid in iced acetic anhydride).[1] Catalyst for O-acetylation of ketones with ketene to form enol acetates.[2] Preparation of crystalline material.[3]

> [1] M. Franchimont, *Compt. rend.*, **92**, 1054 (1881).
> [2] F. G. Young, F. C. Frostick, Jr., J. J. Sanderson and C. R. Hauser, *J. Am. Chem. Soc.*, **72**, 3635 (1950).
> [3] O. Stillich, *J. prakt. Chem.*, **73**, 541 (1906).

31. Sulfosalicylic acid,

$$2\text{-}HOC_6H_3\text{-}1\text{-}CO_2H\text{-}5\text{-}SO_3H \cdot 2H_2O.$$

Mol. wt. 254.22. Supplier: Eastman. More active than *p*-toluenesulfonic acid as catalyst for acetylation and enol acetylation.[1]

> [1] H. V. Anderson, and others, *J. Am. Chem. Soc.*, **76**, 743 (1954); R. B. Moffett and H. V. Anderson, *ibid.*, **76**, 747 (1954).

32. Sulfur, selenium, and catalytic dehydrogenation. The selenium and catalytic methods generally have been preferred to sulfur,[1] but cases are reported where these methods lead to loss of nonangular alkyl groups that are retained when sulfur is used.[2]

> [1] Pl. A. Plattner and E. C. Armstrong, "Dehydrogenation with Sulfur, Selenium, and Plati-

REAGENTS

num Metals," *Newer Methods of Preparative Organic Chemistry*, p. 21, Interscience (1948).
[2] W. Cocker, and others, *J. Chem. Soc.*, 2355 (1953).

33. Sulfur sesquioxide, S_2O_6. Prepared by dissolving 25 g. of sulfur in 375 ml. of 18% fuming sulfuric acid. For preparation of naphthazarin,[1] this solution is added to a stirred suspension of 50 g. of 1,5-dinitronaphthalene in 230 ml. of concd. sulfuric acid and the temperature is checked at 60°.

Naphthazarin

[1] German Patent 71,386; G. Charrier and G. Tocco, *Gazz. chim. ital.*, **53**, 431 (1923); L. F. Fieser, *J. Am. Chem. Soc.*, **50**, 439 (1928).

34. Sulfuryl chloride, SO_2Cl_2. Mol. wt. 134.98. Supplier: Hooker Electrochemical Co. Review of uses.[1] (a) Effects chlorination of aliphatic hydrocarbons[2] in the presence of a catalyst that promotes formation of free radicals: benzoyl peroxide; aliphatic azo compounds such as α,α'-azoisobutyrate

$$(CH_3)_2C(CO_2CH_3)N=NC(CO_2CH_3)(CH_3)_2$$

(catalyst also for bromination with NBS).[3] A tertiary hydrogen atom is replaced preferentially:

$$(ClCH_2)_2CHCH_3 \rightarrow (ClCH_2)_2CClCH_3.[4]$$

(b) Chlorination of ethyl acetoacetate to ethyl α-chloroacetoacetate;[5] of ethyl p-hydroxybenzoate;[6] α-chlorination of aldehydes.[7] In the chlorination of a ketone, sul-

furyl chloride attacks the more substituted position adjacent to the carbonyl group.[8]

[1] H. C. Brown, *Ind. Eng. Chem.*, **36**, 785 (1944).
[2] M. S. Kharasch and H. C. Brown, *J. Am. Chem. Soc.*, **61**, 2142 (1939).
[3] M. C. Ford and W. A. Waters, *J. Chem. Soc.*, 1851 (1951); 2240 (1952).
[4] A. Mooradian and J. B. Cloke, *J. Am. Chem. Soc.*, **68**, 785 (1946).
[5] *Org. Synth.*, **33**, 45 (1953).
[6] *Ibid.*, **29**, 35 (1949).
[7] C. L. Stevens, E. Farkas and B. Gillis, *J. Am. Chem. Soc.*, **76**, 2695 (1954).
[8] B. Tchoubar and O. Sackur, *Compt. rend.*, **208**, 1020 (1939); P. Delbaere, *Bull. soc. chim. Belg.*, **51**, 1 (1942). E. W. Warnhoff and W. S. Johnson, *J. Am. Chem. Soc.*, **75**, 494 (1953).

1. Tetraethyl pyrophosphate,

$$(C_2H_5O)_2POP(OC_2H_5)_2.$$

Mol. wt. 258.19, b.p. 80°/0.1 mm. Preparation and use in peptide synthesis:[1]

$$RCHCO_2H + H_2NCH(R')CO_2C_2H_5 +$$
$$| $$
$$NHCO_2CH_2C_6H_5$$

$$(C_2H_5O)_2POP(OC_2H_5)_2 \rightarrow$$
$$RCHCONHCH(R')CO_2C_2H_5 + 2(C_2H_5O)_2POH$$
$$|$$
$$NHCO_2CH_2C_6H_5$$

[1] G. W. Anderson, J. Blodinger and A. D. Welcher, *J. Am. Chem. Soc.*, **74**, 5309 (1952); V. du Vigneaud, and others, *ibid.*, **76**, 3115 (1954).

2. Tetranitromethane. Test for unsaturation: Chapter 11.4. Suppliers: Monomer-Polymer, Inc.; Aldrich Chemical Co. Preparation (90% yield):[1]

$$4CH_2{=}CO + 4HNO_3 \rightarrow C(NO_2)_4 + CO_2 + 3CH_3CO_2H.$$

Spectrophotometric determination of the color density reveals the number of alkyl substituents on an isolated double bond.[2]

[1] G. Darzens and G. Lévy, *Compt. rend.*, **229**, 1081 (1949).
[2] E. Heilbronner, *Helv. Chim. Acta*, **36**, 1121 (1953).

3. Thiocyanogen, $(SCN)_2$. Preparation in solution by adding 10% bromine in carbon tetrachloride to a suspension of lead thiocyanate

REAGENTS

(10% excess) in the same solvent until the color is discharged, and filtering.[1]

[1] J. L. Wood, "Substitution and Addition Reactions of Thiocyanogen," *Org. Reactions*, **3**, 240 (1946).

4. Thiolacetic acid, CH_3COSH. Mol. wt. 76.12, b.p. 93°, sp. gr. 1.07. Supplier: Eastman. Preparation.[1] Use in S-acetylation of coenzyme A[2] and of pantetheine.[3]

[1] H. T. Clarke and W. W. Hartman, *J. Am. Chem. Soc.*, **46**, 1731 (1924).
[2] I. B. Wilson, *ibid.*, **74**, 3205 (1952).
[3] E. Walton, and others, *ibid.*, **76**, 1146 (1954).

5. Thionyl bromide, $SOBr_2$. Mol. wt. 207.89, b.p. 68°/40 mm., sp. gr. 2.68. Preparation in good yield from thionyl chloride and potassium bromide.[1] For economical conversion of an alcohol to the bromide[2] the alcohol is treated in ether at −10° with 0.5 mole of thionyl chloride and 1 mole of pyridine; the solution is filtered from precipitated pyridine hydrochloride, evaporated, and the residual sulfite, $(RO)_2SO$, is heated with 0.5 mole of thionyl bromide.

[1] M. J. Frazer and W. Gerrard, *Chem. Ind.*, 280 (1954). See *Inorg. Synth.*, **1**, 113 (1939).
[2] M. J. Frazer, W. Gerrard, G. Machell and B. D. Shepherd, *Chem. Ind.*, 931 (1954).

6. Thionyl chloride. Mol. wt. 118.98, b.p. 78.8°, sp. gr. 1.67. Older manufacturing processes give crude, dark-colored thionyl chloride containing sulfuryl chloride (SO_2Cl_2) and sulfur monochloride (S_2Cl_2) and dichloride (SCl_2). If this is refluxed with sulfur, sulfuryl chloride is converted to sulfur dioxide and sulfur chlorides, and on two fractional distillations sulfur monochloride, b.p. 135.6°, is left in the residue and sulfur dichloride, b.p. 59°, eliminated in the forerun.[1] A newer manufacturing process gives material free of sulfuryl chloride, which on distillation in the presence of sulfur and an iron-containing catalyst is freed of sulfur chlorides.[2] The following method of purification of small amounts of reagent is wasteful but simple.

Crude thionyl chloride (50 ml.) is mixed with 10 ml. of quinoline or substitute (Chapter 48) in an all-glass apparatus and distilled. It is then mixed with 20 ml. of raw linseed oil (refined grade, unboiled) and fractionated from it. The distillate is colorless and pure.

The Darzens procedure[3] for effecting the conversion ROH → RCl consists in reaction of the hydroxy compound with thionyl chloride in pyridine; under these conditions a tertiary hydroxyl group is often eliminated:

$$RCH_2C(OH)(R)CO_2C_2H_5 \rightarrow RCH{=}C(R)CO_2C_2H_5.$$

In a new procedure[4] the alcohol is treated in ether at −10° with 1 mole of pyridine and 0.5 mole of thionyl chloride and the resulting solution of the sulfite, $(RO)_2SO$, is filtered from precipitated pyridine hydrochloride. The solvent is removed and the residue is heated with 0.5 mole of thionyl chloride, when the rapidly formed chlorosulfinate, $ROS({=}O)Cl$ slowly decomposes to RCl + SO_2.

[1] D. L. Cottle, *J. Am. Chem. Soc.*, **68**, 1380 (1946).
[2] F. C. Trager, U. S. Pat. 2,539,679.
[3] G. Darzens, *Compt. rend.*, **152**, 1601 (1911).
[4] M. J. Frazer, W. Gerrard, G. Machell and B. D. Shepherd, *Chem. Ind.*, 931 (1954).

7. Titanium tetrachloride. Mol. wt. 189.73, b.p. 136.4°. Less active than aluminum chloride in Friedel-Crafts reactions; solubility in organic solvents a useful feature.[1]

[1] N. M. Cullinane and D. M. Leyshon, *J. Chem. Soc.*, 2942 (1954).

Tollens' reagent: Chapter 21.2.

8. *p*-Toluenesulfonic acid,

$$p\text{-}CH_3C_6H_4SO_3H \cdot H_2O.$$

Mol. wt. 190.22, m.p. 105°. Use of technical product (90%) for promoting coupling of a triazene:

$$ArN{=}NN(CH_3)_2 + C_6H_6 \rightarrow ArC_6H_5.[1]$$

Catalyst for enol acetylation with isopropenyl acetate and in acetylation of tertiary al-

REAGENTS

cohols;[2] catalyst for condensation of ketones with ethanedithiol.[3]

[1] *Org. Synth.* **33**, 56 (1953).
[2] Huang-Minlon, and others, *J. Am. Chem. Soc.*, **74**, 5394 (1952); R. B. Turner, *ibid.*, **75**, 3489 (1953).
[3] J. W. Ralls, *ibid.*, **75**, 2123 (1953); J. W. Ralls and B. Riegel, *ibid.*, **76**, 4479 (1954).

9. p-Toluenesulfonyl chloride. Mol. wt. 190.65, m.p. 69°, b.p. 146°/15 mm. Eastman material is usually satisfactory. The substance can be crystallized from ligroin. For Lossen rearrangement of hydroxamic acids.[1]

[1] C. D. Hurd and L. Bauer, *J. Am. Chem. Soc.*, **76**, 2791 (1954).

10. p-Toluenesulfonylhydrazine,

$$p\text{-}CH_3C_6H_4SO_2NHNH_2.$$

Mol. wt. 186.23, m.p. 112°. Preparation.[1,2] (a) Characterization of sugars;[1,3] glucose forms a mono derivative.[1] (b) For dechlorination of 5-chloroacridine:[2]

$$ArCl \rightarrow ArNHNHSO_2C_6H_4CH_3;$$

this derivative when heated with aqueous alkali yields acridine.

[1] K. Freudenberg and F. Blümmel, *Ann.*, **440**, 45 (1924).
[2] A. Albert and R. Royer, *J. Chem. Soc.*, 1148 (1949).
[3] D. G. Easterby, L. Hough and J. K. N. Jones, *ibid.*, 3416 (1951).

Tosyl chloride. See *p*-Toluenesulfonyl chloride.

11. ω-Tribromoacetophenone, $C_6H_5COBr_3$. Mol. wt. 356.87, m.p. 66°, b.p. 176°/16 mm. Preparation.[1] For selective bromination of methyl ketones and side-chain bromination of hydrocarbons:

$$ArCOCH_3 \rightarrow ArCOCH_2Br;$$
$$ArCH_3 \rightarrow ArCH_2Br.[2]$$

[1] F. Kröhnke, *Ber.*, **69**, 932 (1936).
[2] F. Kröhnke and K. Ellegast, *Ber.*, **86**, 1556 (1953).

12. Tri-n-butylamine, $(CH_3CH_2CH_2CH_2)_3N$. Mol. wt. 185.35, b.p. 216.5°, sp. gr. 0.78.

For dehydrohalogenation of certain α-bromo ketones.[1]

[1] R. E. Lyle and R. A. Covey, *J. Am. Chem. Soc.*, **75**, 4973 (1953).

13. Trichloroacetic acid, CCl_3CO_2H. Mol. wt. 163.40, b.p. 196°, sp. gr. 1.62, m.p. 58°, pK_a 0.08. Preparation from chloral by reaction with nitric acid containing oxides of nitrogen.[1]

[1] G. D. Parkes and R. G. W. Hollingshead, *Chem. Ind.*, 222 (1954).

14. Triethanolamine, $(HOCH_2CH_2)_3N$. Mol. wt. 149.19, m.p. 21°, b.p. 279°/150 mm., sp. gr. 1.12. Satisfactory catalyst for condensation of aldehydes with malonic acid (Knoevenagel reaction).[1]

[1] R. P. Linstead, E. G. Noble and E. J. Boorman, *J. Chem. Soc.*, 557 (1933).

15. Triethylamine. Mol. wt. 101.19, b.p. 89.5°, sp. gr. 0.73, pK_b 3.36. Sometimes superior to pyridine as basic catalyst.

16. Triethylamine benzoate, $C_6H_5CO_2NH(C_2H_5)_3$. For cyclodehydration of alkali-sensitive compounds.[1]

[1] T. Wieland, H. Ueberwasser, G. Anner and K. Miescher, *Helv. Chim. Acta*, **36**, 376 (1953).

17. Trifluoroacetic anhydride. Mol. wt. 210.04. Supplier: Halogen Chemical Co. Alcohols are acylated with the anhydride in the presence of sodium trifluoroacetate[1] or with the anhydride in dioxan without catalysis.[2] The trifluoroacetyl derivatives are stable to acid, but the protective group can be removed easily with dry methanol or aqueous bicarbonate. Two adjacent trifluoroacetyl groups are particularly subject to cleavage by water (no catalyst required). Use in condensation of acids with alkenes and alkines:[3]

$$RCO_2H + RCH{=}CHR \rightarrow$$
$$RCOC(R){=}CHR.$$

[1] E. J. Bourne, C. E. M. Tatlow and J. C. Tatlow, *J. Chem. Soc.*, 1367 (1950); E. J. Bourne, M. Stacey, C. E. M. Tatlow and J. C. Tatlow, *ibid.*, 826 (1951).
[2] A. Lardon and T. Reichstein, *Helv. Chim. Acta*, **37**, 388, 443 (1954).
[3] A. L. Henne and J. M. Tedder, *J. Chem. Soc.*, 3628 (1953).

REAGENTS

18. Trifluoroacetyl hypohalites, CF_3CO_2X.
Prepared by interaction of bromine or iodine with silver trifluoroacetate.[1] Used to effect halogenation of aromatic compounds,[2] e.g.

$$C_6H_5I \rightarrow p\text{-}IC_6H_4I \ (77\%);$$
$$C_6H_5CH_3 \rightarrow p\text{-}BrC_6H_4CH_3 \ (90\%);$$
$$C_6H_5NH_2 \rightarrow p\text{-}IC_6H_4NH_2 \ (51\%).[2]$$

[1] A. L. Henne and W. F. Zimmer, *J. Am. Chem. Soc.*, **73**, 1362 (1951).
[2] R. N. Haszeldine and A. G. Sharpe, *J. Chem. Soc.*, 993 (1952).

19. Trifluoroperacetic acid, CF_3CO_3H.
Mol. wt. 130.03. This substance, prepared *in situ* with 90% hydrogen peroxide in trifluoroacetic acid, is an excellent reagent for hydroxylation of double bonds and for oxidation of aryl amines to nitro compounds and of nitrosoamines to nitroamines:

$$R_2NNO \rightarrow R_2NNO_2.[1]$$

[1] W. D. Emmons, and others, *J. Am. Chem. Soc.*, **75**, 4623 (1953); **76**, 3468, 3470, 3472 (1954).

20. Trimethylene oxide,

$$\begin{array}{c} CH_2CH_2CH_2. \\ \underline{\hspace{1cm}} \\ O \end{array}$$

Mol. wt. 58.08, b.p. 48°/750 mm. Preparation from 3-chloropropyl acetate.[1] Reaction with Grignard reagents.[2]

[1] *Org. Synth.*, **29**, 92 (1949).
[2] S. Searles, *J. Am. Chem. Soc.*, **73**, 124 (1951).

21. 2,4,7-Trinitrofluorenone.
Mol. wt. 315.19. Supplier: Monomer-Polymer, Inc. Preparation.[1] Characterization of aromatic hydrocarbons by complex formation.[2]

[1] *Org. Synth.*, **28**, 91 (1948).
[2] M. Orchin and E. O. Woolfolk, *J. Am. Chem. Soc.*, **68**, 1727 (1946); M. Orchin, L. Reggel and E. O. Woolfolk, *ibid.*, **69**, 1225 (1947).

22. Triphenylmethylsodium, $(C_6H_5)_3CNa$.
Preparation.[1] Use in Claisen type condensations.[2]

[1] *Org. Synth., Coll. Vol.*, **2**, 607 (1943).
[2] See D. F. Thompson, P. L. Bayless and C. R. Hauser, *J. Org. Chem.*, **19**, 1490 (1954).

23. Triphenylphosphine, $(C_6H_5)_3P$.
Mol. wt. 262.28, m.p. 79°. Converts diazonium salts in high yield into arylhydrazines:[1]

$$ArN_2^+Cl^- + P(C_6H_5)_3 \rightarrow ArN{=}NP^+(C_6H_5)_3Cl^-$$
$$\xrightarrow[-\ (C_6H_5)_3PO]{P(C_6H_5)_3\ +\ H_2O} ArNHNHP^+(C_6H_5)_3Cl^-$$
$$\xrightarrow{H_2O} ArNHNH_2 + (C_6H_5)_3PO$$

[1] L. Horner and H. Stöhr, *Ber.*, **86**, 1073 (1953).

24. Triphenylphosphinemethylene,

$$(C_6H_5)_3P{=}CH_2.$$

Preparation of crystalline, yellow material (sensitive to air and moisture) from methyl triphenylphosphonium bromide and phenyllithium.[1] Preparation in solution and reaction with ketones:[2]

$$(C_6H_5)_3P{=}CH_2 + R_2C{=}O \rightarrow$$
$$(C_6H_5)_3P{=}O + R_2C{=}CH_2.$$

Examples: $(C_6H_5)_2CO \rightarrow (C_6H_5)C{=}CH_2$ (84%); cyclohexanone $\rightarrow$ methylenecyclohexane (48%);

$$C_6H_5CH{=}CHCHO \rightarrow$$
$$C_6H_5CH{=}CHCH{=}CH_2 \ (trans).$$

Triphenylphosphinevinylmethylene, prepared in solution by reaction of phenyllithium with the phosphonium salt from $(C_6H_5)_3P$ and allyl bromide, reacts similarly (yield 58%):

$$(C_6H_5)_3P{=}CHCH{=}CH_2 + C_6H_5CHO \rightarrow$$
$$(C_6H_5)_3PO + C_6H_5CH{=}CHCH{=}CH_2.$$

[1] G. Wittig and G. Geissler, *Ann.*, **580**, 52 (1953).
[2] G. Wittig and U. Schöllkopf, *Ber.*, **87**, 1318 (1954).

25. Triphenylphosphite, $(C_6H_5O)_3P$.
Mol. wt. 310.27, m.p. 17–22°. Preparation.[1] Reacts with an alcohol (ROH) and a hydrogen halide (HX) or alkyl halide (R'X) to form the halide RX:[2]

$$(C_6H_5O)_3P + ROH + HX(R'X) \rightarrow$$
$$RX + H(R')PO(OC_6H_5)_2 + C_6H_5OH.$$

Halogens can also be used:[3]

$$(C_6H_5O)_3P + ROH + X_2 \rightarrow$$
$$RX + XPO(OC_6H_5)_2 + C_6H_5OH.$$

If the alcohol is unsaturated, the conversion must be carried out in two steps:

$$(C_6H_5O)_3P \xrightarrow{X_2} (C_6H_5O)_3PX_2 \xrightarrow{ROH}$$
$$RX + XPO(OC_6H_5)_2 + C_6H_5OH.$$

[1] H. B. Gottlieb, *J. Am. Chem. Soc.*, **54**, 748 (1932).
[2] S. R. Landauer and H. N. Rydon, *J. Chem. Soc.*, 2224 (1953).
[3] D. G. Coe, S. R. Landauer and H. N. Rydon, *J. Chem. Soc.*, 2281 (1954).

26. Triphenylphosphite methiodide,

$$(C_6H_5O)_3PCH_3I.$$

Mol. wt. 452.22, m.p. 146°. Preparation; conversion of alcohols to alkyl halides.[1]

[1] S. R. Landauer and H. N. Rydon, *J. Chem. Soc.*, 2224 (1953).

27. Triphenyltetrazolium chloride (red tetrazolium). On reduction it yields a red formazan. Example of use: chapter 21.3. Supplier: Monomer-Polymer, Inc.

28. Triton B (trimethylbenzylammonium hydroxide). Mol. wt. 167.25. Suppliers: Commercial Solvents Corp.; Rohm and Haas Co. This strong base is an effective catalyst for Michael[1,2] and Dieckmann[3] condensations and for cyanoethylations.[4]

[1] *Org. Synth.*, **32**, 86 (1952).
[2] F. K. Kirchner, and others, *J. Org. Chem.*, **14**, 388 (1949).
[3] C. Barkenbus, V. C. Midkiff and R. M. Newman, *J. Org. Chem.*, **16**, 232 (1951).
[4] H. A. Bruson, *Org. Reactions*, **5**, 79 (1949); J. C. Sheehan and C. E. Mumaw, *J. Am. Chem. Soc.*, **72**, 2127 (1950).

29. Trityl bromide, $(C_6H_5)_3CBr$. Mol. wt. 323.23, m.p. 160°. Preparation: Chapter 13.4. Tritylation of D-glucose: Chapter 21.6.

30. Trityl chloride, $(C_6H_5)_3CCl$. Mol. wt. 278.77, m.p. 113°. Preparation from triphenylcarbinol and acetyl chloride.[1] Usual procedure of tritylation of an alcohol: in dry pyridine for 16–20 hrs. at room temperature. Ethers of simple alcohols and phenols,[2] of sugars[3] (primary alcoholic groups are attacked preferentially). The trityl group is stable to

alkali but easily split by acids; hydrogen bromide in acetic acid liberates the alcohol with precipitation of trityl bromide.[4] Hydrogenation eliminates the group as triphenylmethane;[5] reaction with phosphorus pentabromide replaces the trityl group with bromine.[6]

[1] *Org. Synth.*, **23**, 100 (1943).
[2] B. Helferich, P. E. Speidel and W. Toeldte, *Ber.*, **56**, 766 (1923).
[3] B. Helferich, *Adv. Carbohyd. Chem.*, **3**, 79 (1948).
[4] B. Helferich and W. Klein, *Ann.*, **450**, 219 (1926); *Org. Synth.*, **22**, 56 (1942).
[5] P. E. Verkade, and others, *Rec. trav. chim.*, **61**, 373 (1942).
[6] B. Helferich, and others, *Ann.*, **447**, 19 (1926); D. A. Rosenfeld, N. K. Richtmyer and C. S. Hudson, *J. Am. Chem. Soc.*, **70**, 2201 (1948).

1. Urea. Mol. wt. 60.06, m.p. 133°. Used to destroy excess nitrous acid in diazotizations and to free nitric acid of oxides of nitrogen. An acid heated with urea is converted to the amide:

$$RCO_2H + H_2NCONH_2 \rightarrow RCONH_2.[1]$$

[1] E. Cherbuliez and F. Landolt, *Helv. Chim. Acta*, **29**, 1438 (1946).

1. Zinc. Atomic wt. 65.38. Activated for Reformatsky reaction.[1]

[1] L. F. Fieser and W. S. Johnson, *J. Am. Chem. Soc.*, **62**, 576 (1940); *Org. Synth.*, **21**, 52, note 2 (1941); W. Oroshnik, G. Karmas and A. D. Mebane, *J. Am. Chem. Soc.*, **74**, 3807, note 16 (1952).

2. Zinc amalgam. Preparation and use for reduction of $ArSO_2Cl \rightarrow ArSH$.[1] Improvements in the procedure of Clemmensen reduction: addition of toluene,[2] use of freshly poured zinc,[3] mechanical stirring.[3]

[1] *Org. Synth.*, **33**, 47 (1953).
[2] E. L. Martin, "The Clemmensen Reduction," *Org. Reactions*, **1**, 155 (1942).
[3] See L. F. Fieser, and others, *J. Am. Chem. Soc.*, **70**, 3203 (1948).

3a. Zinc dust–acetic acid. For conversion of a halohydrin to the ethylene.[1]

[1] S. Mori, *J. Chem. Soc. Japan*, **70**, 257 (1949); see *Chem. Abst.*, **45**, 4733 (1951); L. F. Fieser and R. Ettorre, *J. Am. Chem. Soc.*, **75**, 1700 (1953).

REAGENTS

3b. Zinc dust–ether–acetic acid. For debromination of a *vic*-dibromide (preferable to Zn–HOAc).[1] Example: Chapter 11.2.

> [1] L. F. Fieser, *J. Am. Chem. Soc.*, **75**, 5421 (1953).

3c. Zinc dust–pyridine. Reduction with this combination, catalyzed by acetic acid, is milder than the usual zinc–acetic acid method.[1] Used for reduction of polyenes, cyanines, and cyanidines.

> [1] R. Kuhn and A. Winterstein, *Ber.*, **65**, 646, 1737, 1742 (1932).

3d. Zinc–HCl. Reduction of an α-ketol to the ketone (in acetic acid or ethanol, with concd. acid or HCl gas).[1] The quality of the zinc is critical.

> [1] V. Prelog, and others, *Helv. Chim. Acta*, **30**, 1741 (1947); **35**, 1598 (1952); M. Stoll, *ibid.*, **30**, 1837 (1947); H. C. Brown and M. Borkowski, *J. Am. Chem. Soc.*, **74**, 1900 (1952).

4. Zinc hydrosulfite, ZnS_2O_4. Mol. wt. 193.50. Relatively stable in aqueous solutions at room temperature at a pH as low as 4, where sodium hydrosulfite is rapidly decomposed. Supplier: Virginia Smelting Co.

Index

Pages citing physical constants are marked with an asterisk.

351

352

DERIVATIVES

	REAGENT *	CHANGE	INCREMENT FORMULA	MOL.WT.
Acetyl	A 4	$-H \rightarrow -COCH_3$	C_2H_2O	42.04
Allophanate	C 21	$-H \rightarrow -CONHCONH_2$	$C_2H_2O_2N$	86.05
Benzal		$=H_2 \rightarrow =CHC_6H_5$	C_7H_4	88.10
Benzenesulfonyl	B 3, 4	$-H \rightarrow -SO_2C_6H_5$	$C_6H_4O_2S$	140.16
Benzhydryl	B 31	$-CO_2H \rightarrow -CO_2CH(C_6H_5)_2$	$C_{13}H_{10}$	166.21
Benzoyl	B 5	$-H \rightarrow -COC_6H_5$	C_7H_4O	104.10
Benzyl		$-H \rightarrow -CH_2C_6H_5$	C_7H_6	90.12
p-Bromophenacyl	B 15	$-H \rightarrow -CH_2COC_6H_4Br$	C_8H_5OBr	197.04
Carbobenzoxy	C 2	$-H \rightarrow -COOCH_2C_6H_5$	$C_8H_6O_2$	134.13
Cathyl (carbethoxy)	E 3	$-H \rightarrow -COOC_2H_5$	$C_3H_4O_2$	72.06
Chloroacetyl	C 4, 5	$-H \rightarrow -COCH_2Cl$	C_2HOCl	76.49
Dimedon	D 19	$=O \rightarrow =(C_8H_{11}O_2)_2 - O$	$C_{16}H_{22}O_3$	262.34
2,4-Dinitrobenzenesulfenyl	D 24	$-H \rightarrow -SC_6H_3(NO_2)_2$	$C_6H_2O_4N_2S$	198.16
2,4-Dinitrobenzal	D 23	$=H_2 \rightarrow =CHC_6H_3(NO_2)_2$	$C_7H_2O_4N_2$	178.10
3,5-Dinitrobenzoyl	D 26	$-H \rightarrow -COC_6H_3(NO_2)_2$	$C_7H_2O_5N_2$	194.11
2,4-Dinitrophenyl	D 27	$-H \rightarrow -C_6H_3(NO_2)_2$	$C_6H_2O_4N_2$	166.10
2,4-Dinitrophenylhydrazone	D 29	$=O \rightarrow =NNHC_6H_3(NO_2)_2$	$C_6H_4O_3N_4$	180.12
Ethanol solvate		$X + C_2H_5OH$	C_2H_6O	46.07
Ethyl		$-H \rightarrow -C_2H_5$	C_2H_4	28.05
Ethylenehemithioketal	E 1	$=O \rightarrow \begin{array}{c} S-CH_2 \\ \mid \\ O-CH_2 \end{array}$	C_2H_4S	60.12
Ethyleneketal	E 6	$=O \rightarrow \begin{array}{c} O-CH_2 \\ \mid \\ O-CH_2 \end{array}$	C_2H_4O	44.05
Ethylenethioketal	M 5	$=O \rightarrow \begin{array}{c} S-CH_2 \\ \mid \\ S-CH_2 \end{array}$	$C_2H_4S_2 - O$	76.18
Formyl	F 8, M 17	$-H \rightarrow -CHO$		28.01
Hydrate		$X + H_2O$	H_2O	18.02
Hydrazone	H 5	$=O \rightarrow =NNH_2$	$N_2H_2 - O$	14.03
Mesyl	M 12, 13	$-H \rightarrow -SO_2CH_3$	CH_2O_2S	78.09
Methanol solvate		$X + CH_3OH$	CH_4O	32.04
Methiodide	M 18	$X + CH_3I$	CH_3I	141.95
Methyl	D 4, 22; M 18	$-H \rightarrow -CH_3$	CH_2	14.03
α-Naphthylurethan	N 2	$-H \rightarrow -CONHC_{10}H_7$	$C_{11}H_7ON$	169.17
p-Nitrobenzyl		$-H \rightarrow -CH_2C_6H_4NO_2$	$C_7H_5O_2N$	135.12
p-Nitrocarbobenzoxy	N 5	$-H \rightarrow -COOCH_2C_6H_4NO_2$	$C_8H_5O_4N$	179.13
Oxime		$=O \rightarrow =NOH$	HN	15.02
Phenylhydrazone	P 8	$=O \rightarrow =NNHC_6H_5$	$C_6H_6N_2 - O$	90.13
Phenylosazone (of α-ketol)	P 8	$\begin{array}{c} -CO \\ \mid \\ -CHOH \end{array} \rightarrow \begin{array}{c} -C=NNHC_6H_5 \\ \mid \\ -C=NNHC_6H_5 \end{array}$	$C_{12}H_{10}N_4 - O_2$	178.23
Phenylurethan	P 9	$-H \rightarrow -CONHC_6H_5$	C_7H_5ON	119.11
Picrate (salt or complex)	P 19	$X + C_6H_2(NO_2)_3OH$	$C_6H_3O_7N_3$	229.11
Pyrano	D 14	$-H \rightarrow \begin{array}{c} -CH \cdot O \cdot CH_2 \\ \mid \qquad \mid \\ CH_2CH_2CH_2 \end{array}$	C_5H_8O	84.11
Quinoxaline	P 7	$-COCO- \rightarrow \begin{array}{c} -C \qquad C- \\ \parallel \quad \parallel \\ NC_6H_4N \end{array}$	$C_6H_4N_2 - O_2$	72.11
Semicarbazone	S 2	$=O \rightarrow =NNHCONH_2$	CH_3N_3	57.06
Tosyl	T 9	$-H \rightarrow -SO_2C_6H_4CH_3$	$C_7H_6O_2S$	154.18
Trifluoroacetyl	T 17	$-H \rightarrow -COCF_3$	$C_2OF_3 - H$	96.01
s-Trinitrobenzene complex		$X + C_6H_3(NO_2)_2$	$C_6H_3O_6N_3$	213.11
2,4,7-Trinitrofluorenone complex	T 21	$X + C_{12}H_5CO(NO_2)_3$	$C_{13}H_5O_7N_3$	315.19
Trityl	T 29, 30	$-H \rightarrow -C(C_6H_5)_3$	$C_{19}H_{14}$	242.30

MULTIPLES OF ELEMENT WEIGHTS AND LOGARITHMS

C	12.01	.07954	H	1.008	.00346	H_{51}	51.41	.71105	OCH_3	31.03	.49178
C_2	24.02	.38057	H_2	2.016	.30449	H_{52}	52.42	.71950	$(OCH_3)_2$	62.07	.79288
C_3	36.03	.55666	H_3	3.024	.48058	H_{53}	53.42	.72770	$(OCH_3)_3$	93.10	.96895
C_4	48.04	.68160	H_4	4.032	.60552	H_{54}	54.43	.73584	$(OCH_3)_4$	124.14	.09391
C_5	60.05	.77851	H_5	5.040	.70243	H_{55}	55.44	.74382	$(OCH_3)_5$	155.17	.19081
C_6	72.06	.85769	H_6	6.048	.78161	H_{56}	56.45	.75166	$(OCH_3)_6$	186.20	.26998
C_7	84.07	.92464	H_7	7.056	.84856	H_{57}	57.46	.75937	$(OCH_3)_7$	217.24	.33694
C_8	96.08	.98263	H_8	8.064	.90655	H_{58}	58.46	.76686	$(OCH_3)_8$	248.27	.39492
C_9	108.09	.03379	H_9	9.072	.95770	H_{59}	59.47	.77430			
C_{10}	120.10	.07954	H_{10}	10.08	.00346	H_{60}	60.48	.78161			
						H_{61}	61.49	.78880	OC_2H_5	45.06	.65379
C_{11}	132.11	.12094	H_{11}	11.09	.04493	H_{62}	62.50	.79588	$(OC_2H_5)_2$	90.12	.95482
C_{12}	144.12	.15872	H_{12}	12.10	.08279	H_{63}	63.50	.80277	$(OC_2H_5)_3$	135.18	.13091
C_{13}	156.13	.19349	H_{13}	13.10	.11727	H_{64}	64.51	.80963	$(OC_2H_5)_4$	180.24	.25585
C_{14}	168.14	.22567	H_{14}	14.11	.14953	H_{65}	65.52	.81637	$(OC_2H_5)_5$	225.30	.35276
C_{15}	180.15	.25563	H_{15}	15.12	.17955						
C_{16}	192.16	.28366	H_{16}	16.13	.20763	O	16	.20412	$OCOCH_3$	59.04	.77115
						O_2	32	.50515	$(OCOCH_3)_2$	118.09	.07221
C_{17}	204.17	.30999	H_{17}	17.14	.23401	O_3	48	.68124	$(OCOCH_3)_3$	177.13	.24829
C_{18}	216.18	.33482	H_{18}	18.14	.25864	O_4	64	.80618	$(OCOCH_3)_4$	236.18	.37324
C_{19}	228.19	.35830	H_{19}	19.15	.28217	O_5	80	.90309	$(OCOCH_3)_5$	295.22	.47015
C_{20}	240.20	.38057	H_{20}	20.16	.30449	O_6	96	.98227	$(OCOCH_3)_6$	354.26	.54932
						O_7	112	.04922	$(OCOCH_3)_7$	413.31	.61628
C_{21}	252.21	.40176	H_{21}	21.17	.32572	O_8	128	.10721	$(OCOCH_3)_8$	472.35	.67426
C_{22}	264.22	.42197	H_{22}	22.18	.34596	O_9	144	.15836	$(OCOCH_3)_9$	531.40	.72542
C_{23}	276.23	.44127	H_{23}	23.18	.36511	O_{10}	160	.20412	$(OCOCH_3)_{10}$	590.44	.77118
C_{24}	288.24	.45975	H_{24}	24.19	.38364						
C_{25}	300.25	.47748	H_{25}	25.20	.40140	N	14.008	.14638	$(H_2O)_{\frac{1}{2}}$	9.01	.95472
						N_2	28.02	.44747	H_2O	18.02	.25575
C_{26}	312.26	.49452	H_{26}	26.21	.41847	N_3	42.02	.62346	$(H_2O)_{1\frac{1}{2}}$	27.02	.43169
C_{27}	324.27	.51091	H_{27}	27.22	.43489	N_4	56.03	.74842	$(H_2O)_2$	36.03	.55666
C_{28}	336.28	.52670	H_{28}	28.22	.45056	N_5	70.04	.84535	$(H_2O)_3$	54.05	.73280
C_{29}	348.29	.54194	H_{29}	29.23	.46583	N_6	84.05	.92454	$(H_2O)_4$	72.06	.85769
									$(H_2O)_5$	90.08	.95463
C_{30}	360.30	.55666	H_{30}	30.24	.48058				$(H_2O)_6$	108.10	.03383
C_{31}	372.31	.57090	H_{31}	31.25	.49485	S	32.066	.50604			
C_{32}	384.32	.58469	H_{32}	32.26	.50866	S_2	64.13	.80706	P	30.975	.49101
						S_3	96.20	.98318	P_2	61.950	.79204
C_{33}	396.33	.59806	H_{33}	33.26	.52192	S_4	128.26	.10809	P_3	92.925	.96813
C_{34}	408.34	.61102	H_{34}	34.27	.53491				P_4	123.90	.09307
C_{35}	420.35	.62361	H_{35}	35.28	.54753	F	19.00	.27875			
						F_2	38.00	.57978	Na	22.997	.36167
C_{36}	432.36	.63585	H_{36}	36.29	.55979	F_3	57.00	.75587	Na_2	45.99	.66267
C_{37}	444.37	.64774	H_{37}	37.30	.57171				Na_3	68.99	.83879
C_{38}	456.38	.65933	H_{38}	38.30	.58320	Cl	35.457	.54970			
C_{39}	468.39	.67061	H_{39}	39.31	.59450	Cl_2	70.91	.85071	K	39.10	.59218
C_{40}	480.40	.68160	H_{40}	40.32	.60552	Cl_3	106.37	.02682	K_2	78.20	.89321
						Cl_4	141.83	.15177	K_3	117.30	.06930
C_{41}	492.41	.69233	H_{41}	41.33	.61627	Cl_5	177.28	.24866			
C_{42}	504.42	.70279	H_{42}	42.34	.62675				Ag	107.88	.03294
C_{43}	516.43	.71301	H_{43}	43.34	.63689	Br	79.916	.90263	Ag_2	215.76	.33397
C_{44}	528.44	.72299	H_{44}	44.35	.64689	Br_2	159.83	.20366			
C_{45}	540.45	.73275	H_{45}	45.36	.65667	Br_3	239.75	.37976	Cu	63.54	.80305
C_{46}	552.46	.74230	H_{46}	46.37	.66624	Br_4	319.66	.50469	Cu_2	127.08	.10408
C_{47}	564.47	.75164	H_{47}	47.38	.67560				Cr	52.01	.71609
C_{48}	576.48	.76078	H_{48}	48.38	.68467	I	126.91	.10350	Hg	200.61	.30235
C_{49}	588.49	.76974	H_{49}	49.39	.69364	I_2	253.82	.40453	Pb	207.21	.31641
C_{50}	600.50	.77851	H_{50}	50.40	.70243	I_3	380.74	.58063	Pt	195.23	.29055
									Se	78.96	.89741

$$\text{Log } C/CO_2 = .43599 \qquad \text{Log } H_2/H_2O = .04883$$